THE BRADY GUIDE TO MICROCOMPUTER TROUBLESHOOTING & MAINTENANCE

The Brady Guide to Microcomputer Troubleshooting & Maintenance

Henry F. Beechhold

A Brady Book
Published by Prentice Hall Press
New York, New York 10023

A Brady Book
Published by Prentice Hall Press
A Division of Simon + Schuster, Inc.
Gulf + Western Building
One Gulf & Western Plaza
New York, New York 10023

PRENTICE HALL PRESS is a trademark of Simon & Schuster, Inc.

Manufactured in the United States of America

2 3 4 5 6 7 8 9 10

Illustrations by Henry F. Beechhold.

Library of Congress Cataloging-in-Publication Data

Beechhold, Henry F., 1928–
     The Brady Guide to Microcomputer Troubleshooting
& Maintenance.

     "A Brady book."
     Includes index.
     1. Microcomputers—Maintenance and repair.
I. Title. II. Title: Guide to microcomputer
troubleshooting and maintenance.
TK7887.B426   1987   004'.028'8   86-30554

ISBN 0-13-580200-8

CONTENTS

DEDICATION

For Renie, my wife,
without whose unstinting maintenance
I would have fallen into disrepair.
With love and appreciation
from the old tinkerer.

FOREWORD

This book, the third of its type that I've written, is a distillation of several years of practical computer experience blended with technical information gathered from a variety of sources—books, colleagues, courses. I've tried to present the material in a way that is both readable and usable. Having checked and rechecked the facts, I am reasonably confident that everything is correct. But being only human, I must be forgiven if some small errors have managed to creep in here and there. I cannot foresee how any such (one would hope nonexistent!) errors will cause the reader difficulty.

Since books like this derive from more than just the imagination of the author, I'd like to thank all those who contributed to the well of knowledge from which I drew. I'd like to thank, as well, the editorial and production staffs of Brady Books, especially Janice K. Mandel, who moved the book from manuscript to print.

Henry F. Beechhold
Trenton State College

Limits of Liability and Disclaimer of Warranty

The author and publisher of this book have used their best efforts in preparing this book and the programs contained in it. These efforts include the development, research, and testing of the theories and programs to determine their effectiveness. The author and publisher make no warranty of any kind, expressed or implied, with regard to these programs or the documentation contained in this book. The author and publisher shall not be liable in any event for incidental or consequential damages in connection with, or arising out of, the furnishing, performance, or use of these programs.

Trademarks

Above Board is a trademark of Intel Corporation.
Framework is a trademark of Aston-Tate.
IBM PC, XT, and PC-DOS are trademarks of International Business Machines Corporation.
KoalaPad is a registered trademark of Koala Technologies Corporation.
LaserJet is a trademark of Hewlett Packard.
Liberty Board is a trademark of Quadram.
Macintosh is a registered trademark of Apple Computer, Inc.
MS-DOS is a trademark of Microsoft Corporation.
Mylar and Teflon are trademarks of E.I. duPont de Nemours & Co., Inc.
Radio Shack is a registered trademark of Tandy Corporation.
ScotchGuard is a trademark of 3M Corporation.
Sidekick and SuperKey are trademarks of Borland International.
Silly Putty is a trademark of Binney & Smith, Inc.
Smart Cable is a trademark of IQ Technologies, Inc.
Static Guard is a trademark of Alberto-Culver Co.
Symphony is a registered trademark of Lotus Development Corporation.
WD-40 is a trademark of WD-40 Co.
WordStar is a trademark of MicroPro International Corporation.
Z80 is a registered trademark of Zilog, Inc.

Chapter 1

WHERE WE'RE GOING

For more than 40 years I've been fascinated by and, from time to time, hip-deep in electronics—as a "ham" (KC2PA, advanced class), a radio technician in the Signal Corps back in the '40s, a technical writer, and . . . well, you get the picture. Yet, "officially," I'm a professor of English, not an engineer or technician. I mention this by way of encouragement. We needn't accept our official categories as limitations. There's a time for poetry and a time for tinkering. At this moment, an eviscerated computer, its innermost parts revealed to the world, sits on my workbench awaiting my attention. When I've graded last week's themes and reviewed the coming week's coursework, I'll head for my "laboratory" and indulge myself in happy hours of fiddling around—cleaning, fixing, and modifying.

WHAT THIS BOOK WILL DO FOR YOU

If all goes as planned, this book will:

- take you on an easy jog around the insides of your computer equipment;
- introduce you to the basics of computer logic and electronics;
- provide you with the conceptual tools for, and practical techniques of, simple troubleshooting and routine maintenance;
- encourage you to hand over equipment exhibiting complex malfunctions to a professional repair facility;
- help you to understand what you can expect from professional technical service;
- add to your vocabulary (in a painless, casual way) a whole bunch of techno-jargon; and
- reduce your technophobia or technological *Angst* to manageable levels.

WHAT THIS BOOK WON'T DO FOR YOU

This is a beginner's book for the nontechnically oriented. It is not intended as a technical training course for professional repair persons. Therefore, in this book:

- you will not learn *all* about the internal operations of a computer;
- you will not be prepared to open a computer repair facility or even go to work for one;
- you will not be prepared to perform maintenance and repair operations that require advanced knowledge, tools, and techniques.

HOW THE BOOK IS WRITTEN AND ORGANIZED

The book's principal readership will be those computer users in search of help with common computer and software malfunctions. For these readers, the technical materials, as presented in the chapters on computer operations and communications, can be passed over until such time as such information may seem appealing. For the reader in search of help *and* with some technical background, *or* with an interest in learning computer hardware fundamentals, the book offers a healthy bonus in the form of a once-over-lightly mini-course in computer science.

This book attempts to avoid the failures of most technical books written for nontechnically trained readers. It is clear, direct, and neither overly technical nor inanely simple. To help you retain information, I use a technique that might be called "incremental repetition," whereby certain facts and concepts reappear throughout the book, each time in a slightly different form or context, with no fancy memory tricks needed. So, while you can go directly to the **Troubleshooting Guides** and track down your problem and its solution, you'll cheat yourself of a great deal of the book's value by doing this.

The three chapters immediately following this one constitute the inner core of (and reason for) the book: troubleshooting and maintenance. Chapter 2, **When Disaster Strikes**, contains (1) general troubleshooting principles and (2) a set of guides to troubleshooting the various parts of your computer system. The **Troubleshooting Road Map** is meant to be a "guide to the guides." Chapter 3, **Hardware Care**, shows you how to perform routine maintenance on your computer and peripherals. In Chapter 4, **Software Care**, you'll get help with problems related to (1) the actual storage media (disks and tapes) and (2) the programs stored thereon.

Chapters 5, **Tools and Techniques**, and 6, **The Technical Reference Manual**, directly support the suggested troubleshooting and maintenance activities, giving you insights into tool use and into the various road maps that technicians use to diagnose and cure various computer ills.

Chapters 7, **How Computers Work**, and 8, **How Computers Communicate**, provide a gentle introduction to electronics and to the inner workings of computer systems.

Chapter 9, **Making Changes**, shows you how to modify your computer system to make it more useful for your particular needs. This chapter shows you that *modifying* and *troubleshooting/maintenance* are part of the same garment, so to speak.

Chapter 10, **Technical References**, contains supplemental technical reference material. Finally, there's a **Glossary**, in which some terms used in the book do not appear because they are clearly defined in context and easily located through the **Index**.

Supplementary information is included at the end of each chapter.

USING THIS BOOK

Computer Problems

Turn to the **Troubleshooting Road Map** (foldout following the Index) and follow the path to the correct **Troubleshooting Guide**, which will direct you to possible causes and possible cures.

Particular Information

Looking for information on a particular topic? Start with the **Index**.

Sources

Need tools, supplies, repair parts, ancillary equipment? Check the appropriate chapter source listings.

AIMS

This book, then, has three general aims: (1) to help you cure a variety of computer hardware ills, (2) to help you to expand and enhance your computer system(s), and (3) to introduce you to some of the fundamentals of computer electronics. Because *software* can give your hardware fits, there's a chapter on the care, repair, and maintenance of software. The central feature of the book—a set of **Troubleshooting Guides**, identifying symptoms and suggesting cures—can be used independently of the other material in the book.

To give you some insight into the "magic" of the computer, I've included what I hope are easy-to-understand explanations of basic digital electronics. Although many—perhaps most—problems can be solved by rote, it's satisfying to grasp the principles underlying problems and their solutions. For me, a "black box" is a challenge. I want to know what's inside and how (within my ability to understand) it works. Put it down to a meddlesome curiosity, if you will, but it certainly makes life entertaining!

RULES

Every game has its rules and traditions. Computer care and repair is a game like any other; that is, you are faced with one or more obstacles to surmount in order to win a prize—in the present case, an operational computer. Because a computer is a system (or a system of systems), there must be a systematic way to solve those problems. "Inspired randomness" can work, of course, but there's no such thing as an "inspired random **methodology**," nor can the outcome of a catch-as-catch-can approach be predicted. Pinching, poking, smacking, twitching, tweaking, and twiddling—perhaps even praying—have all contributed to problem-solving. Who hasn't straightened out an errant appliance through a righteously delivered thwack? It's a rare computer problem, however, that is amenable to such treatment, alas. On the other hand, there's rarely need for despair.

Troubleshooting Considerations

The very first thing you should do before the need for troubleshooting arises is to set up a computer-system journal (notebook, logbook, diary, whatever you wish to call it). Divide it into sections for each part of the system—computer, disk drive(s), video monitor, printer and other peripherals, and software. Make subsections for malfunctions and solutions, system modifications, and interfacing problems and solutions. The journal will eventually prove a valuable reference tool. You'll be able to discover, for example, exactly when you bought a certain product, how it was installed, how it functioned or malfunctioned, and what you did about the latter.

Back to troubleshooting. What you need to do is take a cold look at your ailing computer system and follow these guidelines:

(1) Note the precise conditions under which the problem arose.
(2) Note the precise nature of the foul-up, checking for smoke and/or funny smells, and physical damage such as might have arisen from spilling something (coffee, tea, milk, or whatever) into or onto one or more parts of the system.
(3) Check the obvious potential sources of trouble:
  (a) **Power**—Are fuses and breakers intact, cables connected, switches on?
  (b) **Software**—Is system disk in place? Is the disk okay?
(4) Refer to the **Troubleshooting Road Map**, which, in turn, will refer you to the appropriate **Troubleshooting Guide**.
(5) Prepare a clean, well-lighted place for your ministrations.
(6) Follow the instructions in the **Troubleshooting Guide**(s), using correct tools and maintaining the proper frame of mind (serene).
(7) When in doubt about a course of action, do nothing until you've resolved your doubts. If you can't resolve them, pack up your computer and take or ship it (with a detailed written explanation) to a reliable (preferably factory-authorized) repair facility.
(8) Work within the limits of your understanding of the problem and its solution. On occasion, swallowing your pride will prove the best first move in bringing your computer back to health.
(9) Work within the limits of your alertness. Some jobs are better done over several workbench sessions.
(10) In your journal, make detailed entries of symptoms and cures. The next time something similar happens (and it probably will), you can

refer to your personal fix-it book as a shortcut. Don't rely on your memory; believe me, it's unreliable.

Prevention

Certain difficulties can be forestalled by a program of preventive maintenance. But don't assume that becoming a fussy computer house-keeper will free you from disaster. About all you can actually "maintain" are the mechanical components of the system, namely, disk drive read/write (playback/recording) heads, keys and buttons, wheels, gears, rollers, pulleys, cables and cable connectors, and the like—objects found mainly in or among floppy disk drives (forget hard disks), keyboards, printers, plotters, and tape drives.

Environmental Considerations

Electronic parts—integrated circuits and that sort of thing—need no care beyond keeping them reasonably cool, reasonably free of grunge (airborne contaminants), and **totally** free of moisture or uncommonly high humidity ("dankness"). Using a computer at home will generally subject it to a higher grunge level than is usually the case in a typical office (of nonsmokers). Cooking grease, wood-stove or fireplace soot, general household dust, tobacco smoke, and various household and cosmetic sprays all contribute to buildup in your computer. About all you can do is keep the computer as far from the kitchen as possible, as far from heavy dust sources as possible, and out of damp basements. Should water find its way into the computer, you can probably save the machine. Assault with liquids like milk, beer, and soda (or anything containing sugar) is nearly always fatal.

The buildup of contaminants, even tarnish, on connector and integrated-circuit (IC) pins can cause intermittent failures in electrical contact. Certain inexplicable computer problems may be traceable to so unglamorous a cause. A related type of failure is that arising from poor mating of the IC pin and IC socket. (The metal connector in the socket is called a *wiper*. If it doesn't "wipe" well, the pin may not be making efficient and reliable contact.) The problem can be cured by removing the plugging element (IC or connector), spraying the pins and receptacles with electrical contact cleaner (available at any electronic or electrical supply store), and carefully reseating or replugging the parts. For defective parts, the cure isn't so simple because they should be replaced—a hassle, especially in the case of IC sockets. Let's not worry about this right now!

A computer can be kept cool by (1) its internal fan, (2) placement in a cool environment, and (3) placement where air can circulate freely. If your computer has a wimpy fan, or none at all, replace it or add another one, as appropriate. (See Chapter 9.) A hot and stuffy site can be mitigated by judicious placement of an external fan. Above all, **never** block the ventilation holes and slots of any of your computer equipment.

Electrical Considerations

The electricity that powers your equipment can also damage it. Your system needs between 110 and 120 volts of relatively "clean" AC (alternating current). Electrical quality can be enhanced by both types of gadgets listed below; constant voltage can be guaranteed only with the second. Sources and catalog numbers for all of the electrical devices mentioned below will be found in the **Source Listing** at the end of this chapter.

Plug all of your computer equipment into a single switched outlet strip, one that contains a circuit breaker, transient suppressor, and line filter. Don't buy a "bargain"—it won't be worth whatever you pay for it. A power "command center" that sits atop the computer box is a sensible and attractive solution. Plug the equipment, *via* a common plug strip, into a conditioning power source; those with battery backup are ideal, but cost the most.

NEVER defeat the ground pin. If your outlets provide for only two-prong plugs, use a three-prong-to-two-prong grounding adapter, grounding the "pigtail" wire of the adapter to the screw that holds the face plate onto the outlet box. If the screw is painted, scrape off the paint.

Static electricity is another cause of glitches, crashes, and worse. Here are some suggestions on this shocking subject: (1) Use antistatic mats under your computer and under your chair. (2) Spray carpeting in the vicinity of your computer station with StaticGuard™. (3) Discharge your personal accumulation of static electricity into a large hunk of metal like a filing cabinet or the metal case of your power strip. (4) Try to maintain your computer room at a reasonable humidity level. The ultra-dry air that results from winter heating systems encourages the rapid buildup of static charges.

Regardless of the protection you've installed, however, you should shut down your system whenever any type of electrical disruption threatens—electrical storm and power brownouts in particular.

QUESTIONS

OK, you have questions. I'll pose a few and try to answer them.

Q.   *Can I really repair a computer?*

A.   To answer briefly, yes. But while brevity may be the soul of wit, it's not the soul of candor. Your ability to repair a computer depends on such variables as (1) your willingness to make the effort required, (2) the complexity of the problem, and (3) the correct diagnosis, based on (4) a sound understanding of the troubleshooting principles and practices outlined in this book.

Some problems, in fact, are remarkably easy to solve; others are beyond the casual tinkerer's capabilities. Careful thought about the problem should lead you to a sensible judgment about whether you should tackle it or call for help. Follow my suggestions and you'll stay out of difficulty.

Q.   *Won't I end up making things worse?*

A.   It's possible: Things can *always* get worse. On the other hand, the risk level here is low, and the likelihood is that you'll succeed in getting your equipment back in working order, often at little cost in time and money. Wherever there's a chance for you to do real mischief, I'll steer you into the care of the professional repairperson. I want neither damage to you nor to your computer equipment on my conscience!

Q.   *I can't change a light bulb; how can I work on a computer?*

A.   I've heard *that* one before. It's a matter of attitude. If it's an intriguing and worthwhile activity, and if you have such guidance as afforded by this book, you can do it. Changing light bulbs is boring.

Q.   *Won't I need a lot of expensive equipment?*

A.   You'll need a few tools and supplies, the cost of which you'll cover after the first time or two you have to use them. After that, you'll be well ahead of the game. Consider the cost of your computer system!

Q. *Reading technical stuff puts my head into a tailspin, so how will I be able to make sense out of what you're trying to teach me?*

A. This book is not written for specialists; it's written for you. I've tried to make it clear, readable, and easy to use. In fact, you needn't read anything but the **Troubleshooting Guides**, following them step-by-step to the solution to your problem, or to a recommendation that you shouldn't attempt the job. I'm not going to let you get in over your head.

Q. *Is it a sensible use of my time to tinker with a broken computer?*

A. If you can get your computer system back on line after a couple hours of your time and effort, isn't that a bargain considering the loss of time that might accrue if you sent it out for the repair you could have easily done? Besides, many of the solutions may take only minutes.

Q. *I can use a computer, but I don't have much "manual dexterity." Will this be a problem?*

A. This is related in a way to the "light bulb" question. Anyway, you won't be asked to attempt delicate repair work requiring fancy fingerwork, which, in fact, relatively few professionals indulge in these days. Substitution is the technician's major maneuver. In all likelihood, the defective circuit board that you returned to the computer manufacturer for repair was chucked into the trash bin, and the board you got back came from stock.

Q. *A book like this gives me the scary feeling that my computer system is unreliable and in constant danger of malfunctioning. Is that feeling warranted?*

A. No. Computer systems are extremely reliable. If your computer and associated equipment have been running for ten hours without mishap, it shouldn't need doctoring for a long time to come. Electronic components seem either to die almost immediately or to last until external problems do them in.

Q. *What do you mean by "external" problems?*

A. Environmental, electrical, and physical. That is, heat, dirt, moisture, electrical disturbances (lightning, power brownouts), physical damage (dropping the keyboard, for example)—all those kinds of things. Rest easy: You'll get lots of advice in this book about how to avoid problems that lead to computer system disasters. *Maintenance* really means forestalling or heading off disasters.

Q. *When it comes to expanding my system, wouldn't I be better off to let a professional do it than to attempt the job myself?*

A. Adding "off-the-shelf" items like expansion boards and peripherals (printers, plotters, and so on) does not require professional help. Not only will you get guidance in this book, but knotty problems can almost always be resolved by a phone call to the manufacturer. (Retailers *may* be able to help; but don't count on it!).

You really have to convince yourself—and reading this book should help in this process—that the gadgetry itself is not beyond you. Let's say that you want to expand memory by adding a memory board. This is a simple project: You open the computer, set a switch or two (according to instructions in the memory-board manual), plug the board into the expansion socket, and close up the computer. Do the job yourself and you've saved a $50 to $100 "consulting" fee.

Q. *Come on, most jobs won't be that simple, will they?*

A. In fact, a lot of them will. Setting up a printer and its cabling may take a bit more, but not all that much. Don't slip back into the "I can't change a light bulb" outlook. Put aside that self-defeating attitude! After all, if you can learn to use a serious piece of software, you can easily develop some basic hardware skills.

CAVEATS AND EXCULPATIONS

While this book claims neither completeness (whatever that may be for so large a topic) nor perfection (another undefinable), I've cast a wide net and have made every reasonable effort to achieve clarity and accuracy. No human effort is glitchproof, alas, but I trust that such glitches as may emerge here will not detract appreciably from the usefulness of the book.

SOMETHING EXTRA

At the end of each chapter you'll find a "local appendix" containing odds-and-ends information of the sort you'll find in the **Source Listing** that follows.

SOURCE LISTING

The vendors listed below (and throughout the book) were alive and well at press time. The fact that businesses fail should cause you no problem whatever. Just check a current computer publication like *Computer Shopper*, 407 S. Washington Avenue, Titusville, FL 32781; (305)269–3211.

Please note that a listing in this book does NOT imply endorsement by either the author or the publisher.

Electrical Management Devices

To tame the electricity in and around your computer, you need to consider (1) potential catastrophic loss of power, (2) potential unreliability of power, and (3) static electricity. In addition to protecting your equipment from electrical problems—to the extent that this can be done—you should organize your electrical cabling in a neat and unhazardous manner. The gear listed below is a selection from the riches available, and should not be considered to the exclusion of others you may see advertised.

Surge Suppressors.   These are multiple-outlet strips or boxes provided with transient protection and (usually) some degree of line filtering. The line filtering isn't of great consequence but it won't hurt. The prices fall mostly in the $50 to $100 range. The May 27, 1984 issue of *PC Magazine* (pp.114-146) contains a detailed report on 34 surge suppressors. Dynatech makes a whole family of these devices. Write or call for details:

Dynatech Computer Power Inc.
4744 Scotts Valley Drive
Scotts Valley, CA 95066
(408)438-5760

Uninterruptable Power Supplies.   An uninterruptable power supply not only conditions the electrical power but supplies its own in case of power failure. If you're willing to spend about $400 and up, this is the electrical protection of choice, eliminating the need for anything else but an ordinary multiple-outlet strip (or a "command center," described below). Dynatech's Powerhouse/300 is a first-rate unit at a relatively modest price. For really heavy-duty protection, expect to pay

$1,200 to $2,000. (These units are indeed heavy.) For single systems, this is excessive protection.

Constant Voltage Power Regulators. If flat-out power failures present no problem in your area, you may want to consider using a *power regulator*, that is, a unit capable of maintaining correct constant voltage under varying input-voltage and output-current-demand conditions. The big name in such devices is Sola. Ask them about their PC Computer Regulators:

> Sola
> 1717 Busse Road
> Elk Grove Village, IL 60007
> (312)439–2800

Master Control Units. These are multiple-input, multiple-switch "organizers" or "command centers," most of which contain suppression circuitry. A number of them are meant to match your computer and to be placed right on the computer between it and the video monitor. The Power Managers made by Black Box typify the breed:

> Black Box Corporation
> Box 12800
> Pittsburgh, PA 15241
> (417)746–5530

Antistatic Devices. If you can remember to zap yourself to a filing cabinet or something of that sort before you sit down to compute, and if you spray StaticGuard around on the carpeting in your work area, you probably won't need any other static protection. But to play it safe, you might want to attach a 3M First-Touch Keyboard Strip to your computer keyboard. It lists for $20, and is probably worth having. A source for this and other protective devices is:

> Matterhorn
> 26101 Woodlore
> Franklin, MI 48025
> 1–(800)521–4838

Chapter 2

WHEN DISASTER STRIKES

INTRODUCTION

When a computer problem arises, this is the "official" starting point. I suggest, however, that you read Chapters 5, **Tools and Techniques**, and 6, **The Technical Reference Manual**, in advance of disaster. These chapters will give you the hardware orientation that will expedite troubleshooting and repair. The two chapters on computer electronics (Chapters 7 and 8) are there for those curious about how things work. Satisfying that curiosity will, in fact, enhance your troubleshooting skills. But don't fret, your lacking that background won't prevent you from doing the tasks that follow here.

On Using Tools

Before you attempt any task requiring a soldering iron, please read the section in Chapter 5 on soldering/desoldering technique.
Before you attempt to use a *multimeter* or a *logic* probe, please read the section in Chapter 5 on the use of these instruments.

This chapter opens with a survey of general principles and a miscellany of hints and suggestions. It then moves to a series of specific **Troubleshooting Guides**. Since this book aims to help the nontechnical person to solve common problems, not to train technicians, it will not lead you into the subtleties and complexities of circuit analysis more appropriate to technical education than to emergency first aid.

Nevertheless, as suggested above, the reader who has studied the (1) technical chapters, (2) recommended readings, and (3) computer technical reference manual should be able to go well beyond the efforts explicitly attempted in the **Troubleshooting Guides.** If you are told, for example, that (a) a given complex circuit may be causing certain untoward effects and, therefore, (b) you should send the equipment out for professional repair, you may wish, nevertheless, to press on, exploring the mysteries of that circuit "on your own," and, perhaps, even managing to fix it without benefit of a technician.

WARNINGS

If you open or attempt to repair your computer or any other piece of equipment under warranty, you may void the warranty. Check with the owner's manual.

Danger lurks when you overreach your capabilities or understanding. Don't be too proud to pack the equipment off for professional service.

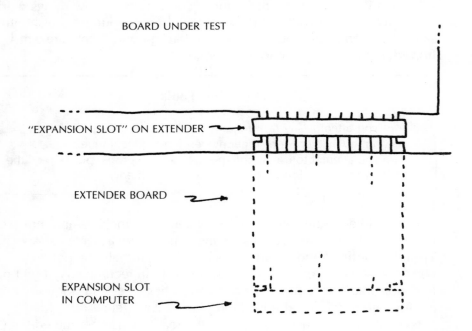

Figure 2–1.   **Extender Card Installed.**

The Extender Card—A Useful Gadget

In some computers, it' s easy (or relatively easy) to get at powered-up expansion boards for troubleshooting. In others, it's well-nigh impossible. But if you're unable to test for voltages and signals because test points are inaccessible, how do you troubleshoot the board? The *extender card* is the solution. You plug this circuit board equivalent of a multiconductor cable into an expansion slot and plug the board under test into the extender card's expansion slot. It's remotely possible for this extension of the bus lines to cause untoward effects. But the alternative is to do nothing. (See **Source Listing** for one source of the IBM PC type of extender card.)

Big Hint

If there is a "royal road" to computer troubleshooting and repair, it lies in the technique of SUBSTITUTION. Wherever possible, substitute a working whatchamacallit for the presumably defective one. Example: If the disk drive is suspected, substitute a known good one. You'll get your computer back on line faster by this method than by any other, assuming that the bad component is bad all by itself. A chain of disasters will take a bit more time to work through. But if you can get your hands on the required substitutes, you've got it licked! Selective pickwork may save you money, but unless you're a troubleshooting whiz, it surely won't save you time.

GENERAL PRINCIPLES

In broadest terms, computer illnesses arise from (1) electrical/electronic failures, (2) mechanical failures, and (3) software failures.

Internal Diagnostics

When you turn on a microcomputer, the built-in diagnostic routine checks memory, disk I/O, and, perhaps, a few other basic functions. The user manual will detail the boot-up tests and explain the meaning of the various error codes and messages that may appear. Unfortunately, these explanations are often sketchy, poorly expressed, or both.

The technical reference manual may adequately supplement the user manual, and it may not. In this case, you should add yet another book to your computer collection; you know the name: *Inside Brand X Computer*, or words to that effect. Several such books are available for each of the popular micros. Browse through them at the bookstore or library and decide which one gives you "more of what you want": clear explanations and illustrations, copious details. In any event, as a tinkerer/troubleshooter, it behooves you to familiarize yourself with the system diagnostics.

Disk Diagnostics

Extended diagnostics on disk are available for most computers from the manufacturer, outside suppliers, or both, and should be part of your troubleshooting arsenal. These diagnostic programs, usually accompanied by extensive printed documentation, will take you through every major subsystem of your computer system. The Texas Instruments diagnostics menu, for example, includes the following choices:

Overall Unit Test
CRT Test
CRT Graphics Test
Diskette Verify Test
Diskette Read/Write Test
Keyboard Test
Memory Test
Parallel Printer Test
Communication Port(s) Test
Display System Configuration
Print Test Results

Selecting an option will put you into a submenu dealing with the specific tests to be performed. Before you have any problems with your computer, you should run the whole battery of diagnostics just to familiarize yourself with the computer system and its potential ills.

Initial Diagnoses
Electrical/Electronic Failures

Power lights. If any part fails to "light up" (turn on), there's obviously some sort of electrical problem. Not long ago, a friend of mine called me in a panic: There was no picture on the video display, despite the fact that the computer itself seemed to be working. Grabbing my traveling toolkit, I made a housecall. I immediately noted that although the computer power light glowed encouragingly, the video monitor light was out. Was the power cord plugged in tightly? Was the monitor switch on? Yes to both. The fault obviously lay with the monitor itself. Sure enough, hooking up another monitor proved the truth of the assumption. (The defective monitor **might** have had nothing worse than a burned-out power light. Alas, it wasn't so simple. Monitors, being similar to TV sets, should be serviced **ONLY** by technicians experienced in this particular branch of electronics repair.)

Smoke and funny smells. These indicate burnout, and, more often than not, can be traced to the power supply. This is another part of any piece of computer equipment you should **stay out of**.

Switches. Nonworking equipment that turns on but neither smokes nor smells bad may very likely be electrically sound, but improperly switched or interconnected, or it may be truly sick, electronically. In such situations, you need to begin by trying to isolate the area of failure. Let's consider how.

The switch problem exemplified: Consider the case of the printer that refused to work despite its having just been professionally repaired and tested. An hour's worth of diddling with configuration switches, an RS-232 breakout box, and software options resulted in nothing (except much heat around the collar). At the point of total exasperation, I noted that one of the rocker switches on the front panel was set neither here nor there. That is, it sat stupidly in the **middle** of its "rocking range." The result was that since the printer didn't know whether it was supposed to be operating at 10-pitch or 12-pitch, it operated at neither. It just acted dead.

External connections.   You can obviate external interconnection problems by checking cables and connectors for integrity and proper seating. To start in on potentially more complex problems: What, if any, diagnostic messages appear on the screen?

Make a note of the symptoms, listing the obvious areas of difficulty. Some examples: The keyboard seems dead; the video monitor isn't displaying anything; the video monitor is displaying garbage; the disk drives are erratic; or the printer grinds out garbage.

Make a note of the precedence or timing of the symptoms: Does the system boot, then fail? Does it boot, work, and then inevitably fail? Does it fail only sometimes. Partially? Entirely? Do odd sounds accompany failure? Beeps? Grinding?

Mechanics

The last named point brings us to mechanics—wheels, gears, pulleys, motors, and that sort of thing. Disk drives, printers, plotters, joysticks and other pointers ("mice", digitizing-pad cursors) exemplify the gadgetry in your system that can malfunction *mechanically*.

Motors.   Major sources of failure are disk drive and printer/plotter motors, which can burn out or seize ("freeze up"), and then burn out. Motors that are impeded from their normal actions go smokeward.

Reflect on the not-so-strange case of the ailing plotter, which lost its pen-carousel drive motor as a result of improperly mounted pens causing the carousel to bind. The raucous chattering of the motor went unheeded by the operator, who, instead of turning off the plotter to get things organized, just let the motor fry itself out. The lesson in this is to turn off the equipment as soon as it starts doing strange things or making funny noises.

Before starting your computer operations, check all equipment for freedom of movement.

(1) Are disk drives clear of anything that might cause a jam? On some drives, you can reach in from the front door and spin the hub. On others, you'll have to open the computer to do this. If the drive doesn't seem to be working or is making a strange noise, try spinning the hub. A hub that doesn't spin easily indicates a jammed or defective disk drive.

(2) Are two disks jammed into a single slot? It's possible, and it happens.

(3) Are printers cleared of paper jams? Lift top cover and examine interior.

(4) Are platens and tractor feeds free to feed? Turn the platen knob to test. (Power OFF.) Paper clips and other alien material can get into the drive mechanism. If the platen and tractor are binding, examine all the accessible gears and other mechanical elements.

(5) Is external tractor feed properly seated?

(6) Is fanfold paper path clear from the source through the printer?

(7) Is sheet feeder properly mounted, electrically connected, and supplied with paper?

(8) Does the print head move freely? (Try this only with the printer turned OFF.) If not, explore for trash.

(9) Are plotter arms and pen carousels unimpeded?

(10) Is the mouse ball clean and free to roll? Most mice can be disassembled for cleaning. You can either snap or rotate the bottom of the mouse open. Let the ball drop into your hand (not onto the floor!). Blow out or mini-vacuum the cavity. Wipe the ball with a damp sponge, dry, and drop back into the cavity. Replace the cover.

(11) Do all the power and other frequently used switches feel "healthy"? That is, do they snap and click as you remember their doing when the equipment was new? A loose or mushy feeling switch is going or has gone west. It should be replaced as soon as possible. Some switches are easily replaced, some are best left to professional repairpeople. (See Chapter 9, **Making Changes**.)

Any equipment that betrays a mechanical malfunction during the preflight checkout **must be not be turned on** until the malfunction is corrected.

Any equipment that starts to malfunction mechanically during a computing session should be **shut down immediately**. At the first unfamiliar noise, turn off the offending device. In the case of disk drives, perform a graceful system shutdown, then troubleshoot.

Software

It is commonly the case that a perfectly healthy computer is driven silly by defective software. Remember that software can force the computer hardware to do just about anything. There are even a few cases on record of software actually causing the destruction of ICs! Fortunately, such digital unfriendliness is extremely rare and not likely to arise in the current generation of microcomputers.

Although Chapter 4, **Software Care**, is devoted to software-related problems, here are some helpful hints. When your computer acts in unwonted ways, and you have satisfied yourself that cables, connections, and switches are all in proper condition and order, run through the following list before going up the wall:

- Is the disk drive door securely closed? Open it and close it, just to make sure.
- Was the diskette inserted correctly? In all computer systems, it must be inserted with the disk label toward the operator. In most systems, the label should be facing up.
- Has the diskette been inserted into the right drive? If the system has been configured to boot from Drive A, it probably won't cold-boot a disk from Drive B. Or, in some hard disk systems, if you put a nonsystem diskette in one of the floppy drives, the hard disk won't boot. Remove the diskette and reboot.
- Did you accidentally insert the boot diskette into the "slot" **between** two stacked floppy disk drives? Don't laugh. It happens—a lot!
- Are you using a good copy of your software? Is it possible that the diskette has been damaged? Try another copy. You should have backups of all program software. If a piece of software doesn't allow you to back it up at your convenience, don't buy it in the first place. Don't think that you can't find a noncopy-protected alternative to some coveted program!
- Are you trying to boot up from a nonsystem disk? On many computers the operating system resides principally on the disk itself. No system, no bootup.
- Have you accidentally pressed the wrong key at some stage? Well-designed software should prevent you from inadvertently crashing the system, but a lot of software isn't that well designed. Reboot and try again. Note when and if the crash occurs.
- Have you tried to transmit data to a device (e.g., a printer) that isn't turned on or online? Many programs and operating systems will let the computer hang itself on this trick. Turn on the device, reboot the computer, and try again.
- Are you using the right version of the operating system for the particular piece of software? (Or *vice versa.*) A program that demands, for example, XYZ DOS 2.x or higher, will not run properly or at all with XYZ DOS 1.x.
- Have you tried to access an empty or open disk drive? On some computers this will crash the system, requiring a reboot. On others, you'll get a "drive-not-ready" message.

Reprise

Difficulties can arise from (1) electrical/electronic malfunctions, (2) mechanical malfunctions, and (3) software malfunctions. A considerable number of difficulties can be identified and resolved by following the preceding lists and suggestions. Many computer failures turn out to be simple matters, easily set right. But it's not in the nature of things to let you slip through your computing life without having to go at least a step or two beyond the obvious.

What follows, now, is the promised set of **Troubleshooting Guides** offered with my hope that you won't have to resort to them very often!

TROUBLESHOOTING TRICKS

Having exhausted the previous lists, and still faced with something that doesn't work, you'll have to press on. Before going to the specifics, let's review some troubleshooter's hints and tricks that may help when you do. Some of these have already been touched on.

Questions to Ask

Every component of the system (the computer and each peripheral) contains subsystems, circuits, and individual parts. You should ask of each, and attempt to answer, the following questions:

- What's the function of the component, circuit, or part?
- How does the component, circuit, or part seem to be deviating from its assigned function?
- In what ways does the behavior of the component, circuit, or part normally depend on the proper action of other components, circuits, or parts? (Example: The video monitor is designed to display visual images. These images can be distorted or absent because of problems in the monitor itself or because of problems in the output of the computer's video circuitry, or even because of a faulty cable.)

Miscellaneous Whatnots

Senses

Since your eyes, nose, and sense of touch are your primary troubleshooting tools, use them early and often.

Visual Inspection

Signs of overheating
Discoloration (fried resistors)
Bubbling or swelling (fried ICs, capacitors)
Vaporization (blown fuses)
Separation (blown fuses)

Disconnections

Separated plugs/sockets
Loose wires
Loose jumpers
Cracked traces

Misconnections

Wrongly connected plugs/sockets
Wrongly connected wires
Wrongly configured jumpers
Shorts between traces, wires, parts

Mangling

Parts bent over (potential shorts)
Parts with twisted leads (potential shorts)

Obviously, any visual evidence of distress should be acted on as appropriate. A disk capacitor, for instance, might be bent in such a way as to be causing an intermittent short through one of its leads. Being the neatness freak that I am, I like to see every such part standing tall in perfectly aligned rows. There's something about sloppily mounted parts that jangles my sensibilities. Anyway, as you neaten up a board, you can spot potential problems. Don't get too compulsive about bending leads—they have a limited "bending life."

FRAGILE LEADS—A WARNING REPEATED

"Officially," IC leads can be flexed three times. Beyond that, expect one lead to become two pieces! Other leads (capacitors, etc.) will usually survive more than three flexes, but don't count on it.

Tactile Inspection

Excessive heat in individual parts
Loose cable and wire connections ("wiggle test")
Loosely mounted board(s) ("wiggle test")
Improperly seated boards ("press-down test)
Improperly seated ICs ("press-down test")

Wiggling will reveal a problem. Pressing down will both reveal and solve.

Discolored, peculiar smelling, and excessively hot components are all signs of trouble. Of course, without a baseline for comparison, how will you know what constitutes a dangerous deviation? The appearance of your computer's insides when you do your first thorough cleanup provides you with the baseline. This assumes, of course, that the cleanup was done while the computer was still functioning perfectly!

Overheating

A computer that acts flaky but isn't actually smoking or making audible complaints can be studied with the power on. To locate overheating ICs and other parts, you'll need to open the computer and power it up. EXERCISE CAUTION! So long as you keep out of the power supply, your life won't be in danger, but the computer's life may be.

CAUTIONS

Never work inside of live equipment wearing rings, watches, bracelets, or necklaces. Never allow metal—such as a probe tip—to bridge computer parts.

Before you touch anything inside of the computer, make certain that (1) you ground yourself to the power-supply cage briefly and (2) you NEVER touch anything carrying AC voltage (such as the wires connected to the computer power switch).

ICs, especially the bigger ones, normally get fairly warm. Regulators (recognized by their heat sinks or cooling fins) can get very hot, as can power transistors, also mounted with heat sinks. But an "unsunk" IC should not burn your finger. If it does, it's suffering and needs attention. Although may work, the overheating could be caused by another problem. Additional troubleshooting may reveal the truth.

Testing by Cooling

Spraying Component Cooler (RS 64-2321) on particularly hot ICs can tell you if a chip is failing. The cooler will temporarily reduce the temperature to the point where the chip may behave normally. If the difficulty the computer has been experiencing vanishes for a time, you've found the proximate, if not the ultimate, cause.

Temporary IC Replacement

Where your troubleshooting researches have led you to ICs that are soldered into the board, hence not easily substituted, you can use piggyback ICs on the originals for testing. This technique demands that you buy one or more ICs of the correct type. Since many ICs, especially the smaller support ICs, are likely to be soldered rather than socketed, you might want to buy a full replacement set. Since I get nervous about not having at least one backup for just about every part, I tend to be compulsive about this sort of thing.

Note that piggybacking will help if the questionable chip is open ("blown"). But if that chip has an internal short (a rare occurrence), you may gain nothing.

Here's how to piggyback a chip:

(1) TURN OFF the power.
(2) Identify the chip for testing by marking the pin 1 location with a dab of easy-to-see nail polish.
(3) As necessary, straighten new IC pins in the lateral dimension, but bend all the pins evenly inward a small amount to aid them in gripping the pins of the suspect IC.
(4) With pin 1 on the new IC matching pin 1 of the suspect IC, press the chip down. The pins should match and grip snugly, one for one, with no pin touching any but its own mate.
(5) Power up the computer to check the results.
(6) Keep doing this with the correct replacement ICs until you isolate the errant IC.

Suppose now that you've located the rotten apple. In theory, you could just leave the piggybacked chip in place. What the heck—it's working, let it alone. Wrong. Suppose the chip pops off some day. What started out as a useful device has transmogrified into a menace. Let's do the repair properly.

To begin, pull off the piggybacked IC and place it on a piece of foil. Now you need to get rid of the old IC and prepare the site for receiving the new one. To remove the old soldered IC:

(1) TURN OFF the power.
(2) Pull the board from the computer and do your work on a proper work surface, with plenty of light.
(3) Clip each pin of the bad chip close to where it emerges from the body of the chip. Use a fine-bladed flush cutter. No butchery allowed!
(4) Discard the old chip body.
(5) During the following soldering-iron operations, DON'T OVERHEAT THE BOARD! This can damage the board by causing the solder pads and traces to come loose.
(6) From the bottom of the board, heat one pin, pulling it from the top of board with a narrow-nose plier. Repeat this process until you have removed all of the pins.
(7) To clean out the holes, use solder braid. Place a clean section of braid over a hole and heat with the iron just enough to "wick out" the old solder. You may to do this on both sides of the board. Remember not to "cook" the board.
(8) When all the holes are clear and the area looks neat (no solder splashes), swab both sides with a little rubbing alcohol. If there is a

heavy deposit of burned rosin (solder flux), you should clean it off with Rosin Flux Remover (RS 64–2324).

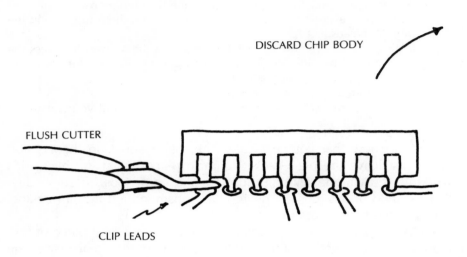

DISCARD CHIP BODY

FLUSH CUTTER

CLIP LEADS

Figure 2–2.   IC Removal.

Installing a New IC

You can add a socket if you wish. Some technopersons disapprove, claiming (with reason) that sockets are troublemakers and that the best possible electrical connection can be had only with direct soldering. I won't argue the point. Yet, unless space prohibits socketing, I socket. After all, some of the chips are already socketed anyway. Suit yourself.

(1) Insert the socket so that the pin 1 indicator marked on the socket is properly oriented. This is for convenience only. Pin 1 on a socket is the same as any other pin.
(2) Check to make certain that all the pins are properly seated in the holes and protruding a little bit above the surface of the foil side.

(3) Use only enough heat and solder to do the job. Heat each pin ("1001, 1002, 1003"), touch the solder to the pin, remove solder, remove iron. The solder should flow brightly and evenly around the pin. No "frost," globs, or drips.

(4) Press the socket tightly to the board and solder a corner pin.

(5) Solder a second pin at the opposite corner.

(6) Solder the rest of the pins.

(7) When cool, insert the IC, taking care not to bend the pins. Seat it.

(8) Replace board and test.

To hard-solder an IC, follow the same procedure as that listed above for soldering in a socket. Mind the heat!

TROUBLESHOOTING GUIDES

Each of these guides is aimed at a major chunk of your computer system. Please remember, however, that the system is a coherent whole and that the dividing line between one part of it and another may not be easily demarcated. For example, the I/O port circuitry of the computer will probably be in the computer itself, either on the main system board or on one or more expansion boards plugged into the main board. Problems with a peripheral device may be at the I/O port end or at the device end, or the one may affect the other.

To put a finer point on it: Is the cable an extension of the computer I/O port, or of the device interface; or is it something in its own right, separate from both? As you've surmised, it's all of these.

Where **exactly** does software "end" and hardware "begin"? Without hardware, software is meaningless; without software, hardware is useless. Each affects the other profoundly. If you have a speculative turn of mind, you may find much delightful intellectual exercise in reflecting on the nature of the computer system as hardware, software, and machine/human interactor.

When your computer presents you with an aggravation, use the commonsense approach first. Disaster hasn't truly struck until you've run out of simple solutions, as outlined above.

The general rule in using the **Troubleshooting Guides** is to try each presumed cure in order—as convenient or feasible. (For example, substituting a disk drive controller board may be both convenient and feasible in some circumstance and not at all in others.) Note the results. At the point that you've achieved success, stop. Then make a dated, written record of what was wrong and what you did to fix it.

NOTE: Work that should be carried out by a professional repairperson is designated **PR**.

Troubleshooting Guide: Power-Related Problems

A large proportion of "no-shows" and crashes are directly related to electrical power problems. These problems may arise externally or from within the computer system. External power problems may arise either from the power (AC) source or between the source and the system. A total lack of electrical power is a computer problem only to the extent that the computer can't be turned on.

SYMPTOM

No electrical power whatever.

CAUSE

Main service box breaker or fuses open or blown.

CURE

Check electrical service panel or box; reset breaker or replace fuse as necessary.

SYMPTOM

General power is okay, but individual piece of equipment won't turn on.

CAUSES

Power cable unplugged.
Power switch off or defective.
Fuse blown.
Equipment power supply defective.

CURES

Plug in power cable.
Turn on switch. (Replace if necessary if you are up to it; if not, **PR**.)
Replace fuse *of correct value*. If fuse blows again, see next item.
Where feasible, remove old power supply and subsitute an exact re-
placement; where not feasible, **PR**.

Some smaller pieces of equipment use the "wall-charger" type of power unit. In certain cases, this is just the *dropping-transformer* part of the power supply (a transformer that drops the AC voltage to the level needed by the rest of the power supply). In others, it's an entire power supply unto itself. If the legend on the device indicates an AC output, it's just a transformer. Try replacing it with one of the **same** voltage value and **at least** the same current rating (e.g., 9VAC, 0.5A). Other-wise, borrow an exact duplicate of the original for testing purposes.

In many computers, replacing a power supply requires no more than unplugging the power connectors and removing the mounting screws of the old supply and reversing the process for the new. Replacement supplies are widely available. See Chapter 9, **Making Changes**.

The power supplies in some computers and most other pieces of equipment are not drop-in (modular) units. Hence, power-supply-re-lated repair of such equipment should be left to the professional.

SYMPTOM

Computer or other equipment turns on and seems to function, but there's no power-light indication.

CAUSE

Burned out power lamp or LED.

CURE

Replace if feasible, or ignore, or **PR**.

There's no harm in a burned-out power indicator light. Replacing it may be more time-consuming or costly than the cosmetic effect is worth. On the other hand, your sense of the fitness of things may nag at you until you set this to rights.

Here's what I would do:

(1) If the lamp can be replaced by a common part readily available from a local store or through a catalog, then replace it. CAUTION: Use **only** the exactly correct replacement part.

(2) Many indicator lights are light-emitting diodes (LEDs). Being diodes, they're polarized. Being polarized, they must be mounted with *anode* (+) and *cathode* (−) correctly oriented. On a new LED, the anode lead is the longer one. The cathode side of the diode is marked with a flat spot impressed on the body of the device.

(3) Before removing the burnout, note where the flat is oriented.

(4) Clip the old leads, leaving the wire to the cathode a little longer, and to the anode a little shorter.

(5) Since the new leads will undoubtedly be longer than necessary, clip them down to size, maintaining the original pattern of longer anode, shorter cathode. Everything will match correctly.

(6) Slip a short length of "spaghetti" (insulator tubing, not pasta) over each of the two leads to which the LED will be connected and slide away from the connection points.

(7) With your narrow-nose pliers, form a tiny hook at the ends of each LED lead and each destination lead.

(8) Hook the cathode lead to the correct wire and pinch with pliers to hold. Heat with soldering iron and flow a **small** amount of solder over the joint. DON'T OVERHEAT. When cool, slide the insulator over the union.

(9) Repeat for anode lead.

(10) Dress wires to avoid shorts, pinching, and twisting.

Troubleshooting Guide: Disk Drive Problems

Professional repairpersons report that disk drive failures are the most common of all computer problems other than those related to cables. Given the hybrid nature of the disk drive—electronic and electro-mechanical—and the hazards of use, it's remarkable that this "large number" of failures proves to be a relatively small number. Hence, there's no need to absolutely *expect* the worst. A little *anticipation*, however, won't hurt.

When disk drives first appeared on the microcomputer scene, they were fearfully expensive and not very reliable. As the cost fell, the

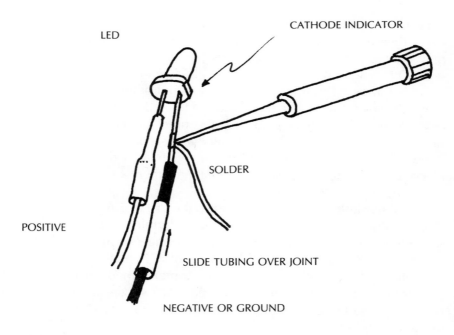

Figure 2–3. Replacing an LED Indicator.

quality rose. Professional computer repair services can run as high as $100 an hour. A new 5¼-inch disk drive can be bought for as little as $60. Does it pay to keep a couple of new replacement drives around? You bet. Computer downtime may be even more costly for you than either repair or purchase costs. In most PCs, an old drive can be pulled and a new one installed in about 30 minutes.

Here are two hints about disk drives:

(1) Buy replacement drives from a company specializing in disk drives (see the **Source Listing** at the end of this chapter), not your standard retail computer dealer. You'll save a bundle. Disk drives embossed with a famous three-letter logo are no different from those without the logo—except in price!

(2) Inquire around about disk drive reliability. There are differences, and price isn't necessarily the best indicator of quality. I must preserve the appearance of neutrality.

Even if you have a replacement drive, you needn't rush to install it every time a drive seems to have failed. Some of your drive problems may indeed prove to be catastrophic failures, requiring heroic measures. Others may be small matters easily attended to on the spot.

Since it rubs my puritan soul raw to toss out potentially useful equipment, I'll tinker until I've either fixed the thing or know for sure that it's beyond hope. For those who lack the time, patience, and tinkering savvy, a sensible approach is to immediately replace an unequivocally nonworking drive and send it out for repair as a down-the-road replacement for the replacement. (Count on there being another time when the need will arise!)

This **Troubleshooting Guide** assumes the use of 5¼-inch floppy disk drives, either single- or double-sided. A double-sided drive has two read/write heads that close down on the long slot in the floppy disk envelope, gripping it on both sides of the disk. A single-sided drive has a single read/write head, pressure being maintained on the opposite side of the disk by a small pressure pad. On single-sided drives, the read/write head does its work on the underside of the disk (that is, on the unlabeled side).

Eight-inch drives are subject to the same ills as their smaller siblings; hence, symptoms, causes, and cures are virtually the same. Refer to the eight-inch drive tech manual. The same is true of 3½-inch drives.

We will do nothing with hard (Winchester) drives other than recommend professional repair in the event of unequivocal (as opposed to a software-induced) crash.

WELL-DISK DRIVE CLINIC

Always insert disks gently. Don't slam drive doors or latches. **Ease** drive latches and doors open—don't let them spring, pop, snap, or bang. Every time a door or latch flies freely open, its life is shortened appreciably, and a day of aggravation brought closer. Slam-banging can also damage read/write heads.

Disk Drive Problem Areas—Overview

(1) Electrical power
    (a) Low voltage.
    (b) No voltage.
(2) Control
    (a) Computer disk controller circuitry.
    (b) Disk drive logic board.
    (c) Servo board (rotational speed adjustment).
(3) Mechanical
    (a) Door latch.
    (b) Spindle assembly.
    (c) Drive belt.
    (d) Head assembly (alignment).
(4) Electromechanical
    (a) Drive motor.
    (b) Head-loading solenoid.
    (c) Head-stepper motor.
    (d) Index light assembly.
    (e) Write protect light assembly.
(5) Connections
    (a) Power cable.
    (b) Interface (data and control) cable.
    (c) Head and other cables.
(6) Read/write head(s)
(7) Media (diskettes)
(8) Software

A note on orderly troubleshooting. There are various ways to be an orderly troubleshooter. The approach given here for disk drives is to (1) note symptoms occurring from the "outside in," that is, from the point of trying to insert a diskette, (2) suggest possible causes, and (3) suggest possible cures. You won't need much in the way of tools and equipment, because I don't recommend your attempting any but the easiest and most obvious repairs and adjustments.

SYMPTOM

Disk drive door jammed (either open or closed).

CAUSES

Disk jammed inside.
Door mechanism sprung.

CURES

Remove drive from enclosure and inspect for problem. You may have to lift the disk drive circuit board to see what's going on.
If a door part is broken, replace drive. Or **PR**.
If a disk is jammed inside, try to free it. Several types of door-latching and disk ejecting mechanisms are in use. Determine the "logic" of yours and work accordingly. For example, there may be a hook designed to release a return spring that's supposed to kick the disk partway out of the drive slot. The hook or the latch may be bent enough to prevent ejection. If the mechanism isn't broken, a little twiddling will fix it. Otherwise, **PR**.

In Chapter 3, we will remove disk drives for cleaning. Here's a review of the removal and disassembly procedure.

Removal and partial disassembly of a disk drive:

(1) TURN OFF power.
(2) Open enclosure.
(3) Unplug disk drive power cable (four-wire cable).
(4) Unplug disk drive interface cable (wide-ribbon cable).
(5) Remove disk drive frame mounting screws. Don't allow drive to drop.

(6) If the circuit board is covering the latching mechanism, move it out of the way by removing the board mounting screws and any connectors mounted on **top** of the board. The connectors lining the rear edge can be left in place.

(7) Gently bend the circuit board back out of the way.

(8) Reverse the procedure when you're through inspecting and tinkering.

SYMPTOM

Disk cannot be inserted.

CAUSES

Another disk is already in place.
Latching mechanism is defective.
Head is being held down by head-loading solenoid.

CURES

Remove offending disk.
Check condition of latching mechanism. Fix if possible, or **PR**.
Turn off computer system and reboot. If head-loading solenoid is okay, the head will release and disks can be removed or inserted.

SYMPTOM

Disk cannot be removed.

CAUSES

Two disks are jammed in together.
Defective latching mechanism.
Head is being held down by head-loading solenoid.

CURES

Remove jammed disks. You may have to open drive (see above) to accomplish this.
Check and repair latching mechanism, or **PR**.
Reboot system to release head solenoid.

SYMPTOM

Disk drive won't run.

CAUSES

Jammed disk.
Jammed spindle.
Dirt and grunge.
Broken drive belt.
Broken or disconnected power or interface cable.
Defective power supply.
Defective disk drive interface circuitry (in computer).
Defective disk drive control circuitry (in disk drive).
Burned out drive motor.

CURES

Correct mechanical problems (jammed disk, spindle, etc.).
Clean drive thoroughly, including electrical contacts (for cables). Lubricate as recommended by disk drive tech manual. Drive motor/spindle should spin freely.
Replace drive belt. For a quick test, take one from a spare good drive. If this is the problem, leave the borrowed belt in place and restore the donor's belt at your leisure.
Check cabling; reconnect or replace as needed.
With power cable disconnected, turn on the power and test for correct voltages on the power-connector pins. (**Exercise extreme caution whenever working on powered equipment!**) The most common power

configuration (four-wire connector at back of drive) is +12VDC (pin 1) and +5VDC (pin 4). The center pins are the respective return lines. Use your multimeter in DC voltmeter mode to test voltages. (For meter technique, see Chapter 5.) If they are okay, the problem is not in the power supply feeding the drive, but there may be power problems in the drive itself.

The most likely cause is a dead drive motor.

Interface and control circuitry troubleshooting and repair is beyond the scope of this book. Nevertheless, if substitute disk drive control and logic boards are available to you, you might want to try playing swap. You'll need *exact* duplicates for this game. So far as the drive itself is concerned, this is mainly an academic exercise. Obviously, you're better off just replacing the bad drive with a known good one.

The computer disk drive controller is another matter. If board substitution works, you might then consider replacing the major chips on the defective board. The most expensive of these, the FDC (floppy disk controller chip), is oftentimes the cause of the problem. The replacement process requires that you replace an IC, test the board, replace another IC, test the board, and so on until it works as it should. It can take time, but you may get lucky. Alternatively, you can chase logic signals around on the board, if it's convenient to get at the board while the system is powered up. (Secret: Most professional repairpersons just substitute, starting with the obvious problem areas.)

A burned out motor needs **PR**, unless, again, you're up for the effort required. You'll have to locate an exact replacement motor, and you'll have to disassemble the drive enough to get the old motor out. Try it if you wish.

SYMPTOM

Drive makes funny noises, and doesn't "run right."

CAUSES

Jammed disk.
Trash and grunge (dust, grease, loose screws, bits of broken plastic, etc.).
Loose drive belt.
Electrical problems.
Defective drive motor.

CURES

Remove jammed disk.

Clean disk drive. Lubricate as necessary according to disk drive tech manual instructions. Drive motor and spindle should spin freely.

With power cable disconnected, turn on the power and test for correct voltages on the power connector pins. (**Exercise extreme caution whenever working on powered equipment!**) The most common power configuration (four-wire connector at back of drive) is + 12VDC (pin 1) and + 5VDC (pin 4). The center pins are the respective return lines). Use your multimeter in DC voltmeter mode to test voltages. (For meter technique, see Chapter 5.) If they are okay, the problem is not in the power supply feeding the drive, but there may be power problems in the drive itself. The most likely cause is a dying drive motor.

Clean all electrical connectors, and check for defective cabling. Replace as necessary.

If other measures don't solve the present problem, and the evidence points to the drive motor, **PR**. (Or try a replacement yourself, if you feel up to the task. See page 37.)

Rotational speed can be easily adjusted on most drives using the variable resistor (potentiometer, "pot") specified for this purpose by the disk drive tech manual. On Tandon drives, for example, the pot is called "spindle speed control" and is located on the small *servo* board mounted on the back of the drive chassis. The idea is to get at this part of the disk drive while leaving the drive fully connected to the system.

SYMPTOM

Disk drive runs, but will neither read from a disk nor write to a disk.

CAUSES

Door not latched.
Dirty read/write head(s).
Defective read/write head(s).
Defective disk.
Electrical and/or electronic problems (power, control, cables, circuit boards).
Drive rotational speed out of specification.
Head misaligned.

CURES

Open door/latch fully; reclose firmly.
Clean head(s) with either swab and alcohol or head cleaner.
Defective head(s) must be replaced: **PR**.
Try another disk.
Substitute boards as convenient, or **PR**.

In some systems, you may have to remove the screws that mount the drive in the computer or drive enclosure, and turn the drive out, resting it on a piece of cardboard. In others, the speed adjustment will be readily available merely by opening the enclosure lid. Check it out and use your good judgment.

With the pot accessible, insert a speed diagnostic disk in the drive. These disks are available for nearly every computer system. Alternatively, dim the lights and shine a neon AC test lamp (from the hardware store) on the disk drive flywheel, usually marked with a 50/60Hz strobe disk. In the United States, you want to monitor the 60Hz strobe ring. Using either the diagnostic disk or the strobe method, let the disk run by trying to access it, and adjust the pot until either method tells you that the speed is correct (300 rpm). The diagnostic disk will display the numbers on the video screen. The strobe will "lock" or appear to stand still at the correct speed.

Alignment is not for the casual tinkerer/troubleshooter; **PR**.

SYMPTOM

Various disk-related error messages appear during computing session.

CAUSES

Defective diskette.
Defective software.
Electrical/electronic/mechanical problems as discussed above.

CURES

The error messages, interpreted with the help of the appropriate manual (*i.e.*, user, technical, operating system, software), should point you in the right direction. First step: reboot the system. If that proves fruitless, reboot the system with a known good copy of the software on a new diskette. Failure at this point must lead you to suspect the hardware. Check for possible electrical and other non-software problems as discussed above.

Troubleshooting Guide: Tape Drive Problems

Tape drives are specialized tape recorders subject to the same ills as any tape deck. There's little you can do for a tape drive beyond routine maintenance as suggested in the product manual: head and drive mechanism cleaning, and (possibly) lubrication. Regular maintainance of this type should forestall breakdowns.

Tape Drive Problem Areas—Overview

(1) Electrical power
   (a) Low voltage.
   (b) No voltage.
(2) Control
   (a) Computer tape drive controller circuitry.
   (b) Tape drive logic circuitry.
   (c) Motor control circuitry.

(3) Mechanical
   (a) Cassette-latching mechanism.
   (b) Spindle assemblies.
   (c) Drive belts.
   (d) Head assembly (alignment).
(4) Electromechanical
   (a) Transport motor.
   (b) Rewind motor.
(5) Connections
   (a) Power cable.
   (c) Interface (data and control) cable.
   (c) Head and other cables.
(6) Read/write head(s)
(7) Media (tape)
(8) Software

Since many of the symptoms duplicate those of disk drives (unit does not run, runs but makes funny noises, fails to read, fails to write, and so on), refer to the disk drive **Guide** for help. Generally speaking, if a tape drive goes bad, it should be professionally serviced.

Troubleshooting Guide: Keyboard Problems

Think of a keyboard as a set of switches and some support electronics mounted in a metal and/or plastic shell, either integral with the computer or attached to it by a cable. The switches, which are usually mounted on a large circuit board, are of varying quality, some with greater, some with less susceptibility to dirt and other contamination. If kept dry, reasonably clean, and not subjected to physically stressful actions (banging the keys with excessive force, dropping, yanking on connecting cable), keyboards will not give you a lot of grief.

Still, things happen.

WELL-KEYBOARD CLINIC

Go easy on keyboard cables: they shouldn't be twisted, tugged, and otherwise tormented. Keep liquids, cigarette smoke, and cigarette ashes away from the keyboard. Vacuum often—especially between keys.
Don't drop the keyboard, and don't pound the keys. Remember, they're electrical switches, not merely mechanical plungers.

SYMPTOM

Striking any of the keys produces no result on the screen.

CAUSES

Cable disconnected.
Cable plug defective.
Cable broken.
Keyboard electronics defective.
Interface electronics defective.

CURES

See that cable is securely plugged in.
Check cable for continuity. This can be easily done as follows:

1. Unplug keyboard cable.
2. Open keyboard enclosure.
3. Locate cable wires.

Using your multimeter in the ohmmeter mode, touch one probe to a connector pin and the other to each wire of the cable inside the enclosure. One of these should give you an indication of continuity. (An analog meter needle will deflect fully; a digital meter will display zeros. See Chapter 5 for meter technique.)

Move to the next pin and repeat. When you're finished, you should have established that the wire for each pin is unbroken, and that no wires are shorted, that is, each wire shows continuity to one pin only. Typically, there will be five conductors.

Replace cable if you discover a broken conductor.

Replace cable if plug is defective. You may be able to squeeze the plug shell or bend the pins for a temporary fix.

Substitute a known working keyboard, if feasible. Should the replacement work, the problem lies in the keyboard electronics. **PR**, or replace with a new keyboard.

If the substitute doesn't work, the problem lies within the computer; **PR**.

One test of the computer side of the equation is a voltage check of the keyboard connector on the computer system board. With the computer turned on and using your multimeter in the DC voltmeter mode, check each pin. On computers with five-conductor keyboard cables, you should read between about +2 and +5VDC on all but the ground pin, which should read 0. Any gross deviation from these values signals trouble. Cure: **PR**.

SYMPTOM

Some keys transmit characters, some don't.

CAUSES

Dirt, poor electrical contact.
Defective keys.
Defective keyboard electronics.

CURES

If possible, remove keycaps and thoroughly vacuum keyboard. If you do remove keycaps, draw a keyboard template to guide you in replacement.

Keycaps on most keyboards can be removed by gentle prying with a miniature flat-bladed screwdriver. They are replaced by pressing them straight down on their posts until seated.

With keycaps removed, spray key contacts with electrical contact cleaner (e.g., RS 64–2320). This should also free up keys that stick down or travel sluggishly.

Keys not revitalized by cleaning and spraying need replacement: **PR**.

Defective electronics require **PR** or keyboard replacement.

Troubleshooting Guide: Video Display Problems

There are three kinds of video monitors in common use:

(1) Ordinary TV set used with a *video modulator*.
(2) Composite video monitor.
(3) RGB video monitor.

Monitors—Explanatory Notes

The term *composite video* refers to a single signal that carries all the information needed to construct an image, even in full color. In terms of image quality, composite video is at the low end of the scale. The advantage is that the entire signal can be carried on one wire.

An *RGB* signal is one in which the three primary video colors, red, green, and blue, are carried as discrete signals, each on its own wire. In principle, and generally in practice, an RGB monitor will produce higher-resolution color images than a composite monitor of equal cost.

Composite video output must be fed to a composite video monitor. Likewise, RGB output must be fed to an RGB monitor. There's no crossover, unless you happen to have a monitor that can be switched between the two types.

Standard TV sets—color or black and white—can be used only for computer displays up to 40 columns wide. In order to use a TV, the composite video signal from the computer must be *modulated* so that the TV tuner can make sense of it. Not only is the inherent resolution of TV set poor, but adding the modulator degrades the image even more.

The perceived sharpness or "resolution" of a video image results from several factors, among them *video bandwidth*, *scan rate*, and *dot pitch*. These terms are defined in the **Glossary**.

WELL-VIDEO MONITOR CLINIC

Keep monitors as cool and dust-free as possible. **Never** block ventilation slots. Don't mount the video monitor in an unventilated enclosure. Cigarette ashes, foreign objects, and liquids must not be allowed to fall into a monitor. Don't boost contrast and brightness any higher than needed to comfortably read the screen. If the computer is left on (as it should be) between computing tasks, blank the screen by turning the brightness and contrast all the way down. Fixed images left at normal brightness for long periods can damage the display screen enough to degrade the image quality. A number of software utilities, *SuperKey*, for example, provide routines for automatically blanking the screen after a user-determined idling time.

WARNING

The casual tinkerer/troubleshooter should NEVER open a video monitor of any type. Not only is there the danger of breaking the tube, which can implode with injurious force, but lethal voltages are present in this equipment—even after the power has been turned off.

The display technology of AC-powered monitors is essentially the same regardless of the specific type. A high-voltage tube is driven by electronics that control the horizontal and vertical movement of an electron beam. The technology is mature, a fact contributing to reliability. But since the picture tube is a "boiling filament" device, and since video equipment generates considerable heat, heat-related failures are not uncommon.

SYMPTOM

Computer seems to be working, but video display is blank.

CAUSES

User video controls (contrast and/or brightness) turned down too far.
Monitor power cable loose or disconnected.
Power switch off.
Video cable disconnected or defective.
Blown fuse.
Defective video electronics.
Computer video output defective or missing.

CURES

Readjust **brightness** and **contrast** controls to suit. In a monochrome display, the characters should be clear—not overly bright—against a black background. Never increase brightness or contrast to the point where (1) the characters "bloom" or (2) the background lightens to visibility.
Secure power cord.
Turn on power switch.
Secure video cable. Check cable connectors for soundness. Check cable for continuity. Repair or replace cable as warranted.
TURN OFF power switch. Replace fuse. If it blows immediately, **PR**.
Computer video circuitry needs **PR**.

SYMPTOMS

Display is dim, overly bright and blurry, or otherwise unpleasant.

CAUSES

User video controls need readjustment.
Internal video controls need adjustment.
Video circuitry defective.

CURES

Readjust **brightness** and **contrast** controls to suit. In a monochrome display, the characters should be clear—not overly bright—against a black background. Never increase brightness or contrast to the point where (1) the characters "bloom" or (2) the background lightens to visibility. On color monitors with accessible controls for *black level*, *color level*, and *tint*, adjust for satisfactory color balance. Your system software may include a color bar display to help in these adjustments.

Some monitors provide additional "fine tuning" controls such as *focus* accessible from the back panel with a TV tuning tool. If you feel that your monitor needs additional touching up, give it a try. Make very small changes to a single control. Check the appearance of the screen and repeat as necessary. Don't expect perfection—it doesn't exist. Settle for a picture you can live with comfortably!

If touching up the controls doesn't do much good, the monitor needs **PR**.

SYMPTOMS

Display is off-center; characters are distorted; display rolls or jitters.

CAUSES

User horizontal and/or vertical controls need readjustment.

(1) Horizontal misadjustment: tearing, horizontal displacement of picture.
(2) Vertical misadjustment: rolling, jittering.
(3) Horizontal distortion of characters (squeezed, expanded): horizontal linearity.
(4) Vertical distortion of characters (stretched, compressed): vertical linearity.

Video circuitry defective.

CURES

Readjust *horizontal hold* and *vertical hold* for stable picture.

Readjust *horizontal linearity* and *vertical linearity* for consistent character size. These controls may be accessible only through the back panel with a TV tuning tool. Or they may not be accessible without opening monitor—**not** a recommended procedure.

Some monitors provide a user-adjustable **vertical size** control. This is similar in effect to **vertical linearity**. Experiment.

If adjustments fail to improve the picture appreciably, **PR**.

SYMPTOM

The video display waves and ripples.

CAUSE

Defective monitor power supply.

CURE

Professional repair.

SYMPTOM

Video display fades and brightens.

CAUSES

Periodic fading and brightening suggests fluctuating AC voltage. Permanently weak display, unhelped by adjusting brightness and contrast controls, suggests defective monitor power supply.

CURE

Check main voltage at time of fading. If voltage lies in the range, 110-125VAC, AC is okay and the problem is in monitor power supply, or in monitor's video drive. In either case, **PR**.

SYMPTOM

Shadowy images detectable under the normally displayed images or when the monitor is turned off.

CAUSE

Fixed images at standard or excessive brightness left on the screen for long periods of time have burned the picture tube (CRT) phosphor.

CURE

Have the tube replaced. This is a job that can be done by the knowledgeable tinkerer, but **do not** attempt it without full confidence in your tinkering skills! A source for replacement tubes can be found in the **Source Listing** at the end of this chapter.

Troubleshooting Guide: Printer Problems

All impact printers, whether dot matrix or letter-quality (daisywheel or other typing element), are fundamentally alike: Signals from the host computer activate the printer, causing (1) the printhead to move back and forth while printing the transmitted text and (2) the platen (or tractor mechanism) to advance the paper. Two motors are required: one to drive the printhead, one to advance the paper. Circuitry in the printer powers and controls the electromechanical operations as well as the logical operations (character selection or formation). Dot matrix printers are, in effect, "slave" computers, able to produce a wide range of characters, symbols, and graphics elements, as well as to place dots in any pattern demanded by your software. A modern printer is actually a dedicated computer.

For details on interfacing protocols and cabling, see Chapter 8, **How Computers Communicate**.

WELL-PRINTER CLINIC

Keep printers scrupulously clean and carefully lubricated (printhead rails and platen/tractor gears). Keep the mechanism clear of paper scraps. Align tractor feed (fanfold) paper carefully on tractor pins. Turn off printer immediately if a paper jam occurs. Don't impede paper movement or paper-advance mechanism. Observe the product manual recommendations for printhead duty cycle. Printing high-density graphics for long periods of time will shorten the life of a printhead appreciably. Keep printhead and printwheel clean. Don't use "no name," bargain cartridges and ribbons. Good quality dot matrix ribbons are reasonably lintless and inked with proper (lubricating) ink.

Printer Problem Areas—Overview

(1) Electrical power
   (a) Low voltage.
   (b) No voltage.
(2) Connections
   (a) Power cable.
   (b) Interface (data and control) cable.
   (c) Printhead and other cables.
(3) Control
   (a) Printer interface circuitry.
   (b) Computer interface circuitry.
   (c) Printer logic circuitry.

(4) Mechanical
  (a) Printhead drive assembly.
  (b) Paper-advance assembly: Platen; Tractor; and Sheet-feeder.
  (c) "Typewriter" components (gears, rods, etc.).
  (d) Printhead alignment.
  (e) Printwheel.
(5) Electromechanical
  (a) Printhead drive motor.
  (b) Paper-advance drive motor.
  (c) Dot matrix printhead.
  (d) Control panel switches.
(6) Software (configuration)

Printer Repair Note: Internal electrical and electronic problems should be attended to by a professional.

SYMPTOM

Printer will not turn on.

CAUSES

Power switch off.
Power cable loose or disconnected.
Blown fuse.
Defective power supply (in printer).

CURES

Turn on power switch.
Secure power cable.
Turn OFF power, and replace fuse. If fuse blows immediately after powering up, **PR**.
Defective power supply requires **PR**.

SYMPTOM

Printer turns on, runs self-test, but won't print under control of computer.

CAUSES

Printer offline.
Interface cable loose or disconnected.
Incorrect interface cable.
Incorrect configuration switch settings (mismatched with operating system or applications software).
Printer interface circuitry defective.
Computer interface circuitry defective.

CURES

Press printer *online* switch (sometimes called *select* or *ready*).
Secure interface cable.
Match cable to current computer/printer combination according to manual. You may have to open the connector shells to ascertain whether the conductors are connected as required by the manual. Some RS-232 devices, for example, require that you cross lines 2 and 3. In others, lines 2 and 3 are left parallel.
Check the compatibility of software interface selections and hardware configuration. The printer's configuration switches will need to be set for word size, parity, baud rate (if a serial interface), and so on. The software will need to match these settings exactly.

Interface circuitry can be tested for power (using voltmeter) and the presence of signals (using logic probe). If you determine that something is awry according to the tech manual, you can either attempt parts replacement or send the printer or computer, as appropriate, for **PR**. Where feasible, substitute a known working interface board. (See Chapter 5 for logic probe technique.)

SYMPTOM

Printer turns on, but won't run self-test.

CAUSES

Interlock switch open.
Defective self test selection switch.
Jammed printhead or paper advance mechanism.
Defective printer CPU (logic) circuitry.
Defective motor control circuitry.
Defective printhead motor.

CURES

Some printers are protected by one or more interlock switches that will shut down the printer if, for example, the top cover is not tightly closed. Check to see that all covers and panels are secure.

Check self-test select switch. Since the self-test is usually initiated by holding down either the *linefeed* or the *formfeed* switch simultaneously when turning on the printer, you can test these switches simply by turning on the printer and doing either a linefeed or a formfeed. If both work, the switches are okay.

Turn off the printer and clear jams and impediments. Move printhead and turn platen knob to assure free movement.

Motors and internal circuitry are best left for **PR**.

SYMPTOM

Printer works normally for a while, then quits.

CAUSES

Intermittent power supply.
Intermittent logic and control circuitry.
Loose interface cable.
Improper printer control codes sent from host.
Printhead or paper path impeded.

CURES

At the first sign of a printer ''crash,'' turn off the power.
If printer works only during the first few minutes after being powered up, the problem lies in the power supply, or the printer logic and control, or both: **PR**.

If the printer stops only once in a while at random intervals, the interface cable and/or the interface connector on the printer itself may be loose or defective. Replace with a new (properly configured) cable. Examine the printer connector for bent or loose pins; fix or replace as necessary. Replacing a chassis-mounted connector takes tinkering dexterity and patience. You'll have to desolder a lot of pins from the circuit board, a hazardous enterprise for the board. Don't attempt it unless you're confident of a successful outcome. See the directions on pages 25–27 on how to remove and replace ICs.

If something—a paper clip, perhaps—drops into the paper-advance gearing, the printer will lock up. Likewise, the printhead can be impeded. Examine for anything that might interfere with the free movement of either printhead or paper-advance mechanism.

SYMPTOM

Printer prints garbage.

CAUSES

Configuration mismatch between printer and host.
Incorrect interface cable.
Electrical "noise."
Defective printer interface circuitry.
Defective printer logic circuitry.
Defective computer interface circuitry.

CURES

Match configuration of printer and host using switch settings and software. Generally, it's easier to set the printer switches and bring the software into conformation. But you may have to do it the other way if the software is inflexible in this regard (as some is).
Check the cable for correct wiring. Most problems in this respect arise in RS–232 systems. (Chapter 8 explains serial interfacing in considerable detail.)

Electrical noise may be leaking into the data stream from fluorescent lighting fixtures, cash registers, computer systems, and any number of other "broadcasting" sources. Start by testing. Turn off the fluorescent lights and try a print run, etc. Replace the interface cable with a better quality, well-shielded one. The connectors should be electrically shielded as well. If you're using a parallel interface, the cable may be too long.

Electrical noise can also enter through the power line. Is your system on a particularly noisy circuit? If feasible, try another. If not, add a beefier transient suppressor. Add a constant voltage transformer. Add an uninterruptable power supply. Do whatever you can afford.

Test the logic and interface circuitry for the flow of data. Replace parts to the extent of your confidence, otherwise, **PR**.

SYMPTOM

Erratic print speed.

CAUSES

Impediment.
Gummy lubricant.
Inadequate lubrication.
Malfunctioning printhead motor.

CURES

Clean printer thoroughly, checking for hidden paper jams, paper clips, and other trash that can impede movement of printhead and paper-advance mechanisms.
Clean out gummy lubricant with degreaser or alcohol. DO NOT USE *acetone* or other "plastic-eating" solvents.
Lubricate gears and rails with fine machine oil or other high-quality lubricant (preferably Teflon-based).
If cleaning and lubrication don't help, the printhead motor is the likely cause: **PR**.

SYMPTOM

Printhead operates, but paper won't advance.

CAUSES

Obstruction in paper path.
Obstruction in advance mechanism.
Defective paper-advance motor.

CURES

Clear obstruction(s).
Replace motor (**PR**).

SYMPTOM

Printhead moves, but produces no characters.

CAUSES

Dot matrix pins not firing.
Printing element striker not functioning.
Printing element missing or improperly seated.
Ribbon missing.
Ribbon improperly installed.
Ribbon broken.

CURES

If the dot matrix printhead is not firing, the printhead cable may be broken or disconnected, the printhead may be burned out, or the printhead control circuitry may be defective. Examine the cable, reconnecting if necessary. A broken or defective cable will probably have to be replaced by **PR**.

Printheads are easily replaced. Just follow the instructions in your printer manual.

Control circuitry failure requires **PR**.

The striker or hammer mechanism in a formed letter printhead may be defective, or the control circuitry may be defective. This type of head replacement and control circuitry repair are in the province of the professional repairperson; **PR**.

Check for the presence and proper seating of daisywheel, ''cup'' or ''ball.'' Correct as needed. Daisywheels can be fairly easily damaged in both insertion and removal. If a wheel is distressed in any way, discard it.

Check for missing, broken, improperly seated, or improperly routed ribbon. Correct as needed.

SYMPTOM

Printed characters are irregular, weak, partial, or occasionally missing.

CAUSES

Printhead out of alignment with respect to platen.
Platen improperly seated or aligned.
One or more dot matrix printhead striker wires inactive.
One or more "petals" missing from printing element, or bent out of tolerance.
One or more printing element characters worn beyond acceptable tolerance.
Dot matrix printhead dirty.
Printing element dirty.
Ribbon dried out or excessively worn.
Ribbon improperly seated.
Ribbon improperly routed.

CURES

A badly misaligned print mechanism should be serviced professionally. However, you can try minor adjustments on the printhead. Merely loosening the head mounting screws and shifting the head slightly may do the trick. Printing element hammer force can be increased or decreased on some printers by a screw adjustment near the hammer.
On printers with typewriter-like removable platens, release the platen and reseat it. Beyond this, you'll need a typewriter service person.
If one or more dot matrix wires are not firing, the head must be replaced.
Printing elements with any defect, including age, should be replaced. Except for cleaning, they cannot be "serviced."
Dirty printing elements and dot matrix printheads can and should be cleaned regularly.
Check ribbons for "health," seating, and routing.

SYMPTOM

Paper is mishandled through the feed mechanism.

CAUSES

Tractors or pins improperly set for width of paper.
Paper improperly installed on tractors (or pins).
On double tractors, paper not installed on rear tractor elements.
Tractor closure left open.
Tractor locks left unlocked.
Tractor unit improperly installed.
Multipart forms too thick for tractor mechanism.
Platen tension bar left on (down) while using tractor feed mechanism.
Friction feed mechanism worn loose.
Tension bar left up when using friction feed.
Fanfold (continuous) paper used with friction feed system.
Multipart forms too thick for friction mechanism.
Sheet-feeder paper guides not properly set for paper width.
Sheet-feeder overloaded with paper.
Sheet-feeder improperly installed.

CURES

Examine tractors for (1) proper installation, (2) proper paper installation, and (3) proper closure and locking. Correct as necessary. Use multipart forms no thicker than the printer manual recommends.

Examine friction feed mechanism for (1) freedom of movement, (2) positioning of bars and guides as recommended by manual for a particular usage, and (3) adequate tightness of mechanism. Don't use continuous paper with a friction feed printer that will be printing unattended. The paper will wander and eventually jam up. Don't use excessively thick multipart forms or overly stiff paper. A badly worn friction feed mechanism will need professional servicing.

Use the correct type of paper for sheet-feeding, setting the paper guides correctly. Load sheet-feeder with no more than the recommended number of sheets, and see that it is seated properly.

Troubleshooting Guide: Computer Problems

You're less likely to have difficulty with the computer itself than with any other part of your system. The computer is purely electronic. It has no wheels, gears, hammers, or other moving parts. Although it can be insulted, even killed, by electrical mishaps, accidents (falls, fire, flood, and such), and excessive heat, in the course of an unexceptional (unstressful) existence, it will behave well.

Computer electronics and operations are covered in Chapter 7, **How Computers Work**. Browsing this chapter will give you some helpful insights with respect to the computer malfunctions touched on below.

WELL-COMPUTER CLINIC

Set up your system in a dust-, smoke-, grease-, and moisture-free environment, using as much electrical power conditioning as you can afford. Clean the computer regularly (see preceding chapter), and protect it from spills, hard knocks, and excessive heat. Because powering up can jolt electronic circuitry, it's best to leave the equipment on throughout the work day, even when you're not actually computing.

At the beginner's level of tinkering/troubleshooting, you can be expected to attempt (1) diagnosis through substitution as well as basic voltage and logic tracing and (2) simple repairs.

Computer Problem Areas—Overview

(1) Electrical power
   (a) Mains.
   (b) Power supply.
(2) Connections
   (a) Keyboard cable.
   (b) Disk drive and other interface cables.
   (c) Internal cables and wires.
   (d) I/O Connectors.
(3) Logic, timing, control
   (a) CPU.
   (b) Firmware.
   (c) Memory.

(d) Clock.
(e) Input/Output: (1) Video interface; (2) Keyboard interface; (3) Audio Interface; (4) Peripheral interface; and (5) External storage controller.
(f) Software.

TINKERING RULE

NEVER remove or insert circuit boards or ICs or anything else with the power on!

SYMPTOM

Computer appears not to turn on.

CAUSES

No power at mains.
Power cord loose or disconnected.
Outlet strip switch or computer power switch off.
Power indicator light burned out.
Blown fuse.
Computer power supply dead or disconnected from system board.

CURES

Check for power at the mains. Is the outlet controlled by a wall switch that was inadvertently turned off? Is there an open breaker or blown fuse at the service box?
Secure power cord.
Are all pertinent switches turned on?
If indicator light proves to be burned out, replace it or let it be. Its absence affects nothing, but I couldn't live with a dead light! See directions above for replacing power lamp.
Turn off power, check fuse. If blown, replace. If fuse blows immediately upon turning on power, there's a power supply problem. **PR**, or substitute a working supply of the same type. **Do not attempt to repair a power supply.**

SYMPTOM

Computer is on, but (seemingly) will not do anything.

CAUSES

Video monitor disconnected or turned off.
Defective power supply.
Defective system clock.
Defective CPU.
Defective memory chip(s) or missing memory card.
Defective system ROM.

CURES

The monitor may be turned off or the cable may have come loose. In either case, there will be no display and you may be led to assume that the computer is not working. Set the monitor to rights and, nine times out of ten, the computer will prove to be perfectly sound.

Check power supply voltages at main board connections. **Exercise caution when working on powered equipment.** If voltages are not within specifications indicated in tech manual, replace supply where feasible, or **PR**.

With your logic probe, check for the presence of a clock signal as it enters the clock pin on the CPU. You should get some indication of logic. If the oscillator circuit has failed, you'll get an unequivocal zilch. But if it is still alive, it may have gone out of specification, resulting in what looks like a good signal. What's a troubleshooter to do? If you want to experiment, replace the oscillator components one at a time, saving the crystal for last. Figure 2-4 shows a typical oscillator circuit under test.

It's also possible that the CPU has gone bad and that the good clock signal going into the CPU is being mangled internally. About all you can easily do is substitute a new CPU chip for the possibly defective one.

Using your logic probe, check for the presence of a signal on the CPU reset line. This line should come to life, as revealed by your probe, whenever the reset switch is pressed. If the RESET on the pinout diagram for your CPU is marked with a line across the top of the word, it means "not reset." This tells you that the line becomes active when it is "pulled" low by the reset circuitry (*active low*). Therefore, in a proper reset operation, the green LED of the logic probe will light up, indicating a logical low (0). On those CPUs in which the reset line is not marked with a bar, the line is *active high*, meaning that a proper signal will light the red LED on your probe. If there's any doubt about the operation of this line, replace the CPU.

Missing or defective memory will leave the computer unable to function. Replace the memory card. (Simply reseating it *might* work.) In computers with memory on the main board, try a "walking substitu-

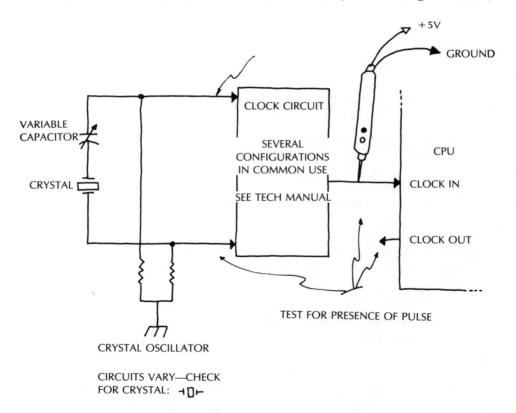

Figure 2–4. Testing the Oscillator Circuits.

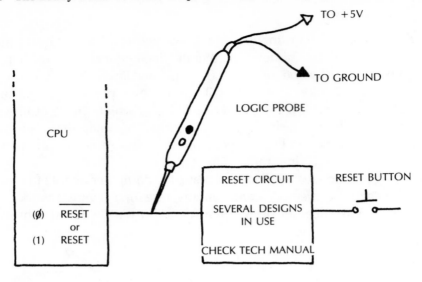

RESET — LOGIC PROBE SHOULD SHOW 0 (GREEN)
         WHEN RESET BUTTON PRESSED

RESET — LOGIC PROBE SHOULD SHOW 1 (RED)
         WHEN RESET BUTTON PRESSED

Figure 2–5.   Testing the CPU Reset Line.

tion.'' Pull the first memory chip and replace it with a new one. Move the pulled one to the next position. Walk through all the chips, observing the result. If you've got a single bad memory chip (a common enough circumstance), you'll find it eventually. The computer MUST be turned off when you remove and insert ICs.

If the system ROM is shot, the computer will act brain dead. Fortunately, this is a relatively rare occurrence. Should you be led to conclude (after other tests and guesses have proved futile) that the system firmware has failed, you'll either have to order a new ROM (or several, as the case may) from the manufacturer, or borrow it (them) from an indulgent friend. You can test for voltage to see if the chip is electrically alive. And you can test for logic on the ROM's data, address lines, and *chip enable* (CE) line. If the chip isn't being "enabled," it won't function.

SYMPTOM

Startup diagnostic routine reports one or more errors.

CAUSES

The diagnostic message, which may come in the form of speaker "beeps," plaintext messages, numbers, or any combination thereof, will usually give you enough information—in conjunction with user and/or tech manual interpretation—to get you started on a search for the specific cause(s). For example, in an IBM PC, a string of short beeps means that the main circuit (system) board is ill. Coded message 401 indicates a problem on the monochrome display adapter board. Zenith Z-100 PC messages look like this:

```
+++ ERROR RAM Failure! Address: XXX:YYYY, Bit: N, Chip: UXXX +++
```

Owners of IBM PC/XT and literally compatible computers, who have access to a fully functional PC, can get additional help with a piece of software called *SERVTECH*. In response to the diagnostic code you enter, this program will, among other services, draw the problem board on the screen and flag the offending IC. (See **Source Listing** at the end of this chapter.)

CURES

Dictated by the error.

SYMPTOM

Computer boots, but displays junk.

CAUSES

Electrical glitch.

(1) Voltage drop in power line.
(2) Voltage spike in power line.
(3) Static electricity.
(4) Defective computer power supply.

Expansion board(s).

(1) Defective board(s).
(2) Improperly seated board(s).

Defective system clock.
Defective CPU.
Defective video driver and output circuitry
Defective video memory.

CURES

Check for and clean up external power problems to the extent you are able.

Turn off power, then restart the system.

Turn off power. Check boards for proper insertion and seating. Restart.

Turn off power. Remove all nonessential boards. Restart. If computer works, the fault lies in one of the boards. Turning off the computer each time, reinstall the boards until you find the culprit. The board itself will probably need **PR**, unless you want to try substituting ICs. If connector contacts are begrimed, a good cleanup may save the day.

For clock and CPU problems, see the symptom "computer is on, but (seemingly) will not do anything."

Video driver, output, and memory sections can be tested for voltage and logic. Two fairly common problems are the failure of the video interface chip and the failure of one or more video memory chips. Check the tech manual diagrams for the location of these chips. Substitution is the remedy of choice.

SYMPTOM

Computer boots up, but functions erratically.

CAUSES

Electrical glitches.

    (1) Voltage drop in power line.
    (2) Voltage spike in power line.
    (3) Static electricity.
    (4) Defective computer power supply.

Defective program disk.
Defective software.
Intermittent clock, CPU, or memory failures.

CURES

Turn off computer. Check for external power problems. Correct as feasible. Restart system.
If problem persists, check internal power supply for proper voltages. In an intermittent situation, however, this may not reveal anything useful.
Substitute a known working power supply where feasible.
Reboot system; use a fresh copy of software.
Reboot system; use a different piece of software to ascertain whether the program itself is at fault.
For clock, CPU, and memory problems, see the symptom "computer is on but, (seemingly) will not do anything."

SYMPTOM

Computer boots up, runs normally, then "crashes."

CAUSES

Electrical glitch.
Voltage drop in power line.
Voltage spike in power line.
Static electricity.
Defective computer power supply.
Expansion card, clock, CPU, and/or memory problems.
"Illegal" procedures.
Defective diskette.
Defective software (program stuck in endless loop, etc.).

CURES

For expansion board, clock, CPU, and memory problems, see the symptom "computer is on, but (seemingly) will not do anything."
Review "legal" procedures. For example, in some systems, attempts to communicate with an offline or non-existent device will crash the computer.
Reboot, using a fresh copy of software.
Reboot, and test system using a different program.

Troubleshooting Guide: Other Problems

A review of the preceding **Guides** will give you a good idea of how to examine and cope with computer system disasters. You know that computer equipment can fail because of electrical, electronic, electromechanical, mechanical, cabling, and software malfunctions. You know that certain pieces of equipment must be properly configured via switches and/or software in order to perform correctly. So even if you have no specific **Troubleshooting Guide** at hand, you'll now be able to look with understanding at almost any piece of errant gadgetry.

Suppose, for example, that your hardware print spooler refuses to transmit data from computer to printer. You have already determined that computer and printer are working properly. (How? By hooking them up directly, that is, without the spooler in line.) To troubleshoot your spooler, use a checklist like this:

(1) Electricity
    (a) Spooler turned on?
    (b) Spooler power supply functioning?
    (c) Power indicator light burned out?
(2) Connections
    (a) Cables okay?
    (b) Connectors okay?
(2) Electronics
    (a) Spooler CPU and support ICs okay?
    (b) Spooler memory okay?

This pattern, *mutatis mutandis*, can be applied to any piece of ailing equipment. It's detective work. You assemble the clues and let them "speak" to you, within the logical framework of the system.

Final Thoughts on Troubleshooting

On that day when your computer system crashes for the first time, steer clear of the panic button. Take a deep breath, and tell yourself that people make gadgets and people can fix gadgets. What's required from you is an orderly approach to the problem, suitable books and tools in hand. The intervention of higher authority isn't usually necessary! Tell yourself further that you can correct most common computer system failures at little cost in time and money—especially so if you've put away a few odds and ends (spare disk drive and whatnot) against that dark day.

SUMMARY

This chapter is the heart of the matter, troubleshooting your ailing computer system. To give shape and substance to the general principles of troubleshooting outlined at the beginning of the chapter, you've been taken through a panoply of specific problems and their possible solutions. With the material presented here, you should be able either to put the equipment back on its feet yourself, or to determine that the difficulty is beyond your competence.

Important Point

Knowing what you can do and what you shouldn't attempt to do will save you time, money, and aggravation. Why pay high-priced service personnel to replace a bad cable? On the other hand, why send your computer (or, perish the thought, yourself) into oblivion because you stuck your fingers into something you didn't understand?

SOURCE LISTING

Diagnostic Aids—Software

Apple

MASTER DIAGNOSTICS
NikROM Technical Products, Inc.
176 Fort Pond Road
Shirley, MA 01464
1–(800)835–2246

This program guides you through routine maintenance procedures and provides a full kit of diagnostics, identifying problems and offering solutions.

IBM

HDTEST
Proto PC Inc.
2424 Territorial Road
St. Paul, MN 55114
(612)644–2383

HDTEST is a menu-driven hard-disk diagnostic program.

SERVTECH
Rylos Technologies, Inc.
10213 Heron Pond Terrace
Burke, VA 22015
(703)250–3028

SERVTECH, currently available only for IBM PC/XT and true compatibles, shows you via screen display how to disassemble the computer, and interprets in detail the IBM's own diagnostic messages, directing you to solutions. A first-rate addition to the IBM computerist's toolkit. Versions for other systems are under development.

Zenith

> DISK-BASED DIAGNOSTICS
> Zenith Data Systems
> St. Joseph, MI 49085
> (616)982–3860

Available for both IBM compatible and non-IBM compatible Heathkit and Zenith computers, this program is representative of extended diagnostics software. It tests for malfunctions in all major sections of the system. A detailed manual walks you through the whole process and explicates the error messages reported.

Diagnostic Aids—Books

The technical reference manual(s) have to come first on the list. See Chapter 6.

Since the publication of my own book, *The Plain English Repair and Maintenance Guide for Home Computers*, New York, Simon & Schuster, 1984, several such books have appeared. Here are two useful ones:

Robert C. Brenner, *Apple II Plus/IIe Troubleshooting & Repair Guide*, Indianapolis, Howard W. Sams, 1985.

Robert C. Brenner, *IBM PC Troubleshooting & Repair Guide*, Indianapolis, Howard W. Sams, 1985.

Disk Drive and Printer Information

Michael G. Peltier, *Commodore 1541 Troubleshooting & Repair Guide*, Indianapolis, Howard W. Sams, 1986. For the 1541 disk drive only.

John J. Williams, *Disk Service Manual*, Consumertronics, 2011 Cresent Drive, Alamagordo, NM 88310. J.J. WIlliams **is** Consumertronics. (Booklet.)

John J. Williams, *Printer & Plotter Manual* (publication information as immediately preceding).

Other Aids

Computer clubs and special interest groups, through meetings and newsletters, can help out with many (if not most) hardware and software difficulties. In these groups resides a vast, nearly untapped resource for free help. The dedicated computer tinkerers populating these groups are often more knowledgeable and more skillful than the paid professionals at your local computer dealer!

Faculty and students in the electronics engineering and technology departments of local college and universities will also lend a hand. Don't be shy about soliciting help, but don't expect endless hours of free consultation time!

Online information services and electronic bulletin boards are fruitful sources of help with computer problems. Many are sponsored by computer clubs. An extensive listing of clubs and electronic bulletin boards can be found in *Computer Shopper*, a publication well worth subscribing to for its wealth of parts and equipment advertisements alone:

> *Computer Shopper*
> 407 S. Washington Avenue
> Titusville, FL 32796
> (305)269–3211

An electronic information exchange service covering all aspects of computering, from simple hardware problems to abstruse explorations in the rarified upper atmosphere of computer science, is sponsored by *Byte* magazine. You'll have to pay a nominal, one-time entry fee as well as per-minute network usage fees. Some of the one-on-one and teleconference discussions are printed each month in the magazine. Check out a recent issue and decide whether you would benefit from signing on.

> BYTE Information Exchange (BIX)
> 70 Main Street
> Peterborough, NH 03458
> (603)924–9281

Sources of Disk Drives and Other Repair/Replacement Parts/Service

Adahk Inc.
7260 Collamer Road
East Syracuse, NY 13057
(315)656–399
printer parts and service

Computer Parts Galore, Inc.
56 Harvester Street
Batavia, NY 14020
1–(800)431–9008
(716)343–6133 (in NY)
extender cards, IBM PC/XT and expansion board compatibles

Floppy Disk Services
39 Everett Drive, Bldg. G
Lawrenceville, NJ 08648
1–(800)223–0306
disk drives, parts, and service

JIC Associates
1584 Pershing Place
South Plainfield, NJ 07080
(201)753–2270
power supplies

Langley-St. Clair, Inc.
132 West 24th Street
New York, NY 10011
(212)989–6876
replacement video monitor tubes

Proto PC
2424 Territorial Avenue
St. Paul, MN 55114
(612)644–2383
disk drives, parts, and service

Chapter 3
HARDWARE CARE

INTRODUCTION

Neatness doesn't count all that much, but cleaniness counts a lot. Over the long haul, a clean computer system (with "clean" power) will serve you better than a dirty one. Appreciate, however, that even if you keep your computer looking as though it just came out of the shipping carton, it can—and, one day, surely will, go awry. Preventive maintenance stretches the time between, but does not eliminate, failures. This brief chapter will review simple preventive maintenance procedures.

"If it ain't broke, don't fix it." Despite the fact that this is a mighty tired old saw, long bereft of its humorous tang, it's worth thinking about any time you're overcome by the urge to tinker. On the other side of the argument, some "fixin' " when it's not apparently needed can save your needing it later on.

Recommendation

Before tackling any of the activities suggested in this chapter, you should look over Chapter 5, **Tools and Techniques**.

THE WORKSTATION ENVIRONMENT

Electrical Considerations

In Chapter 1, I suggested various protective ways to hook your computer system up to AC service. You can, of course, just plug all the power cords into any available outlet and hope for the best. In many cases, this expedient will work satisfactorily, barring the unforseen (!). No doubt, a lot of computers out there are running "bare." I suspect that in many, if not most, computer classrooms, what comes from the outlet is what the computer gets, period.

Yet, how many inexplicable crashes might be traced to dirty electrical power? There's no firm answer, of course, just surmise. Nevertheless, here's a round number: plenty.

Since the philosophy here is *play it safe*, let's not take the quick and (definitely) dirty way out of the electrical problem. This means an expenditure of as little as a few bucks to as much as a lot of bucks, depending on the circumstances.

These circumstances include (1) your willingness to spend additional money on your computer system's noncomputing gadgetry (equipment that doesn't actually seem to *do* anything); (2) the known (un)reliability of the electrical power in your neighborhood; and (3) the importance you attach to the long-term reliable operation of your computer system.

If you can think of protective electrical devices as being fundamental to your system—therefore, part of the *cost* of your system—no different in a sense than the video monitor, keyboard, or printer, you may have an easier time justifying the cost involved than if you think of these things as luxurious add-ons that you can probably get by without.

Having now convinced you to get out your checkbook, my best recommendation is an *uninterruptable power supply* with all the bells and whistles (filtering, transient suppression, tight voltage regulation). A super-fantastic setup would be a power regulator *and* an uninterruptable power supply. There are parts of the country where the quality of electrical service almost mandates such a system for the serious computer user. Check around your own area. Talk to local computer folks—users, not sales clerks. Your local electrician can usually give you a good insight into the raw electrical conditions. Unless you have good reason to trust the salespeople at the computer store, don't count on a lot of expert guidance from that quarter.

ELECTRICAL HOOKUP HINT #1

Plug the final cord going to the wall outlet into an electrical circuit that isn't being used for other kinds of electrical equipment, especially equipment using motors, which are notorious for generating nasty spikes.

If you choose less than full-bore protection, you're playing "electrical roulette." Still, for your circumstances, an outlet strip with a good-quality transient suppressor might be adequate (until that fateful day!). In Chapter 9, you'll find an easy-to-do project that turns an ordinary outlet strip into one with excellent transient supression.

ELECTRICAL HOOKUP HINT #2

DON'T use the AC convenience connector(s) on the back of your computer for anything but a video monitor. Plug each piece of equipment into a common strip or into a multi-outlet unit like a good-quality power regulator.

An outlet strip offers its own potential, if remote, hazard, the "ground loop." All those power cords can act as antennas, capturing a variety of radio, TV, and electrical interference signals. These signals can get into your computer, turning it into a demented radio receiver and causing various kinds of electrical disruption to its normal operations. The following hint will help you avoid the nefarious ground loop.

ELECTRICAL HOOKUP HINT #3

Make a neat "cable" of the various power cords plugged into the outlet strip, binding this cable with several equally spaced *cable ties* (available from Radio Shack, etc.). Don't allow any cables to form into loops. Remember, wire loops are *inductors*; they *induce* electrical current (see Chapter 7).

Have I scared you? I didn't mean to—not exactly. I'm just trying to impress on you the importance of electrical current and its behavior. We tend to take it for granted, not realizing how irregular and, for computers anyway, dangerous it can be. You wear a seatbelt when you drive; you drive defensively; you wear hat, gloves and muffler against the cold; and put fuses, not pennies in your fuse boxes. It's not unreasonable to carry your intelligently cautious behavior over to your computing.

Static electricity can end the life of an IC or a board full of ICs. It behooves you not to pop your personal sparks around your computer. You can minimize static buildup by (1) forgoing a carpet at your work-place, or by spraying the carpet regularly (especially during cold, dry periods) with a static eliminator like Static Guard; (2) using an antistatic strip on your keyboard; (3) discharging yourself into a large metal object before sitting down to compute; and (4) wearing cotton instead of wool or man-made fiber clothing. Okay, it's settled, then. Clean power from now on. And no static.

Ambient Cleanliness

Before servicing your computer, **TURN OFF ALL THE POWER SWITCHES** and **UNPLUG** the main power connector.

Your computer system wants to live in a dry, dust-free, grease-free, smoke-free environment. It also wants to be away from direct sunlight. These are ideal conditions, and, happily, not all that difficult to achieve closely enough to satisfy your finicky computer.

COMPUTER CLEANLINESS HINT

When not in use, your computer equipment should be protected by static-resistant dust covers. For the last word in keyboard dust-and-mess shielding, there's a product called "SafeSkin Keyboard Protector" available from Ultimate Computer Supplies. This shaped, transparent, and highly flexible plastic "cocoon" is meant to be left in place permanently. (See **Source Listing** at the end of this chapter.)

Environmental Considerations

You've probably seen that picture of the cross-section of a human hair, a dust particle, and a smoke particle in relation to the surface of a computer disk. We're talking ugly-looking boulders that will grind away at disk drive heads and disk surfaces. Other hazards to the computer include airborne contaminants (especially grease), moisture (high humidity and spills), and heat.

Computing at home. Since airborne grease will gum things up quickly, do your home-based computing as far from the kitchen as possible, but don't compute in the basement unless you've got a dry one. Computing in an apartment poses problems, nothing being very far from anything. If you can afford the cost (not great) and the space (perhaps in a bedroom) for a bookcase type of work center, you've solved your problem. The worst approach is to set your computer up in the breakfast nook (or whatever room you have adjacent to the kitchen).

Likewise, avoid dust-raising activities around the computer; you know: roughhousing with pets, gallumphing around on the carpet, shaking and folding clothes, whacking the overstuffed furniture, and so on.

Computing at the office.   Although offices generally don't present grease hazards, dust and smoke are not all that uncommon. Dust and smoke can be especially harmful to disk drives. Perhaps you can't set up a "clean room" in the manner of an IC manufacturer. But you can chase the dust regularly and discourage dusty activities in the vicinity of the computer.

Smoke.   Even if you are addicted to tobacco beyond even the thought of ever giving it up, you should snuff your butt, or set aside your pipe or stogy before settling at the workstation. You should demand that others in the vicinity do so as well. When you're overcome by a nicotine fit, think how grand it'll be to take a stroll elsewhere and puff yourself into smoker's nirvana.

Liquids.   Beverage-guzzling and snacking likewise belong somewhere else. Take it from one who knows, it's mighty easy to drop drinks and crumbs into a keyboard. Once in, not easily out. Liquids can, in fact, damage a keyboard beyond the hope of repair. Anyway, repairing a keyboard may cost as much a replacing one!

Heat.   It kills. Electronic parts get warm, even hot, while they work. They don't need additional heat. Ideally, they should be cooled to some extent. Internal fans help, but an external fan (or better yet, air conditioning) may be in order. Blocked ventilation slots, an overly hot workroom, and exposure to long hours of direct sunlight all take their toll. Chips can overheat and turn flaky or fail outright. Lubricants (in disk drives, for example) can dry out or even sublimate into areas where they are not wanted. Floppy and hard disk media can be damaged by heat, resulting in partial, even total loss of data.

That's the environmental scene. The absence of heat, dampness, dust, grease, food, drink, or smoke will help your computer stay as healthy and as wise as it's supposed to be.

CLEANING

Exterior Cleaning

Computer and Keyboard

Dust. The computer work area and the external surfaces of the computer should be dusted with a vacuum cleaner no less than weekly. Use the vacuum cleaner's small circular tool. In between these major weekly cleanups, it won't hurt to do a beginning-and-end-of-day keyboard dusting with one of those mini-vacuum cleaners advertised in many computer supply catalogs. (See **Source Listing** at the end of the chapter). At first, I was skeptical about the effectiveness of these "dollhouse" gadgets, but I've satisfied myself that they do an especially good job down between the keys.

Vacuum all slots and openings. Carefully move the computer to clean underneath. The amount of dust that accumulates under a computer in a short time will astound you. Vacuum the video monitor all around, including the screen. Then wipe the screen with a barely damp sponge or cloth, drying it immediately thereafter. DON'T allow ANY moisture to dribble down between the video tube and the mounting bezel. When you're finished, the screen should be bone dry, and free of dust and fingerprints.

VIDEO TUBE ANTISTATIC HINT

Use antistatic screenwipers to clean the video display screen and reduce the buildup of dust-attracting static. See **Source Listing** at the end of this chapter.

Hair. Some computer keyboards are susceptible to "failure by pet hair." That is, dog or cat hairs can get into the keyboard and prevent proper contact. (In most keyboards, keys are just simple switches, and if the contacts can't close, no switch.) So the rule is to keep pets away from the keyboard—and check for your own errant hairs as well.

Hand contamination.   Even if you wash your hands before every computing session, the natural oil from your fingers will gradually form an ugly residue on the keys. This isn't particularly harmful, but it is unsightly. The area of the keyboard where your palms rest accumulates this grunge even faster. Keep it clean. In addition to regular vacuuming, therefore, keyboards should be cleaned from time to time with a sponge barely moistened with soapy (or detergenty) water; moist, NOT SOPPING. Rinse with a barely moist, unsoapy sponge. Wipe bone-dry with a lint-free cloth.

Disk Drives

Remove floppy disks, and leave the drive doors open. Place the circular cleaning tool over each disk slot for a few seconds. If your drives are in an external box, vacuum the ventilation slots.

Standard Printers

Before vacuuming the printer, remove the ribbon. The mini-vacuum is good for getting down, in, around, and under.

While you're at the printer, make certain you don't leave any scraps of paper behind. A little bit of unwanted paper here and there can cause the printer a good deal of grief (jams, for example).

Laser Printers

Keep the exterior clean with a vacuum and damp sponge, as needed. It's extremely important that the ventilation slots be free of any obstruction. These printers generate a great deal of heat. After all, a typical laser printer uses about 850W when actually printing. That's a lot of heat-producing power.

For interior cleaning of a laser printer, follow the manufacturer's instructions. Do this job as often as recommended in the user's manual and save yourself grief later on.

WARNING: Don't work on the interior of a laser printer for at least an hour after the printer has been turned off. There is *very hot* stuff in there!

Other Equipment

Vacuum and sponge as needed. Ventilation slots MUST in all cases be kept free of dust and other obstructions to the free movement of air. Moisture should NEVER be allowed to make its way into any electronic equipment. Sponges or cleaning cloths should be wrung out almost dry before use.

Interior Cleaning

Computer

Field stripping. I have found that *field stripping* the computer every six months or so can save you grief. Dust and other kinds of dirt may build up to levels that will prove troublesome to your computer. It's a simple task, requiring only that you open the computer enclosure and remove the expansion cards. This allows for a thorough cleaning of the inside and of the various accessible contacts, should they appear dull and filmed over.

Your owner's or tech manual will guide you in the opening and removal procedures. Opening the box generally requires that you remove or loosen a few screws and lift off the top cover. (Some screws are "captive," hence they are loosened, not removed.) Put the cover out of the way and pull the various plug-in boards. There may be retaining screws holding the boards in place. Remove them and store in a muffin tin or other suitable container, labeled as to original location. If all the screws are the same size and type, labeling isn't a must. But sometimes this isn't the case. Why waste time figuring out what goes where once the job is done? Labels lighten your labors.

Wrap each board in a piece of aluminum foil to defeat the static gremlins. Label the foil with the board's original location (slot), and the locations of connectors to be reattached.

Assuming a PC type of computer, you'll now be looking at the main circuit board at the bottom of the box, a power supply, and one or more disk drives. The main board (the system or "mother" board) contains a number of electronic components and the slots into which the removable boards are inserted. These slots are called *female card-edge connectors*. The male connectors are sometimes called *fingers*.

Dust. If you've never cleaned the computer, there will be a fair amount of dust distributed about. Don't be surprised to find actual dust monsters (fluff balls) and other bits and pieces of trash. You may even turn up solder blobs and orphaned screws. Pick up the big pieces of detritus by hand, and then go to work with your vacuum cleaner, again using the round utility brush. Give the power supply careful attention, holding the brush to all the vent holes, including the fan grill. Follow up with the mini-vac for hard-to-clean-places, such as the insides of the expansion slots and around the disk drives.

Degreasing

Grease and grime.   Computers subject to grease and grunge need serious cleaning at more frequent intervals than those in a relatively clean environment. Grease buildup can best be cleansed away using a degreasing agent like Radio Shack's Cleaner/Degreaser (RS 54-2322). When the computer has been stripped down and all the boards and other parts thoroughly vacuumed, spray all exposed connectors—slots, fingers, cable ends and mating connectors—with degreaser. Catch the drips on a paper towel. Blow dry with canned air (available from photo stores as well as electronic and computer supply stores).

Pin and contact cleaning.   Really bad cases of grease contamination will interfere even with the proper contact between IC pin and IC socket. Your eye and your finger will tell you whether your computer is nearing this parlous state. Preventive maintenance demands that you pull each socketed IC and spray both pins and sockets with degreaser, blowing everything dry as you go.

CAUTION

This is not a job for the impatient or for those who have serious doubts about their manual dexterity! It is a tedious, intellectually empty task requiring a calm mind guiding careful fingers. Don't do it when you're tired and cranky. And don't do too much of it at one time.

Removing, cleaning and replacing ICs:

(1) Note the location of pin 1. On an IC it is always the first pin to the right of the small indented or cutout area of the IC as you face this cutout head on. Sockets may be numbered or otherwise distinctively marked to match the IC cutout, as will the circuit board itself.

(2) Loosen the IC with the blade of a miniature screwdriver by prying alternately at each end. Work gently and take care not to bend the pins. **NOTE:** The metal-fatigue specification for IC pins allows them to be bent three times only—then failure.

(3) When the IC comes free, immediately press the pins through aluminum foil (static protection).

(4) Spray the pins with degreaser, and blow dry.

(5) Spray and dry the socket.

(6) Carefully align the pins with the socket holes, pin 1 to hole 1. Double-check to see that no pins are bent away from their holes or bent under the IC.

(7) When the pins are all started straight down into the holes, press gently until they are seated.

(8) **Check pin 1 location once again. This is extremely important. A chip that has been socketed wrong will be destroyed.**

ERRATIC COMPUTER BEHAVIOR?
A POSSIBLE SOLUTION

Removal and reseating ICs will sometimes solve an otherwise intractable computer problem. Erratic behavior, as opposed to total failure, can result from flaky components. But it can also result from components in poor contact with their mating elements (e.g., pins and sockets).

Disk Drives

Vacuuming.   The mini-vac is ideal for disk drive cleaning because it is small enough to reach into the head area. CAUTION: Never touch the heads themselves with anything but a soft brush or swab.

Head cleaning.   When you've finished with the vacuum, you can clean the disk drive heads using a cotton utility swab (Q-Tip) moistened with *clear* isopropyl (rubbing) alcohol (90% strength). Once again, moist doesn't mean sopping wet! Rub the head gently, turning the swab to continually present a clean surface. The swab will probably turn a bit brown—especially if you've never done this before. If you have been using a disk drive cleaning kit, swabbing probably won't be necessary, but it won't hurt. It's better to swab than to use a cleaning kit because kits have been known to damage drive heads—especially in the hands of overly zealous users. Cotton swabs and alcohol do absolutely no harm, even if used daily.

As an alternate to swabbing, you can spray with disk drive head cleaner. Aim precisely at the head with the plastic nozzle and don't overspray. Figure 3-1 shows you where to swab or spray.

Removing a disk drive. In a system with stacked floppy disk drives, you'll need to remove the top drive to clean the bottom drive heads. This is easily done.

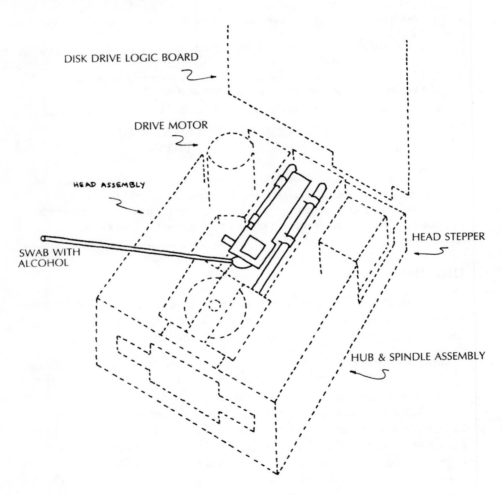

Figure 3–1. Disk Drive Head Cleaning.

Here's how to remove a disk drive (check your manual):

(1) Unplug wide-ribbon cable connector, noting location of red stripe marking pin 1.

(2) Unplug 4-pin power connector. As this is "keyed," it can be replaced only one way.

(3) Remove mounting screws while holding the drive to prevent its dropping when the last screw is removed.

(4) Ease the drive out of the drive cage (mounting bracket arrangement).

(5) Take care not to disturb any switches or jumpers that may be mounted on the disk drive circuit board.

With the upper drive removed, it should be easy to clean heads of the lower drive. Removal probably won't be necessary.

Removing drive circuit board. On some drives, the drive circuit board covers the head area, making it nearly impossible to get at the heads. In such cases, you'll need to remove the circuit board. The following list on page 86 shows how.

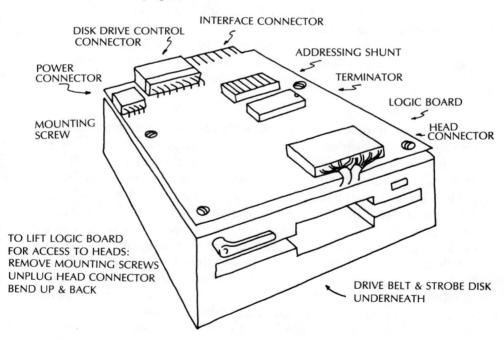

DISK DRIVE CONTROL CONNECTOR

INTERFACE CONNECTOR

ADDRESSING SHUNT

POWER CONNECTOR

TERMINATOR

LOGIC BOARD

MOUNTING SCREW

HEAD CONNECTOR

TO LIFT LOGIC BOARD
FOR ACCESS TO HEADS:
REMOVE MOUNTING SCREWS
UNPLUG HEAD CONNECTOR
BEND UP & BACK

DRIVE BELT & STROBE DISK UNDERNEATH

Figure 3–2. Floppy Disk Drive.

(1) Remove the drive, as described on page 85.
(2) Remove the mounting screws (usually four) holding the disk drive circuit board in place. Store screws safely, labeling their location in case of different sizes.
(3) Unplug small connector (usually toward the front of the drive).
(4) Lift circuit board, hinging backward. The line of connectors at the rear of the board needn't be unplugged.
(5) Take care not to disturb any switches or jumpers that may be mounted on the circuit board.

With the board back out of the way, the heads are readily available for swabbing.

Hard disk drive maintenance.   There's nothing to be done for hard disk drives other than keeping the computer clean inside to allow free movement of air.

Boards

Open the foil wrapping around a board, exposing the components but leaving the foil in contact with the backside of the board. Run the vacuum brush over the components. Then on the component and foil sides of the board, swab the connector fingers with alcohol. If the fingers look dull and tarnished, burnish them *lightly* with a pink (non-gritty) eraser. Swab off residual erasings.

Reassembly

In exactly the reverse order, replace everything you took apart and removed. Don't overlook any screws or connectors. Make sure you match mating elements, pin 1 to pin 1. Keyed connectors will mate only one way. Disk drive cable connectors may not be keyed, but the cable itself will usually have a red (or a blue) stripe marking pin 1. Pin 1 on a disk drive board will be to the right as you look to the back of the drive. (It will also be on the underside. Not to worry, for so long as the cable stripe is to the right, everything will work out correctly.)

When you replug the boards, press each one down with sufficient force to seat it properly. You should feel it snap home. Reattach cables or wires to the various boards as required. Route cables neatly around the inside. Try not to allow them (especially the broader ones) to interfere with air circulation around the ICs on the various boards. Ideally, each board should have its own free air space. Cables can usually be dressed clear of contact with the boards.

Replace retaining screws. Then do a double-check and replace the cover.

External Disk Drives

An external disk drive box is just an enclosure holding one or more disk drives, hence disassembly and cleaning operations are no different from those in which the drives are mounted in the main computer box.

Other Peripherals

Plotters, digitizing pads, and other peripheral equipment should be cleaned up at the same time as you clean the computer.

Printer

Opening the printer.   Most of what needs to be cleaned in most printers can be reached without disassembly beyond popping off a friction-held plastic lid. Some larger printers (e.g., Facit, Diablo, NEC Spinwriter) have hinged covers that give you access to virtually everything. The smaller printers can be laid bare by removing four (rarely more) body shell screws (from the underside of the shell). To get the top half of the shell clear, you'll also have to pull the platen knob—a friction fit—and unplug the connector to the control panel if your printer's controls are on the top shell.

Dusting.   With the top shell off, you can do a thorough vacuuming and trash-collecting job. If absolutely necessary, the bottom shell can also be removed. This gets a little complicated. Use the printer tech manual for guidance here. Keep track of all the screws and connectors.

Lubricating.   While you're in the printer, you should wipe the head-travel rail(s) with a clean, lintless rag and relubricate it with a few drops of a high-quality machine oil, preferably one with Teflon added. (Teflon-based lubricant: Jensen Tri-Flow, Y616B009. Machine oil: Nyoil.)

Smooth the oil evenly over the rail(s). A fine film is all that is necessary. No drips, please! Oil is a great dust collector. If the manual tells you about other lubrication points, now's the time to do the job.

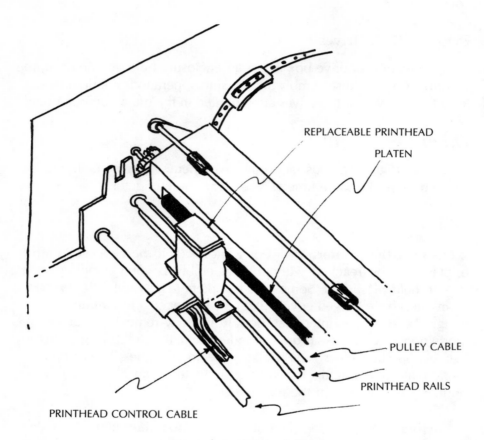

REPLACEABLE PRINTHEAD

PLATEN

PULLEY CABLE

PRINTHEAD RAILS

PRINTHEAD CONTROL CABLE

Figure 3–3.   Printer Interior.

Now get out the WD-40 and apply a small amount to the various gears, wheels, and pulleys inside your printer. Keep any lubricant away from the rubber platen, and keep all petroleum products away from rubber and plastic. If the platen looks particularly hard and shiny, it may need to be replaced. It's been said that platens can be rejuvenated with baby oil, but I've neither tried this technique nor intend to.

The rails of an externally mounted tractor feed need not be lubricated, just wiped dust-free. Ditto for a sheet-feeder.

Printwheel cleaning.   Printwheels will get as messy as typewriter type slugs and should be cleaned regularly. Use cleaning fluid that won't damage plastic. Your office supply store will guide you.

Dot matrix printhead cleaning.   Dot matrix printheads will eventually get clogged with ink and ribbon fibers. Most printers allow you to remove the printhead by simply loosening or removing two screws. Remove the head and clean the pin area by blotting with a good quality of paper toweling moistened with printwheel cleaner. DON'T RUB, just blot, otherwise you'll clog the pin channels with paper fibers. When the head is clean and dry, carefully replace it.

PRINTER-RIBBON-RESTORATION HINT

Fading **fabric** printer ribbons can be rejuvenated with WD-40, a trick that works best with cartridge ribbons. Open the cartridge by popping off the top cover (held in place by several plastic snaps). Be careful not to overturn the bottom part of the cartridge. The ribbon will fall out (and you'll pull out your hair). Spray the coiled up ribbon with WD-40: back-forth-back-stop. Don't drown the ribbon. Turn the ribbon advance knob ten turns in the direction of the arrow marked on the cartridge. One more quick spray. Replace the top cover, snapping it down all around. Store the cartridge in a sealed plastic bag for about a week. The ribbon will imprint like new. You can do this two or three times.

Cleaning Other Peripherals

Plotters, digitizing pads, and most other peripherals require external cleaning only.

TROUBLESHOOTING CONSIDERATIONS DURING CLEANUP

Opening up your computer for periodic housecleaning affords you the opportunity to check for potential problems, such as those arising from cable wear and damage.

Cable Maintenance

Damaged and/or improperly connected cables are among the most common causes of computer malfunctioning. Sad to say, these all-important components are often grossly mistreated when they are not being entirely ignored. We're going to change all of that right this minute.

Connectors. While you're doing your computer housekeeping, press all the cable connectors home tightly. Connectors that fit loosely or sloppily may need to be replaced. An alternative is to replace such connector hoods that lack chassis-mounting screws with those that have them. The DB type of hood (for many printers and joysticks) can be bought at Radio Shack. By fastening the cable to the chassis with screws, you maintain a secure electrical fit and help prevent damage to both plug and socket. Not infrequently, an interface cable is heavy enough that its own weight will help pull the plug from the socket. After this happens a few times, the connectors begin to deteriorate. Worse yet, you can accidently squash the connector underfoot.

In the event that you can't screw down the connector, just plug it in and crisscross it with strapping tape, sticking the tape to the chassis wherever there's room. It's inelegant, but it works.

Cable hazards. Since cables that are sharply bent or strewn carelessly on the floor are highly susceptible to damage, they should be carefully routed to avoid the hazards of torsion, crushing, abrading, and the other ills thoughtlessly heaped on these dull but all-important components of your system. At the very least, you should avoid stepping on the poor things.

At cleanup time, it's a good idea to check the physical integrity of the insulating material on the cables. Should you detect any breaks or abrasions, you may be looking at a cable in need of replacement. At the very least, you should wrap the abraded area with vinyl insulating tape.

Internal cabling. The cables and various interconnecting wires inside the equipment should be examined for damage that might arise from rubbing (from printhead movement, for example), heat (being routed against the cooling fins of a voltage regulator), or crushing (being squashed between enclosure and chassis). A conductor whose insulator has been damaged to the point of revealing the wire itself is in danger of causing a short circuit and should be replaced. If this is not easily accomplished, the damaged area should be wrapped with insulating tape and the wire routed so as to avoid contact with any metallic surface.

Miscellaneous Observations

Sights and smells.   Look and sniff around the inside. Should you spot signs of excessive heat (a scorched looking resistor, perhaps) or note that acrid electronic burning smell, some heavy-duty troubleshooting may be in order. If such is the case, turn quickly to the **Troubleshooting Guides.** It's not likely that such severe damage would occur without giving you some warning during a computing session, but sneaky damage is *possible*—perhaps a part consistently overheating yet continuing to work just well enough. Trouble is definitely on the way.

Printer.   In a printer, you may note that the printhead cable is starting to fray, or that wheels or gears are wearing. These are warnings. Repair, replace, or get service as soon as possible.

Floppy disk drives.   You won't be able to tell much visually about the condition of a disk drive beyond noting the dirt that someone has neglected to clean out. A drive that's been in steady use for a year or more—especially one that hasn't been kept clean—is in imminent danger of crashing.

Hard disk drives.   Hard disks can probably be repaired more cheaply than they can be replaced, particularly the larger capacity drives. For five- to ten-megabyte drives, replacement might be a better choice. When you do replace, you can move up to a larger capacity than the original.

Tape drives.   High-speed tape drives need fairly frequent attention. These should be kept as clean as possible, and the heads should be regularly demagnetized. Follow the instructions for maintenance interval and method in the product manual.

FLOPPY DISK DRIVE HINT

Since it will generally cost you about as much to have a floppy disk drive repaired as it will to buy a new one, it pays to keep one or two spares on hand, and to replace drives as needed. This limits downtime and minimizes computer-user stress. Replacing drives is an "any adult and most children can do it" job. See Chapter 9, **Making Changes**.

SUMMARY

We've considered the importance of a clean environment and a clean physical environment for your computer system. We've noted that a regular program of computer equipment cleaning can forestall failures or note their imminence. In accordance with the essential truth that a clean computer system is a happy computer system, we've opened the system for cleaning and other maintenance. In actuality, there isn't a whole lot of maintenance to be done in computer equipment beyond cleaning. A little lubrication and occasional part replacement is about all there is to it. A floppy disk drive gone bad can be repaired, but in most cases you'd be wise to retire it, replacement costs being as low as they are.

SOURCE LISTING

Electrical Equipment

See Chapter 2, **Source Listing**, page 73.

Cleaning Supplies, Equipment, and Miscellaneous Stuff

Most of the following items are available from almost any computer supply house. Two additions to the listing in the Chapter 2, **Source Listing**:

Global Computer Supplies,
45 S. Service Road,
Plainview, NY 11803
1–(800)845–6225

Ultimate Computer Supplies Inc.
1690 Oak Street
Lakewood, NJ 08701
1–(800)–370–2440

Supplies and equipment for the conscientious maintainer:

Antistatic dust covers
Antistatic video screen wipers
Canned compressed air
Cotton swabs
Disk drive cleaning kit
Degreaser/cleaner
Formed keyboard protective cover
Isopropyl alcohol
Magnetic head-cleaning spray
Miniature vacuum cleaner
Tape head demagnetizer
Teflon-based lubricant
WD-40 lubricant

Chapter 4
SOFTWARE CARE

INTRODUCTION

As we've noted, a sharp distinction between hardware and software cannot be easily drawn. The hardware both runs and is run by the software. Apart from the computer, software has no meaningful existence *as* software. Yes, you can read, even interpret, printed programs. But a printed program is text, not *software*, the very term implying symbiosis with (appropriate) *hardware*. One can further argue that the hardware can claim no meaningful independent existence. Even the act of pressing a single key on a functioning computer involves four levels of software. At the user level, **you** are the "software," which is to say, the programming agency or whatever you want to call yourself in this context. At the machine level, there's (1) an operating system (on disk, in ROM, or a combination of both); (2) a ROM monitor; and (3) the instructions designed into the CPU.

On the assumption that the stuff built into the CPU and burned into the ROM(s) is running as advertised, this chapter will concern itself with keeping the **other** software—the stuff on disk—in good working order. Innumerable computer crashes are traceable to problems with this external program material or its use. These problems may be inherent "bugs" or transient "glitches" brought on either by damage to the electronic media (e.g., disks) or by "pilot error."

GOOD IDEA

Keep a dated log of all disk- and software-related crashes and mess-ups. Identify the system, the drive in question, the operating system and software in use at the time, the exact nature of the problem, and how the problem was solved.

GENERAL HINTS AND INSIGHTS

We who have lived in computerdom for a considerable time tend to forget that everyone now using a computer isn't so tuned in on their behavior. Here, then, are a few observations about the software side of computer use:

- When you retrieve a file from a disk, the file is still on the disk. You can keep retrieving it, and if you change its name after retrieval, it can be saved as a "new" file, the "old" one still available to you.
- When you write a file back to a disk, the newly written version will obliterate the original version unless you've renamed the new version. Some software will automatically save files every so often. If you don't want to wipe out the original version, immediately rename the version you are working on.
- Each disk operating system (DOS) has its own file-naming conventions. What is acceptable for, say, Commodore computers, may be "illegal" for MS-DOS-based computers.
- If you create a large number of small files, you may run out of disk directory space before you run out of actual storage space. Some operating systems allow you to change the value for the number of directory entries allowed. Check the DOS manual.
- MS-DOS and similar operating systems allow you to create sub-directories. These are particularly useful on hard disks, for with subdirectories you can segregate different kinds of computer files, each grouping (e.g., wordprocessing files) in its own "storage bin." To make a directory in MS-DOS, you need merely enter: MD (for "make directory") followed by a suitable name. Then enter CD (for "change directory") to access the directory you've just created. Now you have a blank area in which to store files. Check the DOS manual.
- Trying to save a file that is larger than the disk space left can (but doesn't necessarily) result in a crash. Be prepared. Check your data storage disks before starting a computing session. This point is touched on again in this chapter.
- Using a program without a thorough understanding of its quirks can lead to trouble. There are programs, for example, that will allow you to do things that the operating system does not like. See the discussion below dealing with file names.
- Although some software will allow you to print directly from memory without having saved the file first to disk, never do so until you've saved it. If you attempt to print an unsaved file to a nonexistent, offline, or defective printer, the system may crash and your data will be lost.

Resist the temptation to delete (erase) files using "wildcards" in the deletion command. As you probably know (though it won't hurt to repeat it) in MS-DOS (and PC-DOS), DELete *.* will delete every directory file on a disk. DELete A*.* will delete every file with a name beginning with A. DELete DOC*.* will delete every file with a name that begins with DOC. And DELete MYFILE.* cleans out every file with the "first name" *MYFILE*. If that's what you really want, okay. But suppose that the MYFILE collection contains, say, *MYFILE.SOS*, which you really wanted to save. A wildcard deletion will wipe it out. Better to delete only one file at a time.

If you attempt to save a file to a nonexistent or defective disk drive, all may not be lost. Wait for the error message, follow the instructions (e.g., "Abort, Retry, Ignore?"), and hope for the best. Often, aborting the effort will work. If it does, (that is, if the DOS prompt happily comes back), try saving the file to another drive. But sometimes you'll end up with a crash, requiring you to reboot the system.

Some crashes are so jarring to the computer's sensibilities that a "warm reboot"—[Ctrl][Alt][Del] in MS-DOS computers—doesn't work, and you'll have to turn off the computer, then turn it back on. This is called a "cold boot."

This will be repeated: Make backups, often. Backing up disks should be a normal part of your daily office procedure. Disks are cheap; the data you generate with your computer may be irreplaceable.

Disks are fragile. Treat them carefully. Take to heart the various recommendations in this chapter on disk care.

THE MEDIA

In the solecistic lingo of computerdom, *media* is used as both singular and plural noun. (*Data* too, alas.) Thus, a single diskette is called "media," a single **type** of recording material is called "media," and all the various recording materials are collectively called "media." I would have preferred *medium* for one, *media* for more than one. And where I must use the term, I'll do it that way.

Computer folk distinguish among *removable* and *fixed* media, between, that is, floppy disks (of whatever size) and hard disks. Because of its ubiquity and susceptibility to mishandling, most of our attention at the level of the actual media will be directed at the floppy. A hybrid hard disk technology that might be termed *semi-fixed* offers the removability of floppies and the speed and storage capacity approaching that of ordinary hard disks. A popular trade name for this type of drive is *Bernouilli Box.*

Floppy Disks

A floppy disk is made of a flexible plastic (typically, Mylar) on which a thin coating of magnetically active material has been deposited.

Among microcomputer users, the *floppy disk, disc,* or *diskette* dominates as the external storage medium. And despite the earlier popularity of the 8-inch floppy, the 5¼-inch floppy now rules. Its dominance, however, may not persist much longer, as the 3½-inch diskette finds increasing favor—especially now that IBM seems to be edging that way.

FLOPPY DISK TERMINOLOGY

Density.   The number of bits recorded per unit of recording surface: (1) Single, (2) Double, (3) Quadruple (Quad), and (4) Extended Quad.

Floppy disk.   The term originally denoted an 8-inch diameter disk in a sealed, flexible envelope. Now "floppy" applies to any flexible disk used for external mass storage.

Bernouilli Box.   See *cartridge disk.*

Cartridge disk.   Actually a floppy disk in a stiff cartridge that looks not unlike a large 3½-inch (microfloppy) disk. *Bernouilli Box* is the big name in this technology.

Disc.   A pretentious spelling, though one that reminds us the word comes from Latin *discus*, as, for that matter does *dish.*

Disk.   The more-or-less standard word for the object.

Diskette.   Any floppy disk. This pointless diminutive-feminine confection is happily fading from use.

Microfloppy disk.   A flexible 3½-inch diameter disk in a rigid cartridge.

Minifloppy disk.   A flexible 5¼-inch diameter disk in a sealed flexible envelope. The term has all but disappeared from use.

RAM disk.   A segment of memory defined to emulate a disk. A good RAM disk program will allow you to set up this imaginary disk to match the formatting characteristics of any type of physical disk. The RAM disk, which can be used just as though it were a physical disk, but vanishes when the computer is turned off, stunningly points up software/hardware ambiguities.

Hard error.   Usually the result of physical damage to the disk, causing, for example, bad sectors. If these have been caused after the formatting procedure, which should have locked them out, they can give you grief. (*Soft errors* also exist, but these are program-related, not the result of physical damage.)

Index hole.   A hole punched in the disk that acts as a marker from which the operating system starts its search for intelligent life.

Operational specifications.   Access time and other disk drive hardware parameters.

Access time.   Also called *seek time*, the time it takes the head to hop from track to track, measured in microseconds, with 5ms being a good number.

Error rate.   The number of errors per so many seeks. Hope for a value of no more than 1 per 10^6 (1,000,000).

Latency.   A measure, in microseconds, of the average time it takes for a particular databit to appear at the read/write head of the disk drive, starting from a dead stop. A typical 8-inch drive: 88ms; a typical 5¼-inch drive: 100ms.

Rotational speed.   The normal spin rate in revolutions per minute of a disk drive, 300 for 5¼-inch, 360 for 8-inch; various speeds for hard disks (3000 typical).

Transfer rate.   The rate in bits per second that data can be moved to or from a disk. This number varies with the recording density. The higher the density, the higher the transfer rate. A typical 5¼-inch drive might transfer 250,000 bits per second in double-density recording.

Sector.   A formatted region on a track. Some systems use disks punched with a ring of holes that act as sector markers.

Soft sectoring.   Makes use of a single *index hole*, requiring most of the sectoring information to be provided by the software formatting routine. Although a fair amount of disk space is lost to formatting data, modern high-density recording far overweighs the loss. Used almost exclusively now.

Hard sectoring. Makes use of a ring of 8, 10, 16, or 32 holes punched into the disk to reduce the amount of sectoring information actually written onto the disk. Found mainly in older systems to compensate in small measure for low recording density.

Sides. The number of sides the drive is able to read/write, either (1) single or (2) double.

Tracks. The concentric read/write data paths provided on a disk. These don't exist until the formatting program "writes" them onto the disk. The magnetic density of the recording surface will be greater on disks explicitly manufactured for 96 tracks per inch. Typical values are (1) 77 8-inch (48 tracks per inch); (2) 80 5¼-inch (96 tracks per inch); and (3) 40 5¼-inch (48 tracks per inch).

IBM 3740 format. The first floppy disk standard came from IBM in the form of the single-sided, single-density 8-inch diskette. Since IBM invented the thing, their format became by default the standard. IBM dubbed this format protocol, 3740. It provides 246,272 bytes (call it 240K) of storage space, arranged on 77 *tracks*, each containing 26 *sectors*. Each sector contains operating system information (for enabling the DOS to find a particular sector) and space for 128 bytes of data (program material or user-generated data).

While the 3740 format remained **the** standard, it wasn't long before a number of other formats, modeled on the 3740 format, emerged, allowing 8-inch disks to store a megabyte or more of data. In order to achieve these high densities, new disk drives were developed, able to write information more densely than the earlier models and supplied with two read/write heads, for using both sides of the disk.

In addition to needing a fancy disk drive, high-density data packing takes (1) better quality recording material, (2) new floppy disk controller circuitry, and (3) new software. The operating system software controls the floppy disk controller. The controller, in turn, directs the disk drive to write and read at the desired density.

A fairly large number of CP/M-based micros use 8-inch drives, sometimes alone, sometimes as part of the drive complement. The big advantage of 8-inch drives is storage capacity. The big disadvantage is the dark side of the advantage. Eight-inch floppy disks tend to be rather less

less reliable than 5¼-inch disks because of their size, hence degree of "floppiness." The smaller disk is, perforce, stiffer and less flexible. Every time a disk is flexed, the recording surface (a very thin layer) is put in jeopardy. Furthermore, the larger the disk, the more easily it will go out of round and "off track."

CP/M. Control Program for Microcomputers is a disk operating system used primarily in older, 8-bit microcomputers. The equivalent among the current crop of popular business-oriented micros is *MS-DOS*—Microsoft Disk Operating System.)

Several mutually incompatible formatting patterns are currently in use. Amiga, Apple, Atari, and other non-IBM compatible computers each follows its own DOS star. CPUs from different "families" cannot read each other's software, disk operating systems included. Even among certain MS-DOS-driven machines there are disk-formatting incompatibilities, some subtle, some blatant. For example, one MS-DOS machine uses single-sided, quadruple-density formatting. The motive for this anomalous format could have been nothing more than difference for the sake of difference! Fortunately, there are conversion programs that translate formats among systems in the same CPU family (e.g., 8080, and its descendents, including 8088 and 8086). (See the **Source Listing** at the end of this chapter.)

IBM's version of MS-DOS, called *PC-DOS*, and its disk formatting pattern quickly became a "standard." That is, when IBM PCs hit the marketplace, a whole bunch of other companies leaped in with machines that could read and write in the IBM format, and could use nearly all of the software written for the IBM computers, either with slight modifications or directly.

The most common of the IBM PC/XT 5¼-inch disk formats is double-sided, double-density, 40 tracks (48 tracks per inch), formatted with 9 sectors per track, 512 bytes per sector. An MS-DOS disk formatted this way will have a storage capacity of approximately 360K. The unformatted capacity is somewhat greater, but the formatting information is just more data, after all. It "wastes" space, yet the disk is unusable without it. When DOS formats a disk for use, it is building a "data warehouse" out of the "raw material" provided by the magnetic characteristics of the recording material (magnetic oxides) deposited on the surface of the disk.

Spin rate. The 8-inch disk spins at 360 RPM, the 5¼ at 300 RPM. The disk drive motor may be directly connected to the spindle or coupled through a drive belt. When you access a disk, a solenoid pulls the heads into contact with the surface of the disk, and a stepper motor moves the head assembly back and forth along the read/write slot of the disk. As the disk spins, the sectors for the track being read pass between the head and a pressure pad or between the dual heads. In a double-sided system, each side of the disk is written to or read alternately. The data being sought exists on the disk as magnetic fields (*domains*). These fields are turned into electromagnetic pulses, then into the voltage values that the computer understands as 1's and 0's.

Read/write heads. The read/write head of a floppy disk drive is in actual physical contact with the recording surface of a disk during read/write operations. Eventually, the disk will wear out, just as an audio tape will wear out after a certain number of playings. In fact, the recording surface of disk and tape and the methods of recording and playback differ little. However, a tape is a *serial access* medium and a disk is a *random access* or, better term, *direct access* medium. The tape is thus like a piece of string—just as the grooves on a phonograph record would be if "stretched out." The tracks on a disk, conversely, are arranged as concentric rings, not a unitary spiral. A given file is broken into chunks and scattered around on the disk, a procedure called *skewing*. Information about the location of the parts is included in the file when it is written to the disk. On a tape or phonograph record, each "file" (piece of music) is stored all in one sequential chunk.

FAT. Despite the fact that the DOS causes a given file to be scattered hither and yon on a disk, it reads the file as if it were all of a piece, its *logical* though not *physical* nature. DOS operations are guided on the disk by a *directory*, a *file allocation table* (FAT), and pointers written into a *header* to each sector. Additionally, a *system disk*, namely one that can cause the computer to boot up for normal use, contains operating system program material.

Damage to the system portion of a disk will prevent the disk from booting. Damage to the directory or the FAT will make it impossible to get at the files on the disk without some sophisticated recovery techniques, and perhaps not even then.

Hard Disks

Hard disks, known also as *fixed disks* and *Winchester disks*, are like floppies in some respects and quite different in others. A hard disk is a magnetic storage medium made by depositing recording material on an inflexible substrate (machined aluminum or even glass) instead of on flexible plastic. Within a hard disk drive, there will generally be two or more disks, sometimes called *platters*, each with its own read/write head assembly.

HARD DISK TERMINOLOGY

Flying height. The distance between the read/write head and the disk surface while the drive is running.

Fixed disk. IBM's synonym for *hard disk*. The term refers to the fact that hard disks are not removable in the manner of floppies.

Hard disk drive. A drive using one or inflexible disks ("platters"), typically 5¼ inches in diameter.

Winchester. Synonymous with *hard disk*. The name derives from the code name given to the technology when it was being developed at IBM.

Hard disk read/write head. Whereas the floppy disk drive is open to the elements, the hard disk is sealed and pressurized with its own purified atmosphere. It cannot be evacuated because the read/write heads need an atmosphere in which to "fly." Each head has a minute pair of wings, and when the disk is up to speed, the airflow causes the head to rise fractionally above the surface of the disk. Hence, the only time a head should actually touch the disk is when the system is off. The flying head arrangement eliminates frictional wear, or nearly so. Even the merest impurity can mess up the elegance of this design. And jarring the drive can cause the heads to bang on the disk, damaging the disk, the head, or both.

More and more microcomputers are being delivered with hard disks, or being modified to include them. Only a short time ago, a 5-megabyte hard disk was considered spectacular. Now the 10-megabyte disk is already headed for retirement, with 20-megabyte drives "standard'' and 32-megabyte and larger drives available at relatively low cost.

The fact that the hard disk travels about ten times faster than floppy disks means that disk-access time increases tenfold (more or less). Once you've used a system with a hard disk, you'll not willingly return to a straight floppy system, unless the work on the floppy system demands very few disk accesses.

Hard disks are bothered principally by shock, although the later models can, on the average, take a lot more jolting than the earlier.

Hard disk formatting. Hard disk formatting differs in certain details from that of floppies, but these differences are transparent to the user. Any disk must have tracks, sectors, a directory, and a FAT. Hard disks, because of their large storage capacity, can be *partitioned* to make them look like more than one disk. Because of their large capacity, crashes can put one in peril of cardiac arrest. Software maintenance in a hard disk system means back up, back up, back up!

Other Media

Microfloppy. The microfloppy differs from the standard floppies in packaging and, of course, physical size. The fundamental similarity between it and the others can be seen from the fact that microfloppies can be interfaced with normal floppy systems and made to emulate 5¼-inch drives. After all, a recording surface is a recording surface, irrespective of its size. The big advantage of the microfloppy disk stems from its compactness and robust package (cartridge). Since Apple, as an example, formats these little fellers up to 720K, capacity is more than adequate. The only real disadvantage is lack of direct floppy compatibility, that is, you can't stick a microfloppy into a minifloppy drive. I expect that the microfloppy will not be long in supplanting the minifloppy as the principal medium of removable storage.

Backup tape. Backup tape systems (*streaming tape*) are not meant for anything but archival and disaster prevention storage. That is, software isn't written to run from tape, nor would you want to manage your software this way.

Cassette recorder. If you're devoted to your old cassette system and intend to keep it, back up your tapes periodically, and store them according to the same environmental rules required for safe storage of any magnetic medium. (And don't forget to clean and demagnetize your cassette recording heads periodically.)

SOFTWARE

Software here refers to program material read from and written to floppy or hard disk. First a few terms:

Applications software. Programs specialized for doing particular tasks like wordprocessing and database management.

Operating system (DOS or OS). A piece of software designed for managing basic system operations, especially those concerned with disk input/output. Usually, a small part of the operating system is resident in ROM, the rest on disk. ADVICE: Study the operating system manual for your system. The popular operating systems like CP/M and MS-DOS are rich in helpful goodies that many users little note nor long remember, which is a pity because they can ease some of the travails of computing. Did you know, for example, that the special function key on an IBM or compatible will display your last DOS command on the screen?

Formatter. A program provided with the disk operating system for preparing a disk to receive programs and data. The formatter sets up defaulted or user selected *tracks, sectors, density*, and number of *sides*.

Data disk. A disk generally formatted without an operating system "on board," used to store the data you generate with a piece of applications software like a word processor or a database management system.

System disk. A disk containing the operating system, hence a *bootable* disk. It's common practice to include system on disks with applications programs so that you can boot and go immediately into the program you wish to use. See data disk.

Programming language. A program to allow you to create programs. Some are free-standing like BASIC, Pascal, PROLOG, and so on. Others are included in other programs. *Framework,* for example includes *FRED* (FRame EDitor), a full-fledged programming language, but usable only within the parent program. The term *low-level language* is "low" only in the sense that it is written directly in the instruction set of the CPU. Since a *high-level language* is not CPU specific with respect to its statements, commands, and other instructions, it is further away from the CPU, at a level "higher" than the machine itself.

Assembler.   Like a *compiler*, a program to convert the programmer's lines of instruction code into machine-understandable code, but used with *assembly language*, the language built around the *instruction set* of a particular microprocessor chip.

Assembly language.   The programming language for a specific CPU instruction set. See *Assembler*.

Compiler.   Similar to an *assembler*, but used with languages other than assembly language to turn the programmer's lines of code into machine understandable code.

Interpreter.   A subprogram in certain programming languages (e.g., BASIC) that sequentially translates each instruction of the source code into machine code every time the user runs the program. An interpreted language is "interactive," in that programs are written from within the language itself and parsed for syntax as the program's lines are written.

Machine language.   The machine level (binary) code that all programs must be converted into before they can be run. The system monitor ROM can translate hexadecimal (number base-16) code into binary code, which means that it is possible to write programs in hexadecimal code directly into the computer without benefit of intervening software. Not for beginners!

Protection.   Schemes for either limiting the number of backup copies a software purchaser can make, or preventing the making of copies altogether. Copy protection can be dangerous to the health of your software and your equanimity. Most protected disks can be successfully copied with specialized copy programs. (See the **Source Listing** at the end of the chapter.)

Utilities. Programs to aid in various computer operations, like file recovery, disk copying, and direct control of peripherals. The *disk operating system* typically includes two set of utilities, *resident* and *transient*. Resident utilities are programs like DIR or CAT (directory or catalog), COPY, and TYPE. They reside within the operating system and are not shown in the catalog of programs on the disk. Transient programs are ordinary "command" files like DEBUG, DISKCOPY, and EDLIN (a line-oriented text editor). These appear in the disk catalog and can be moved around (or deleted) like any normal program.

Disk-based software can be categorized as follows.

Operating Systems

    (1) CP/M—Once dominant in the micro world, now fading fast.
    (2) MS-DOS (PC-DOS, ZDOS)—Derivative of, but superior to, CP/M; dominant because of IBM.
    (3) UNIX (Xenix, and others)—AT&T's powerful but complex DOS; may grab an increasingly large proportion of the micro market.
    (4) Others—Apple (AppleDOS, ProDOS), Macintosh, Amiga, Atari, and other manufacturers provide proprietary systems that run only on their own computers.

Utilities

Toolkits. Collections of programs for recovering erased files, restoring directories and FATs, examining non-text files, and indulging in miscellaneous "disk hacking" exercises like unlocking programs that require the use of a *key disk*.

Hard disk backups. Programs for routinely and automatically backing up hard disks to floppies or tape. GOOD ADVICE: Do it often and save yourself much heartache!

Copiers. Programs for backing up software, in particular, copy-protected software.

Managers/shells. Programs for organizing and accessing files through a menu system instead of having to learn the niceties of "DOS-babble."

Printer utilities. Programs for managing printer operations, including font selection, screen dumping, spooling, and port swapping (redirection).

Programming languages. Includes ancillary assemblers, compilers, linkers, loaders, and whatnot.

Graphics utilities. Screen and printer font designers.

Applications. (1) accounting, (2) communications, (3) database management, (4) decision support, (5) desktop publishing, (6) education, (7) entertainment, (8) financial management, (9) graphics design, (10) mathematics and statistics, (11) science and technology, (12) spreadsheets, (13) tax preparation, (14) time managers, (15) word processors, and others.

WHAT CAN HAPPEN AND WHAT TO DO ABOUT IT

Software can fail as a result of (1) media damage, either mechanical or electrical; (2) misuse; (3) poor program design; or (4) protected software foul-ups.

Media Damage—Mechanical

You've been expecting it, now here it is: the "Well-Disk Clinic"—in two parts.

**WELL-DISK CLINIC—MECHANICAL
AND MISCELLANEOUS PROBLEMS**

Always return disks to their protective sleeves.
Always store disks in a closable box or "disk safe."
Never leave disks in drives when the computer is not in use.
Never handle disks except at the label end. Touching the bare disk (accessible through the read/write slot) will damage it.
Don't flex disks. Bending, twisting, or "flopping" a disk can damage the surface.

If you have disks without *hub rings,* don't try to remedy the lack by adding rings. You can buy hub ring kits, but don't. The claimed benefits are far overbalanced by the potential for mischief. The adhesive can ooze and gum up the drive hub. I've seen drives that were so gummed up you couldn't open the drive door. Forget the whole thing.

Don't write on a disk label with anything but a felt-tip pen. The pressure exerted when using a ballpoint pen or a pencil can damage the recording surface. Preferably, write the label before applying it to the disk.

Disks are dimensionally unstable outside of their normal temperature range, 50° to 125°F, with 68°–70°F ideal. When a disk goes out of round, it can be neither written to nor read correctly.

Allow disks that have been in the cold to reach room temperature before using them. This will stabilize the shape of the disk and allow condensation to dissipate.

Excessive heat can permanently damage a disk. Disks left in closed automobiles parked in the sun are at serious risk. A closed car in the summer can reach 130°F or higher.

Airborne contaminants (dust, smoke, grease) and disks do not get along. Dust and smoke particles appear to a disk drive head like spiky boulders and can damage both disk and head.

Protect disks from liquids, especially sticky ones. An accident with plain water might not be fatal. In all probability, alcoholic liquids, milk, and soft drinks will wreck a disk.

Solvents (*acetone*, etc.) are guaranteed to do so. NOTE: You can remove label glue from the protective cover of a disk by wiping it gently with a tissue moistened with lighter fluid. Don't soak the tissue.

Don't pile disks up like magazines on a desk, and don't pile books or anything else on top of disks.

Don't leave disks in the plastic disk sleeves that come with many software manuals: (1) dust accumulates over time and (2) the disks can be crushed by the binder rings. As soon as you've installed the programs as directed, store the disks in a disk box.

Store disk boxes upright like books, not on their sides. Store no more than ten disks in a ten-disk box, etc. In other words, don't crush your disks.

Buy brand-name disks from a reliable dealer. You can pick up super cheap disks at computer flea markets. Sometimes they're perfectly good, sometimes not. It's the unpredictability that really gets you. Brand-name disks can, of course, let you down, though they do so only rarely. Besides, brand-name disks have highly polished, properly lubricated surfaces, both factors contributing to the longevity of drive heads. Unbranded disks may not meet the same standard of finish, even though the oxide itself will be acceptable.

Cull out unwanted programs and disks periodically. Disks—even brand-new ones—have a limited "shelf life." (Insiders assert that five years is the maximum.)

Don't try to save money by turning your single-sided disks into "flippies." Inside the sealed disk envelope there's a papery material designed to catch dust, oxide particles, and whatnot. A right-side up disk always turns in the same direction, setting the liner fibers in one direction. The fibers collect the dirt. Then you turn the disk over and the fibers are forced in the other direction, releasing the stuff they have so diligently cleaned from the disk surface; not good.

Label disk boxes to identify all the major programs and files contained in each. Label all disks as to (1) computer; (2) operating system and version; (3) date disk was started (formatted and programmed); (4) programs included; and (5) loading and running instructions, as appropriate.

A disk that has been physically abused should be discarded immediately after you've rescued usable files. If the disk seems not to be readable, it still may be possible to recover some part of it with a toolkit utility. Be prepared for the worst.

It's a good idea to assume that every floppy in your collection stands in immediate danger of being eaten by the Disk Monster. This being the case, every floppy of any value should be backed up with at least one fresh copy. Two is better. As mentioned above, disks age and should be replaced periodically.

Save the data you've stashed on a RAM disk to a regular disk before you shut off the computer. Or else, good-bye data. (Is this a hardware or a software issue?)

Media Damage—Electrical

Remember that the disk is a collection of "permanent" magnetic charges representing binary information. Neutralizing or inverting one or more of these charges can cause trouble. The principal causes of electrical damage to disks follow on page 110.

WELL-DISK CLINIC—ELECTRICAL PROBLEMS

Keep disks away from any object (e.g., magnetized tool) or device (e.g., electric motor, demagnetizer) that emits a magnetic field. One troubled magnetic domain on a disk can mess up the orderly operation of a disk or a program.

Never insert a disk into a drive whose "busy light" is on.

Never remove a disk from a drive whose busy light is on.

Never stop a disk-writing operation before the procedure is complete unless the software has provided for a graceful interruption: "Press Ctrl C to halt this operation." Or something like that.

Don't try to use a programmed disk formatted for one operating system in a computer using a different system.

Don't try to run software designed for one version of a given operating system on a different version, unless you're using a special conversion program. These, by the way, have been known to trash disks.

Don't shut off the computer in the middle of disk activity.

To avoid potentially scrambled disk data, pile on all the power line conditioning equipment you can afford. Blackouts, brownouts, and strong transients can do dastardly things to a disk if they hit during during an access.

Don't try to save data to a disk just when the electrical power is flickering. Wait for things to settle down first. Why? Because power fluctuations can adversely affect the disk-writing function. Ideally, of course, you should close up shop before the storm closes in.

Disks that are not normally written to, such as program (as opposed to data) disks, should be *write-protected*. Use opaque tabs. Clear or transluscent material is useless for this purpose because most drives use a light beam detector, which can work properly only if the beam is truly interrupted.

Before you attempt to copy any disk, write protect it. Remove the tab afterward if necessary for normal operations. Note that write protection on 8-inch disks is the opposite of that on 5¼-inch disks—the tab must be attached in order to *enable* disk write operations.

Installation of copy-protected software onto your hard disk usually results in two "protective" actions: (1) A counter on the original floppy disk is decremented to disallow a second copy until the installed copy is uninstalled with a special routine provided with the software. (2) Hidden files necessary to the correct operation of the software are written to the hard disk. These files will not appear in a normal directory, nor can they be copied, or even erased. The damage is done should you erase the program from your hard disk without "officially" uninstalling it. You are now stuck with a master disk decremented to zero copies. The trick is to copy the master disk(s) before installation, using one of the protection-breaking copy programs. Make a couple of backups and all will be well.

Difficulties can arise from mixing versions of DOS. Suppose you have booted up your computer using one version of the operating system. In MS-DOS, the "command processor" file *COM-MAND.COM* will be loaded at bootup. This transient disk file sits in memory only while you're using the operating system directly, for it controls the operating system commands (COPY, DIR, TYPE, and so on). Now suppose that you load and run a program that is on an operating system disk containing a *different version* of DOS from the one you boot up with. The command processor will also be different—not much, but enough. When you exit the program, and try to use DOS directly again, the DOS in memory will grab the not-quite compatible command processor from the disk. Generally, you'll get an error message. But under certain circumstances, mismatches between the visible part of the DOS (*i.e.,* COMMAND.COM) and the invisible parts (the hidden SYStem files) can chew up both programs and data. The moral of the story is that you should always start new software with your legitimate version of DOS; never swap versions in "midstream"; and don't accept pirated software, which may start the "DOS worm" eating through your legitimately acquired software.

Recovery

Sometimes, what seems to be a bad disk turns out to be an errant bit generated who knows why or how. Sometimes a nonworking disk will (so it seems) "heal" itself. And sometimes, you must abandon all hope.

GOOD IDEA

A disk that has acted badly once, will act badly again. Don't give it the chance. After copying the disk to a newly formatted one, discard it.

Troubleshooting Guide: Misbehaving Disks

When a disk drive refuses to obey your commands, first test the drive with another disk to ascertain whether it's the disk or the drive. Error messages can help, though you won't always get them. Or they'll be so general as to be useless. I mean, what do you learn from a message like "Disk error"? You already know that!

If you're satisfied that the drive is functioning, remove the malfunctioning disk, boot the system, and try again. In many cases, this will work. Copy the disk onto a freshly formatted disk immediately.

If the disk remains obstinate, use a backup disk to continue your work. If the disk was purely a data disk, all or part of the data may be lost.

Don't throw the disk away yet. First try rebooting the system, and running the disk from another drive. Lacking another drive, or lacking success with the other drive, try one of the recovery utilities like MS-DOS's *Recover* program. Likewise, the *Norton Utilities* and similar software may save the bacon. (See the **Source Listing** at the end of the chapter.)

It may be that the temperature has shifted the shape of the disk just enough to make it unreadable. Let the disk "cool off," then try it again. Or wait until tomorrow and try again.

Alternatively, if the disk proves unusable for normal file operations, and none of your utilities have managed to get the disk into working order, you still may be able to rescue text and data by reading the disk with a *file dump* routine, such as that included in the MS-DOS Debug program. If you can get data on the screen, you can print it out and/or save it on another disk. A file dump won't look remotely like a normal text or data file, but all the text and data that haven't been actually wiped out will be there. Figure 4-1 shows what a dump looks like.

Sometimes, what seems like a disk error proves to be a random system error of some sort. There's an awful lot going on in your computer and it's not surprising that once in a while things get a little out of sync. Reboot and try again. A *warm start* may **not** do the job. Thus, in an IBM PC type of computer, the Ctrl + Alt + Del restart will not necessarily clear out the errant bit(s). You'll need to shut down the system completely, or use the *hard reset* button, if your system has one—and, alas, many don't.

```
Filename= d.com Logical Sector= 01
Relative byte:                 Numeric Data:              ASCII Equivalent
---------------0--1--2--3--4--5--6--7--8--9--A--B--C--D--E--F-------------------
0000 ----->    E9 7F 01 BE 06 00 00 00 00 00 00 00 01 00 00 00   ................
0010 ----->    14 53 74 72 69 6B 65 20 61 20 6B 65 79 20 77 68   .Strike a key wh
0020 ----->    65 6E 20 72 65 61 64 79 20 2E 20 2E 20 2E 20 24   en ready . . . $
0030 ----->    56 4F 4C 2E 20 49 44 3A 20 00 00 00 00 00 00 00   VOL. ID: .......
0040 ----->    00 00 00 00 20 20 20 20 20 20 20 28 4F 70 74 69   ....       (Opti
0050 ----->    6F 6E 73 3A 20 2F 43 6C 73 20 20 2F 44 61 74 65   ons: /Cls  /Date
0060 ----->    20 20 2F 45 78 74 20 20 2F 48 69 64 6E 20 20 2F    /Ext  /Hidn  /
0070 ----->    4E 6F 20 73 6F 72 74 20 2F 53 69 7A 65 29 0D   No sort  /Size).
0080 ----->    0A 24 66 69 6C 65 6E 61 6D 65 2E 65 78 74 20 20   .$filename.ext
0090 ----->    2D 62 79 74 65 73 20 20 2D 2D 6C 61 73 74 20 63   -bytes  --last c
00A0 ----->    68 61 6E 67 65 2D 2D 24 20 20 20 20 20 20 20 20   hange--$
00B0 ----->    24 20 46 69 6C 65 28 73 29 20 20 20 20 24 3C 6E   $ File(s)    $<n
00C0 ----->    6F 6E 65 3E 20 20 20 20 20 44 49 52 2E 20 4F 46   one>     DIR. OF
00D0 ----->    3A 20 40 3A 5C 00 00 00 00 00 00 00 00 00 00 00   : @:\...........
00E0 ----->    00 00 00 00 00 00 00 00 00 00 00 00 00 00 00 00   ................
00F0 ----->    00 00 00 00 00 00 00 00 00 00 00 00 00 00 00 00   ................


C)hange, N)ext, P)revious, M)odify, I)ncrement, D)ecrement, Q)uit
Enter your choice (C, N, P, M, I, D, or Q) = Current Modify Mode = NUM
```

Figure 4–1. File Dump.

HARD DISK CAUTION

If you have a hard disk and you have to shut down your system temporarily (as in the last named case), **DO NOT** restart the system until the hard disk has come to a complete stop. You'll be able to tell by ear. Restarting a hard disk that is still spinning puts a strain on the disk drive motor and on the power supply.

Misuse and Faulty Design

Since we've already noted the contribution of storage media to program malfunctions, *misuse* here means *user misuse* of the software. For example, a certain program tells you that you should insert or remove disks only at flagged stages in the running of the program, but you get anxious and yank out a disk at the wrong time. This may result in (1) electrical damage to the disk, (2) corruption of the data being manipulated by the program, (3) a flat-out program crash, or (4) all of the above. A really friendly program won't allow you to crash it or the system by making keystroke, or worse, goofs. Of course, inserting and removing disks at the wrong time goes way beyond keystroke errors, and it's mighty difficult to armor plate a program against such blatant disregard of disk-handling protocol!

WARNING

No software designed to do complex tasks is bug-free. The bugs may take a while to show up, but beware, for they're lying in wait! Don't panic when they attack.

From the standpoint of potential pilot error, the best software refuses to accept irrelevant keystrokes—beeping at you, sending you messages (*"key not recognized "* or some such)—and lets you find your way back to a master menu simply by repeatedly hitting a particular key (e.g., the ESC key). Any program that attempts to *act* on irrelevant keystrokes will surely lead you into trouble.

A good program will likewise refuse to perform "illegal" actions. My favorite word processor tells me that my outboard 8-inch disk drives are not ready if that's the case when I attempt to save a file to one of them. A lot of software will crash in witless efforts to communicate with the incommunicado. You have a small memory lapse and the software punishes you for it! It's an easy matter to design error traps into the software to prevent this sort of aggravation.

Three Software Errors to Avoid

(1) Don't generate data that is likely to exceed the memory (RAM) capacity of your computer. This can create a variety of weird and generally disastrous effects.

(2) If your software doesn't automatically create backup files (to avoid over-writing the original when you save the current version), think about renaming the current version before you save it. Why? Suppose you have made some drastic changes to the current version and, after saving it (under its original name), you remember that you really need all the deleted material. Tough luck, it's gone. But if you've given the current file its own name, the original, with all that good stuff in it is still on the disk!

(3) Some (thoughtlessly designed) programs allow you to use blanks as part of a filename, but when you try to write the blank-included filenames to disk, MS-DOS, for example, will crash, and your data will be lost. Incidentally, it's legal in MS-DOS to skip the extension part of the name altogether, or to use extensions with only one character. But you **cannot** use a *first name* or an extension with blanks *between* characters.

There's a lot of software out there that does useful things in un-friendly ways. If you are using such software, then learn the quirks by practicing for a while on noncritical tasks. Make a few deliberate mis-takes and note the outcome. You might want to write a little file for each piece of software, specifying its known quirks. Unless you're us-ing the software daily, you're likely to forget.

Overcoming a Common Source of Difficulty

If you try to save a file to a disk lacking sufficient storage space, the file will not be saved. In some computer systems, the program may even crash, causing you to lose the data you attempted to store. Solutions:

- Check the remaining storage capacity of the current data disk prior to a computing session. Use a fresh disk if anticipated file storage will be greater than disk capacity.
- Keep a box of fresh, formatted disks on hand. Some, but not much, software will allow you to format a new disk from within the pro-gram. Better to be prepared before you start the computing session.

Software Repair

Some software with certain bothersome little flaws and infelicities can be repaired by the user. Should you have only minimal software skills, you may still be able do a bit of patching and filling simply by following instructions you'll find in computer magazines or special-interest group and club newsletters. For example, any number of refinements to WordStar have been published in a wide range of computer publications. These refinements eliminate bugs, add features, and enhance the program from the standpoint of speed and ease of use.

If you're willing to dig into the esoterica of software, you can avail yourself of any number of file-editing utilities for examining and modifying your software. WARNING: *Always* do your experimentation on a backup copy.

Here's an example of a simple warm-up exercise. Suppose you have a piece of software in which the help screen confuses rather than clarifies. If the help screen is a separate ASCII text file, you can edit it with your word processor. Often, however, the help screen and other prompts are buried right in the main program. With a file utility like ULTRA-ZAP (see **Source Listing** at the end of the chapter), you can dump the software on the screen as a combination hexadecimal ("machine code") and ASCII display. By scrolling through the file, you'll eventually locate the text materials you want to revise. The utility then allows you to type in the new text, replacing the old, and save the revised file. When you run it, your text will appear instead of the original.

Obviously, as soon as you move beyond revising ASCII text, things get complicated, and unless you really know what you're doing, you can mess up a piece of software gloriously. Still, there are lots of computer persons hacking happily away. It's a great hobby. Keeps you out of bowling alleys and saves you from TV reruns. For serious help in tearing apart and rebuilding your software, start with the books listed in the **Suggestions for Further Reading** at the end of the chapter. The debugging program (DEBUG, or whatever) that came with your operating system may be all you'll need in the way of "hacking software."

Software Protection Problems

Hidden Files

In MS-DOS, as an example, it is possible to hide files so that they will not appear when you use MS-DOS's own DIRectory command. Since these files are accessible to the software that put them there, however, they are accessible to you if you know how to find them and what to do about them.

First you need one of the fancier directory programs that come with a lot of the public domain software disks. These programs go by various names: SDIR, XDIR, and so on. If you call for a disk directory using the hidden files option, the program will display not only the usual directory of accessible files on the screen but the hidden ones, which my directory program prints in lower case.

Here's the scenario: You've decided to dump ScribbleWord in favor of FantastiText. Since you've made your safety backups, you don't bother with the uninstalled stuff, merely wiping out all the ScribbleWord files with DEL. Next, you return to the root directory and get rid of the ScribbleWord directory: "RD Scribble" (remove the directory called "Scribble"). Hold on! MS-DOS comes right back and says that the directory isn't empty and can't be removed. You return to "Scribble," call DIR, and nothing appears but the dots that signify the present and the parent directory. Then you get smart and use the "outside" directory with the hidden-file-revealing option. Sure enough, there are the hidden files. Now that you can read their names, you attempt to delete them. Nothing happens.

The problem you've run into is that the hidden files are *read only*, which means that they are armor-plated so far as the MS-DOS DELETE and COPY commands are concerned. You can read them with the TYPE command, but what good will that do you? No good. What you have to do is change the status of these files from *read only* to *read/write*. You can do it easily with the Norton Utilities, or a simple little program called CHMOD (change mode) on PC-SIG Disk 85 (*Utilities #3*). MS-DOS Version 3 owners can use ATTRIB ("attribute"). As soon as you change these hidden files to read/write, they can be erased and you can get rid of the unwanted directory.

Copying the "Uncopyable"

Software that cannot be copied by copy-breaking software can be copied by a combination of software and hardware. After all, the software developer makes thousands of duplicates. The machines for high-speed, high-capacity copying are extremely expensive. At least two companies make board/software combos for around $150. Mine makes what amounts to an audio copy, bypassing the compulsions of the floppy disk controller to put the copied material onto a properly formatted disk. The point of the protection is to create sector patterns on the disk that are usable by the operating system but unfamiliar to the formatting and copying routines of the operating system. The point of a copy board is to copy exactly what's on the disk, regardless of how peculiar it may be. (See the **Source Listing** at the end of the chapter.)

To free you of the need to use a "key disk," there are programs around with names like *Unkey* and *Unlock*. These are not hard to use, but may not work on the particular piece of software you'd like to unlock. Always experiment with a backup copy of the original!

The ethics of copying. For the record, I **do not** advocate copying software for any reason other than backing it up. Copying for any other purpose is both unethical and illegal. However, life is too short to waste it waiting for a company to ship you a replacement copy of the zonked disk of a program that you need now—not next week or next month. Then there's the sad case of the company that no longer exists, and so forth. Happily, more and more software developers are coming around to the no-protection view of reality.

Warning

Abroad in the public domain are programs that have been designed explicitly to destroy your software. Some can even unformat your hard disk, trashing all the data thereon. This is by no means a major problem, but it does exist. See Alfred Glossbrenner's article, "Trojan-Horse Programs Invade the Public Domain," *Lotus*, July 1986, pp. 13–14.

SUMMARY

Media and software problems arise almost daily. Most of them aren't fatal. In this chapter, we've looked at preventive measures, causes, and cures. Disks are relatively fragile and should be handled with more than a modicum of care. They are subject to mechanical and electrical damage, the former trashing the disk, the latter screwing up disk formatting and/or program material. Software can fail because of disk problems, user mistakes, and built-in bugs. Some software is truly friendly; that is, well protected against user mistakes. Much is only partially so, and much is downright irascible. Learn the limits of your software's tolerance for input errors and other improper actions. But because no software is truly bug-free, don't be shocked, and don't panic, when bugs appear, causing odd things to happen, including flat-out crashes.

We noted that you can modify software, even if you are not knowledgeable in the aracana of program design and structure. You can get a great deal of guidance in computer publications and books devoted to the inner workings of your computer system's software, as well as through clubs and users' groups. Many utilities are available, most of them at very low cost, for examining and modifying software.

Finally, we touched on copy protection and how—for legitimate reasons only!—to get around it.

SOURCE LISTING

Disk Utilities

Public domain software

Send for catalogs. This "freeware" and "shareware" covers the whole range of software, but included are many clever and extremely helpful utilities. Cost is usually around $5/disk.

B&L Consultants & Sales
Box 461
Wabash, IN 46992
Apple and Macintosh

Computer Software International
Route #2, Box 478
Utica, KY 42376
Apple

Heath Users' Group (HUG)
Hilltop Road
St. Joseph, MI 49085
(616)982–3463
Heath/Zenith, IBM compatible

PC Software Interest Group (PC-SIG)
1030D East Duane Avenue
Sunnyvale, CA 94086
(408)730–9291
IBM and compatibles

Public Domain User's Group
Box 1442-CO
Orangepark, FL 32067
IBM, CP/M, Commodore

Specific Utilities

NOTE: The IBM products will run with true compatibles (Compaq, Zenith, AT&T, etc.)

Central Point Software, Inc.
9700 S.W. Capitol Hwy., #100
Portland, OR 97219
(503)244–5782
copy boards/software for most popular computers

CopyWrite
Quaid Software Limited
45 Charles Street East
Toronto, Ontario M4Y 1S2
Canada
(416)961–8243
IBM disk copy program

Disk Toolkit
Morgan Computing Co., Inc.
P.O. Box 112730
Carrollton, TX 75011
(214)245–4763
IBM disk maintenance utilities

Master-Key
Sharpe Systems Corporation
2320 E Street
La Verne, CA 91750
(714)596-0700
IBM software disassembler

Media Master
Intersecting Concepts
4573 Heatherglen Court
Moorpark, CA 93021
(805)529–5073
CP/M, MS-DOS format conversion

The Norton Utilities
2210 Wilshire Boulevard
Santa Monica, CA 90403
(213)453–2361
IBM data recovery, disk management

ULTRA Utilities
The FreeSoft Company
P.O. Box 27608
St. Louis, MO 63146
(Also from PC-SIG)
IBM disk and file recovery

Suggestions for Further Reading

John M. Alswang, *Macintosh*, New York, NY: Brady Books, 1985.

David E. Cortesi, *A Programmer's Notebook: Utilities for CP/M- 80*, Reston, VA:, Reston Publishing Company, 1983.

Alfred Glossbrenner, *How to Buy Software*, New York, NY: St. Martin's Press, 1985.

James E. Kelley, *PC Secrets*, Berkeley, CA: Osborne/McGraw-Hill, 1986.

Robert Krumm *Getting the Most from Utilities on the IBM PC*, New York, NY: Brady Books, 1986.

Gary Little, *Inside the Apple IIc*, New York, NY: Brady Books, 1985.

Gary Little, *Inside the Apple IIe*, New York, NY: Brady Books, 1985.

Peter Norton, *Inside the IBM PC, Revised and Expanded*, New York, NY: Brady Books, 1986.

Chapter 5

TOOLS AND TECHNIQUES

INTRODUCTION

This chapter introduces you to the basic tools and techniques of computer care and repair. Since most of the tools used for household chores—the old pliers, hammer, saw, chisel, file, and so on—won't do for electronic work, you now have an official excuse to buy yourself a new collection of goodies!

A Note to the Tool Shy

The potential troubleshooter who really doesn't want to attempt tool-related activities can rest easy, for most of the troubleshooting and maintenance procedures suggested in this book require *at most* the use of a screwdriver.

TOOLS

Your new tools should be the best you can afford. Jensen (JE) specializes in high-quality tools; but you'll not go wrong at Radio Shack (RS), Heath/Zenith (HZ), and similar suppliers. Bargain hardware, on the other hand, will in the long run prove to be a waste of money. You won't need very many items, so splurge a little! Note: Although I've included catalog numbers for most items, these are representative, not inevitable choices. The **Source Listing** at the end of this chapter includes a list of suppliers.

Handtools

> Phillips and flat-bladed screwdriver set (JE FF23B006)
> Nut drivers (RS 64–1800)
> Miniature nut, screw, and Allen driver set (RS 64–1961)
> Long-nose pliers (about 5") (JE AA66B657)
> Diagonal cutter (about 5") (JE AA1B005)
> Wire stripper (RS 64–1919)
> Hobby knife, tweezers (forceps)—the longer the better

A nifty collection of tools at a (fairly) reasonable cost is Jensen's JTK–6 "Mean Little Kit" (JE FF–6). Neatly stashed in a zippered case, this outfit comes with all the tools you're likely to need for disassembly, reassembly, and tinkering. And it even includes a basic soldering kit (similar to the one suggested below, though lacking a stand and a vacuum desolderer).

Industrial-grade electronic soldering equipment is costly; however, for general-purpose tinkering (making cables and so forth), you can put together an adequate soldering kit. The following sections offer suggestions.

Soldering Tools

> Low-wattage (about 12–25W) miniature soldering iron (JE FF47B120)
> Soldering stand (RS 64-2078)
> Vacuum-type desoldering tool (RS 64-2085)
> Soldering aids (RS 64-2227)
> Desoldering braid (RS 64-2090)
> Rosin core solder, .050, 60/40 (60% tin, 40% lead) (RS 64-006)

WARNING—Do not use your utility soldering gun, which can fry electronic components in an instant.

Test Equipment

The only essential piece of test equipment for the casual trouble-shooter is the *multimeter* (pronounced **MUL**time**ter**), which can be used to test for electrical shorts (that is, continuity) and opens (broken circuits, the opposite of shorts), as well as for AC voltage, DC voltage, resistance, and current. Later on I'll show you how to make these tests.

While not really necessary for general troubleshooting, the *logic probe* can be of inestimable value for those troubleshooters who really want to dig into the computer. With a logic probe, you can determine

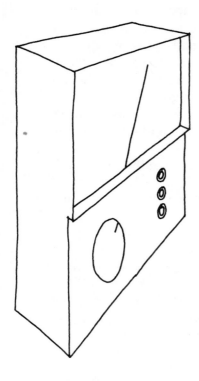

ANALOG MULTIMETER

Figure 5–1a. Analog Multimeter & Meter Probes.

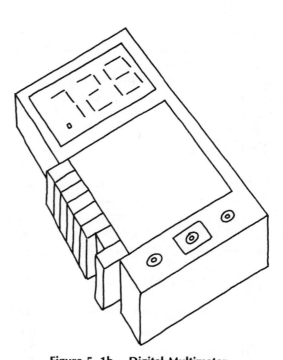

Figure 5–1b. Digital Multimeter.

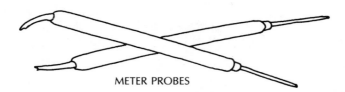

METER PROBES

the presence and state of digital signals entering and leaving particular points in a digital circuit, a circuit made principally of digital circuits called ICs *integrated circuits* or "chips." The status of the signals—the ones and zeros that constitute binary or digital logic—at any given moment determines what's going on. If an expected value isn't at a particular point, you have begun to localize the problem. The logic probe provides an easy way to discover what's going on.

These are moderately priced and entirely adequate: analog multimeter (RS 22–210) or digital multimeter (RS 22–191); and logic probe (OK Industries PRB–1).

NOTE: You don't need both multimeter types. See the discussion of the two types on pages 134–135.

TECHNIQUES

In order to solve hardware problems, you'll need to know (1) how to use various tools—particularly (on certain occasions) the soldering iron, (2) how to disassemble and reassemble the computer or peripheral equipment, (3) how to troubleshoot, and, as part of the troubleshooting process, (4) how to use a multimeter.

Using Tools in General

The overriding principle is to use the right tool for the job at hand. This means, for example, that the blade of the screwdriver should fit snugly into the slot of the screw. A loose fit may damage the slot and/or result in the blade's slipping out while you're working, which can in turn scratch or otherwise damage the equipment or give you a painful gouge. Likewise, it means using pliers of the right shape and size, metric nut drivers on metric nuts, and so on.

Avoid at all costs screwdrivers with worn (rounded) blades. Such tools will slip in use and can damage you and your equipment.

Notes on Tool Use

Loosen and tighten hex nuts with nut drivers (metric or inch, as appropriate), not pliers, and unless the wire is very fine, cut it with cutting pliers not scissors—to protect the scissors.

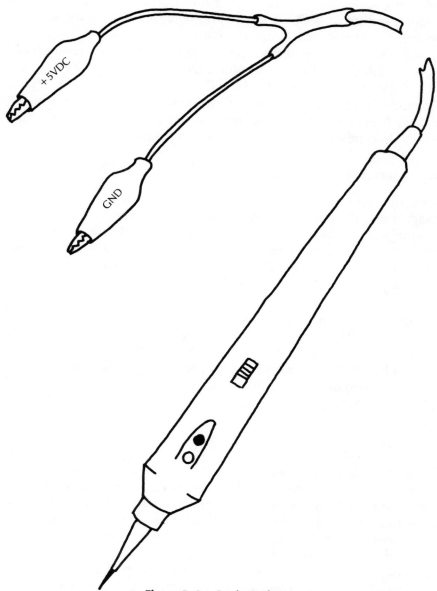

Figure 5–2.   Logic Probe.

Adjust your wire strippers for the gauge of wire you're stripping, unless, of course, you have a stripper that adjusts automatically. You can use a pocket or hobby knife to strip wire, but it's a nuisance and more often than not, you'll nick the wire itself.

If you have to clip a wire on a circuit board, use side cutters or flush cutters, clipping just above the solder. Don't twist as you cut or you may pull the foil away from the board.

Computer tools shouldn't be magnetized, but sometimes they get that way. There's no harm in this unless you plunk such a tool down on a floppy disk, in which case, plan on reformatting the disk!

Demagnetizing Small Tools

One safe application for a heavy-duty soldering gun is as a tool demagnetizer. What this trick does is turn the secondary winding of the soldering iron transformer into a "magnetic flux disorganizer." The same principle is used when you demagnetize a tape deck or bulk erase tapes or floppy disks. However, DON'T use a soldering iron for those tasks! Here's how:

(1) Turn on the iron.
(2) Slide the blade of the magnetized screwdriver (or whatever) between the two soldering-tip holders that protrude from the body of the gun.
(3) Gradually withdraw the blade to a foot or so from the iron.
(4) Do this one or two more times.
(5) Turn off the iron.

Tool Care

It's a good idea to give your tools a wipe with a silicone-impregnated cloth every once in a while, but don't overdo it. Alternatively, you can wipe them with a slightly oily rag, using a paper towel to clean off all but the merest hint of oil. Except for certain pieces of actual machinery in your computer system, electronic equipment dislikes oil as much as it does other liquids, except those like *electronic contact cleaner* and *degreaser*, explicitly made for the purpose. (Note that *silicone* and *silicon* are different materials, the former used in lubricants, Silly Putty, and so on, the latter in integrated circuits.)

Soldering and Desoldering

Soldering

Although there's a lot more to soldering than you might imagine, your purposes will be served without an advanced degree in the subject. In essence, soldering involves the heating of the joint in question with an iron of adequate tip temperature (approximately 700°F) and allowing the solder to flow neatly over the joint, forming a smooth, bright union.

An *important point* to keep in mind, whether you're soldering or desoldering, is to heat electronic components only long enough to get the job done. Think of electronic parts as Alaskans rather than Floridians in their environmental preference.

Heat. To bring the joint to the ideal temperature, hold the soldering tip to it for a count of "1,001, 1,002, 1,003." Then you touch the solder to the joint (not the iron). The solder will melt almost instantly and begin to invade the joint. As soon as the joint is covered with solder, but not drowned in it, remove the solder wire, then the iron. A few puffs of air on the joint hastens cooling and hardening.

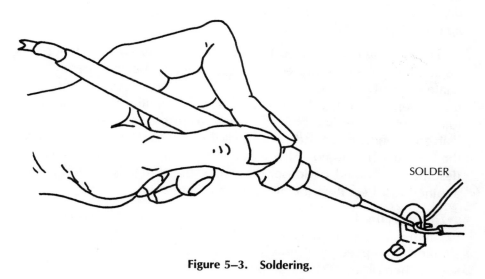

SOLDER

Figure 5–3. Soldering.

Appearance.   The finished joint should be smooth and shiny. If is looks frosty, dirty, or globular, it's a poor joint and should be desoldered (see page 129) and redone.

Tip cleaniness.   As hot as the soldering tip may be, it will not do a proper job of melting the solder if it isn't clean and bright, a condition achieved by wiping the tip on a damp sponge after every connection. Any sponge will do—the denser the better. Note that the sponge should be damp, not soaking wet.

Wire preparation.   Should you need to connect a braided wire, such as you'd use in cable-making or repairing, strip the wire back about ¼ inch, twist the fine wires tightly together, heat the exposed wire, and touch solder to the tip. A *small* amount of solder should be "wicked" into the prepared wire. When you solder the prepared wire to the target point, the solder you've melted into the wire will help in making the connection.

Desoldering

Occasions arise in this business when you have to take apart a solder joint—to remove a bad component, repair a poor soldering job, whatever—a task made easy by using either desoldering braid or a vacuum desoldering tool, or both. Of course, some joints can be simply cut apart, but you'll still have to clean up the old solder.

Desoldering braid.   Desoldering braid, copper wicking that soaks up molten solder, is placed over the point to be desoldered, then heated directly at that point with your iron. You'll soon see the braid turn silver, a sign that the unwanted solder is being drawn out of the joint. Keep moving the braid to expose a fresh section until no more "silvering" occurs, an indication that the joint is desoldered. Remove the heat and the braid. Although the two wires, or whatever you're desoldering, should be loose, they may still be lightly tacked to one another. Just heat them briefly and pull them apart.

Desoldering tool.   This spring-loaded gizmo actually works like a vacuum cleaner, sucking the solder into a small chamber, which should be emptied from time to time. To use the tool, first cock the spring, then place the hot iron directly on the joint you are desoldering and melt the old solder. When the solder is runny, place the tip of the

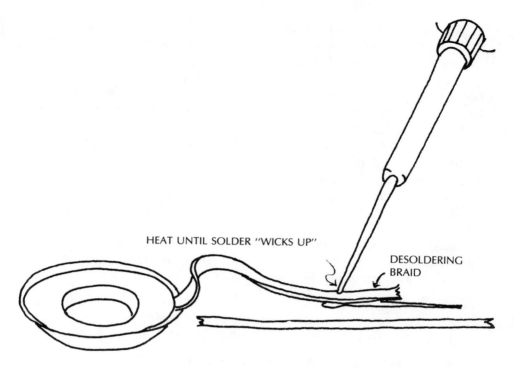

HEAT UNTIL SOLDER "WICKS UP"

DESOLDERING
BRAID

Figure 5—4. Desoldering with Desoldering Braid.

solder sucker into the puddle of solder and press the trigger. It may take more than one go around to clean the joint sufficiently. And you may have to do some final "touching up" with the braid.

Disassembly and Assembly

General Principles

Wherever possible, use the manual that accompanies the equipment for guidance in disassembly/reassembly. In the event you bought manual-less used equipment, order a manual from the manufacturer. It'll cost you something, but it's worth it. You might also check your local bookstore for computer hardware specific books.

Always turn the power to all equipment **off**. To be absolutely safe, disconnect the system power strip from the wall socket.

Don't wear jewelry—particularly dangling things (necklaces, brace-lets) or rings—while you're working on electronic equipment. Short sleeves are better than long sleeves, too.

Make notes to remind yourself where everything belongs. The con-nectors of internal cables may not be "keyed," which means that you have to note the proper orientation of the pins (1 to 1, etc.), labeling with a felt marker or a stick-on label.

Store nuts, screws, and other loose pieces in a labeled muffin tin, or some other compartmented container.

Don't use excessive force. If something doesn't budge under reason-able torque or pull, it may require the release of an unnoted connector of some sort. Check; disassembly screws are sometimes hidden under labels or decorative panels.

Disassemble only far enough to do the job at hand. The large items (like boards) you remove should be placed out of harm's way, each labeled as to original location and orientation.

Cable connectors. To detach cable connectors from their mates, grasp the body of the connector—not the cable itself—and pull gently, "rocking" ever so gently from side to side (if necessary) to break free.

Nuts and screws. Nuts and screws should be tightened firmly, but not torqued down like automotive head bolts! As soon as you feel the turning element (screw or nut) "bite," the job is done.

Enclosures. Using the correct driver of the correct size, remove the screws or bolts (unless they are of the "captive" type), store in the muffin tin, and make a note of the location of each type or size of screw in those circumstances where the manufacturer has been thoughtless enough to use more than one type or size. Then remove the enclosure lid—sometimes by sliding, sometimes by simply pulling apart. Check to make certain that no wires—such as those to a pilot (power-on) light—are attached to the part you are removing. If there are such, they should be easily unpluggable. Make a note of how the wires are oriented.

Circuit boards. Typically, an expansion circuit board comes with a "plug"—nothing but a section of the board itself provided with a bank of contacts, sometimes called "fingers"—that is inserted into a slotted connector on the main computer circuit board, making what is termed a *card-edge connection*. Circuit boards may be held rigidly in their slots by (1) a pair of guides in a *card cage*; (2) a guide and a screw-down bracket (IBM PC type); or (3) merely the slot itself (Apple IIe). Externally mounted circuit boards are either fitted into an *expansion chassis* in the ways already described, or take the form of plug-in cartridges (*e.g.*, Commodore 64).

Where required, remove the screw and put in the muffin tin. Then grasp the board, avoiding the components on the board, and pull up, rocking gently for and aft as necessary to ease the board's connecting "fingers" out of the expansion slot. As soon as the board is out, place it on a sheet of aluminum foil large enough to accommodate the entire foil side of the board. This ties all of the electronic parts to a common ground and minimizes the danger of static electricity's zapping the board.

Remounting circuit boards. Remounting requires that you seat the connecting fingers properly in the slot while making certain that the board slides into the correct board guide (at the opposite end from

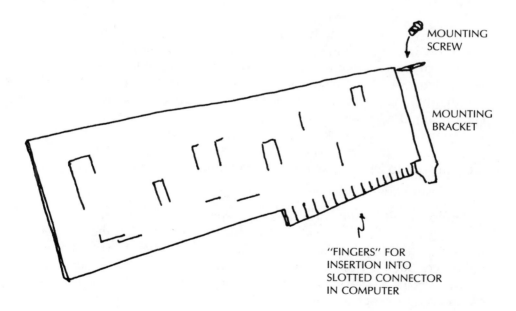

MOUNTING
SCREW

MOUNTING
BRACKET

"FINGERS" FOR
INSERTION INTO
SLOTTED CONNECTOR
IN COMPUTER

Figure 5–5. Expansion Board.

the screw bracket). When you press directly down on the board, you should feel it sort of snap into the slot. Don't forget the mounting screw.

The Multimeter

The *multimeter* is used to measure voltage, resistance, continuity, and current, that is, it can be an *AC or DC voltmeter*, an *ohmmeter*, and an *AC or DC ammeter*.

Voltage and resistance are measured in *parallel* with the circuit; current is measured in *series* with it. But before we take our measurements, let's look at the meter itself.

Meter Types

Each of the two general types of multimeter, *analog* and *digital* has its preferred uses. For measuring fixed values, the digital meter is appropriate. For noting fluctuations or for tuning a value to a given point, the analog meter seems more informative, at least to me. Compare the sense of time you get from an analog timepiece and digital one. With the latter, you know exactly what moment you're in; with the former you know how that moment relates to the passing hour.

So what meter should you buy if you're buying only one? Digital. Why? Because most, if not all, your measurements will be of fixed values, not ranges and fluctuations. Anyway, it's not as if a digital meter can't respond adequately to changes. On the contrary, a digital meter will sometimes flick back and forth between two adjacent values in a most disconcerting way, whereas the inertia of the analog meter's needle will tend to keep it fixed at a given point on the scale. I have both types.

Analog multimeter. The analog meter can be recognized by its swinging pointer and numeric scale. The extent to which the pointer moves is *analogous* to the value of the electrical characteristic being measured. Such a view of, say, variable voltage is valuable when you are looking for a peak value while adjusting a control like a potentiometer (that is, a variable resistor or "pot"). It's easy to watch the needle swing to the point of greatest deflection. However, this type of measurement is uncommon in basic computer troubleshooting. You can get an adequate analog meter for between $30 and $50.

Digital multimeter. The digital meter reveals its measurements as numbers on either a light-emitting diode display (LED) or liquid crystal display (LCD). The former is usually red, the latter grayish. Because LEDs use up a lot of battery power, most the current crop of hand-held meters use the LCD. The principle advantage of the digital meter is the (ostensible) precision of the reading. If a voltage is 4.89V, and the meter is accurately calibrated, the display will show 4.89. You won't have to guess at precisely where a needle is pointing. Of course, the cheaper meters (of either type) cannot be expected to be as accurate over the full range of their capability as the more expensive ones.

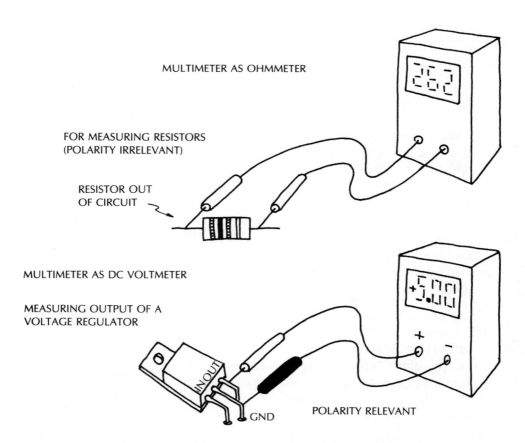

Figure 5–6. Multimeter As Ohmeter and DC Voltmeter.

Using a Multimeter

This table specifies the disposition of *probe points* for measurement:

Measurement	Meter Setting	Probe Points	Power
Resistance or continuity	OHMS	IN PARALLEL with circuit	OFF
Voltage	AC or DC VOLTS	IN PARALLEL with circuit	ON
Current	AC or DC AMPS	IN SERIES with circuit	ON

Figures 5-7a and b show the way the measurements are actually taken.

Before taking any measurement, set the meter for the *type* of measurement (resistance, AC or DC voltage, AC or DC current) and for the highest anticipated *range*.

Measuring DC voltage. Since DC is *polarized*, that is, it has fixed positive and negative poles or values, the probe should be used accordingly, the black probe plugged into the "common" or *negative* socket on the meter, and the red probe plugged into the "hot" or *positive* socket. Generally, meters have a separate "hot" socket for current measuring.

When applying the probes to the circuit itself, the black probe (negative or common) should be touched to a ground on the circuit board. If you're in doubt about where to find one, try a circuit board mounting screw or a wide area of foil. The red probe (positive or hot) should be touched to the point that is presumably producing the voltage you're looking for. **Never** allow a probe to touch two electrical points at the same time! This may cause a short circuit, which, more often than not, is disastrous.

Measuring AC voltage. Since AC is nonpolarized (*i.e.*, lacking fixed positive and negative poles), the distinction between positive and negative meter probes is irrelevant. This means that you measure by touching either probe to one side of the circuit, and the other probe to the other side. For all practical purposes, you can forget about measuring AC inside of your computer. The purpose of a computer power supply is to turn the AC from the wall into DC, the computer's main diet. However, you might want to check the AC voltage level at the mains (the wall outlet) from time to time, as explained on page 138.

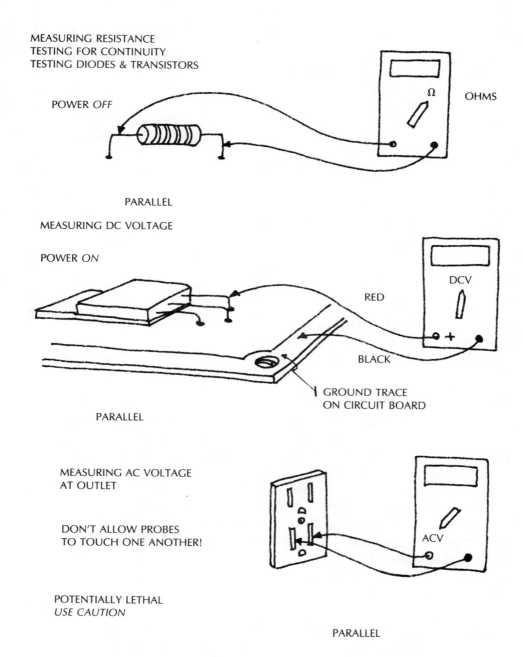

MEASURING RESISTANCE
TESTING FOR CONTINUITY
TESTING DIODES & TRANSISTORS

POWER *OFF*

Ω

OHMS

PARALLEL

MEASURING DC VOLTAGE

POWER *ON*

DCV

RED

BLACK

GROUND TRACE
ON CIRCUIT BOARD

PARALLEL

MEASURING AC VOLTAGE
AT OUTLET

DON'T ALLOW PROBES
TO TOUCH ONE ANOTHER!

ACV

POTENTIALLY LETHAL
USE CAUTION

PARALLEL

Figure 5–7a. Parallel Measurement.

MEASURING DC CURRENT

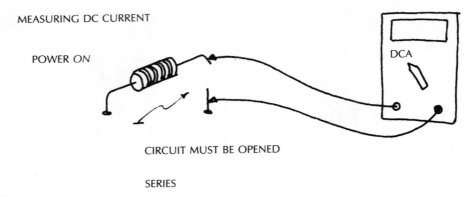

CIRCUIT MUST BE OPENED

SERIES

Figure 5–7b. Series Measurement.

WARNING

Be **EXTREMELY CAUTIOUS** in performing the following measurement. Household current can be LETHAL!

Measuring AC mains voltage.   With the meter turned on, selected for AC volts, and set to a range that includes at least 130 volts, insert one probe into one slot of the electrical outlet and the other probe into the other slot. **DO NOT ALLOW THE PROBES TO TOUCH EACH OTHER.** Your meter should read about 117VAC. As soon as you've got a reading, remove one probe, then the other.

To determine which is the "hot" side of the outlet, place one probe into one slot and the other probe into the ground receptacle (the round one). If you get a reading, you know that the slot is hot. If you get no reading, then the other slot is hot. At the service box (fuse or breaker panel), the "cold" (neutral or return) side of the wiring is tied to ground—or it should be!

Measuring resistance.   When you switch your meter to the *ohms* or *resistance* position, you've turned the multimeter temporarily into an *ohmmeter*.

OHMMETER CAUTIONS

Turn power OFF when measuring resistance and continuity.
Since voltage is present at the ohmmeter probe tips, don't touch the probes to integrated circuit (IC) pins. It's not likely that you'll damage an IC with an ohmmeter, but it can happen.

Because resistance measurements are made with the electrical power turned off, they present no danger whatever to you. You merely turn on your meter, touch one probe to one side of the device or circuit you're measuring, and the other probe to the other side. Polarity is irrelevant—there's no voltage or current in the device other than that provided by the meter itself.

Measuring a particular resistor *in a circuit* will not give you a meaningful reading. Why? Because of the other resistance in the circuit. You have to pull one end of the resistor in question out of the circuit to do an accurate job. Later on, you'll learn about the electrical effects of resistors in circuits.

Resistance-measuring doubles as continuity-measuring. If a circuit or component is unbroken, it should produce a value on your meter. This tells you that the circuit is capable of carrying electricity throughout. A short piece of unbroken wire should show no resistance—at least none measurable by a low-cost meter. If you measure the same wire after having snipped it in two, the meter should show nothing at all, which is to say, *infinite* resistance—the resistance of air. Thus, the unbroken wire is a complete circuit (or a *short* circuit); the broken wire is an *open* circuit.

Short circuit. In practical terms, a *short circuit* is one in which two parts of a circuit that are not meant to be in direct contact have been brought into direct contact. For example, a splash of solder might cause the positive side of the circuit to be shorted to the ground side. Or a probe tip might slip between two pins on an IC, shorting the power input to a signal input.

Open circuit. An open circuit results when two parts of circuit that should be in contact are no longer thus. This may result from a "cold" solder joint, or a faulty IC socket, or a connector with a broken wire. A cold solder joint is one in which the solder has not been heated sufficiently to make an electrical bond. Visual clues suggesting cold joints are (1) frosty appearance of solder and (2) ''globby'' or dropleted solder (instead of smooth peaks).

A resistor is supposed to offer resistance to the flow of electricity. When you measure one, you should get a value close to the designated value of the resistor. Figure 5-8 shows you how to interpret the resistor color code.

A Note on Terminology

For additional information on terms like *diode* and *transistor*, see the next two chapters and the **Glossary**.

Checking diodes and transistors.   The resistance-measuring capability of a meter can be used to determine whether a diode or a transistor is good. ''Good'' is, of course, a relative term. At least the

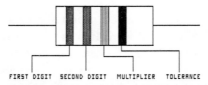

FIRST DIGIT   SECOND DIGIT   MULTIPLIER   TOLERANCE

COLOR	1st & 2nd DIGITS	MULTIPLIER	TOLERANCE
Black	0	1	—
Brown	1	10	—
Red	2	100	—
Orange	3	1,000	—
Yellow	4	10,000	—
Green	5	100,000	—
Blue	6	1,000,000	—
Violet	7	—	—
Grey	8	—	—
White	9	—	—
Silver	—	.01	10%
Gold	—	.1	5%

Figure 5–8.   Resistor Color Codes.

measurement can tell you whether the device is "capable" of being good.

A diode can be thought of as an electrical valve, allowing current to flow in only one direction. Thus, testing it in one direction is like testing an *open* (nonconducting) circuit. With the meter probes switched, the meter reading represents the diode's resistance to the current from the meter tips actually flowing through the diode. *Direction* here refers to the movement of current (negative to positive flow).

Hence, in the case of diodes and transistors, polarity counts, even though they are measured with the power OFF. Turn the meter on and set it to the ohms-measuring range specified for measuring diodes. (See the meter manual for this information.) Then touch the black probe to the *cathode* (banded) end of the diode and the red probe to the *anode* end. You should get a resistance reading of some sort. Reversing the probes should produce zeros on a digital meter or no deflection on analog meter, indicating in both cases infinite resistance (no flow of electricity).

With a transistor, which can be thought of (in part) as a pair of diodes mounted "back to back," one probe should be touched to the transistor's *base* lead and the other to the *emitter* lead and then to the *collector* lead. The polarity depends on the type of transistor. Suffice it to say that one arrangement should result in resistance readings, the other in none. The illustration in Figure 5-9 should make this procedure clear.

Measuring current. Don't. Unless you have a very expensive little gadget called a *current probe*, you have to actually break the circuit under test in order to be able to place your meter probes in series with one side of the circuit. For the purposes of this book, current measurement is irrelevant.

The Logic Probe

A logic probe is a testing device that will tell you whether a particular point in a circuit is carrying a digital signal and whether the signal is high (1) or low (0). By convention, a red LED (light emitting diode) stands for digital 1, a green LED for digital 0. Since the probe responds to voltages, which are, after all, what digital signals are made of, it can be fooled by any voltage source. In order to get meaningful readings, then, test *only* those points that carry **signals** as opposed to **power**.

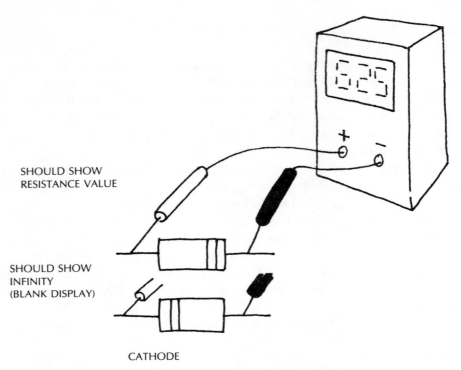

SHOULD SHOW
RESISTANCE VALUE

SHOULD SHOW
INFINITY
(BLANK DISPLAY)

CATHODE

Figure 5–9.   Testing Diodes and Transistors.

To run its own circuitry, the probe requires a +5VDC power source and a ground connection. The red clip can be hooked to the output pin of a 5V regulator, and the black clip to any convenient ground or the negative (−) lead of a polarized (electrolytic) capacitor. The drawing in Figure 5-10 shows you how.

The probe tip is then touched to the pin or trace you wish to analyze. If the red LED lights, the logic is high (1); if the green LED lights, the logic is low (0). Neither LED will light if there is no signal.

CAUTION: Don't allow the probe tip to short one line or pin to another.

Troubleshooting at the level of individual logic signals is pretty sophisticated, and, except in the most superficial way, beyond the aims of this book. Still, once your appetite it whetted, there's no telling how far you may go! When that desire overcomes you, it's time for some serious study. Check the **Suggestions for Further Reading** at the end of the

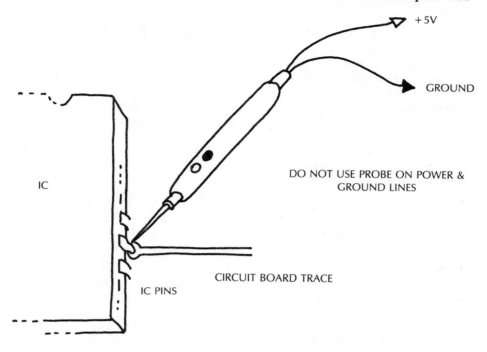

Figure 5–10.   The Logic Probe in Action.

chapter. Meanwhile, before we're finished, you'll have gathered enough information to get you started.

TROUBLESHOOTING

Since there is a large chapter devoted to this topic, I'll do no more at this point than review a few general principles.

A typical computer system consists of:

- **Computer**—The main unit, including one or more circuit boards containing the microprocessor, ROM-based routines for running system diagnostics and other "housekeeping" chores, system memory, input/output ports and circuitry, and expansion slots.
- **Power supply**—The source of the DC voltage required to run the computer. The power supply is often, but not always, mounted in the main computer box.
- **External storage**—Floppy disk(s), hard disk(s), tape drives. These may or may not be mounted in the main computer box.

- **Video display**—Older "home" computers used TV sets as video monitors. Business-oriented as well as the newer home computers use monitors that are basically high-resolution TV sets without tuners. Laptop computers and some "luggables" use liquid crystal displays (LCD) and other technology very different from the TV type.
- **Peripherals**—Printers, plotters, digitizers, modems, spoolers, and other "hang-on" devices not essential to the basic operations of a computer.

The first step toward cure is a diagnosis. A diagnosis requires that you identify, localize, and interpret symptoms. Troubleshooting—a set of diagnostic procedures—can be thought of as an orderly method for isolating the errant component(s), circuit(s), and part(s), and interpreting the meaning of the malfunctions. Having done this, you are in a position to prescribe a cure and, in the role of technician, to effect the cure. (Or to know when it is the better part of valor to let someone else do it.)

The specific problems covered by the **Troubleshooting Guides** can be resolved into those concerning (1) power, (2) signals, and (3) mechanical/electromechanical components. So, at the highest level of abstraction, troubleshooting looks simple. And in certain ways, it is.

Signals. Consider, for example, what would happen if the cable between the video monitor and the video port were loose—a common occurrence with cables terminated in *RCA phono plugs*. Depending on the type, your monitor would be blanked to black or to light (white or amber or green). Pull the cable from the monitor right now and note the result. So now you know to check that cable if your monitor ever comes up nothing. This, by the way, illustrates a loss of *signal*.

Power. A loss of power can occur in a number ways, but the first place to check is the power cable, which can (and often does) come loose. Then move to the fuses or breakers, and so on, until you find the actual place where power has failed. **CAUTION:** Stay out of the power supply itself. The warning label is there for good reason!

Mechanical. Problems arise from such matters as paper jams in the printer; burned out motors (in, a printer or disk drive); failures of various parts (gears, cams, pulleys, and that sort of thing); and physical damage to various components (such as someone's spilling liquid in the keyboard).

Subsystems. In practical terms, you troubleshoot for power, signal, and mechanical failures through the perspective of the *subsystem*.

Physically, the computer is an electromechanical device populated with electrical and mechanical devices under the control of both electrical power (the *energy* to run the computer) and electrical signals (the "thinking" or *logic* of the computer). Thus, you would consider (1) power, (2) cabling and connectors, (3) microprocessor and support circuitry, (4) main memory, (5) I/O (input/output) circuitry, (6) video monitor and video circuitry, (6) disk drives and support circuitry, (7) keyboard and support circuitry, (8) expansion board(s), and (9) peripherals (printer, etc.)

The inner workings of your computer and peripherals are revealed by *technical reference manuals*, valuable books—tools, really—that should be bought with and considered part of your computer system. They can be heavy going. To make them less so is the aim of the next chapter.

SUMMARY

Every trade, craft, and profession has its jargon and its tools. In this chapter, we've focused on electronic tools and—in a general way—how to use them. We've looked in the same general way at the principles of computer troubleshooting. The leaves and blossoms of these bare trees will appear as we move along in the book, with the jargon being covered principally in the **Glossary** and the specifics of troubleshooting in the various **Troubleshooting Guides**. In addition, check the **Suggestions for Further Reading** and the **Source Listing** for this chapter.

SOURCE LISTING

Suppliers: Tools and Test Equipment, Electronic Parts, and Miscellaneous Items

Please note (as said before) that inclusion in this list **does not** imply endorsement by the author or the publisher. These companies are merely representative. There are many others. Check out the computer periodicals pertinent to your particular system, and *Computer Shopper*, 407 S. Washington Avenue, Titusville, FL 32796; (305)269–3211.

All of these companies listed below put out detailed catalogs. This is as good a time as any to start your collection. Many of the companies sell items other than those listed. Call or write.

Black Box Corporation
P.O. Box 12800
Pittsburgh, PA 15241
(412)746–5530
cabling parts and tools

Digi-Key Corporation
701 Brooks Avenue South
Thief River Falls, MN 56701
1–(800)344–4539
electronic parts

Fordham Radio
260 Motor Parkway
Hauppauge, NY 11788
1–(800)645–9580
test equipment

Heathkit Electronic Centers
Nationwide (check phone book)
electronic kits, test equipment, tools, parts

Jameco Electronics
1355 Shoreway Road
Belmont, CA 94002
(415)592–8097
electronic parts

Jensen Tool Inc.
7815 S. 46th Street
Phoenix, AZ 85040
(602)968–6231
tools, test equipment

OK Industries
3455 Conner Street
Bronx, NY 10475
(212)994–6600
test equipment, electronic parts and kits

Radio Shack
Nationwide (check phone book)
electronic parts, tools, test equipment

Valentine's Inc.
658 Whitehead Road
Lawrenceville, NJ 08638
(609)394–8121 Contact: Sandy Hornick
miscellaneous computer supplies

Suggestions for Further Reading

Forrest Mims, *Getting Started in Electronics*, published by and available through Radio Shack. Easy to read and delightfully illustrated.

Robert G. Middleton, *New Digital Troubleshooting Techniques*, New York, NY: Prentice Hall, 1984. A couple of steps up in difficulty, though it does "begin at the beginning."

If you really want to get your hands into electronic tests and measurements, invest in the Heathkit Individual Learning Program, *Electronic Test Equipment*, a two-volume set that includes a package of parts for doing the experiments outlined in the text. Heath Company, Benton Harbor, Michigan 49022; (616)982–3411.

Computer Smythe is a quarterly journal aimed at computer hardware hackers. It offers projects and tinkering advice from simple to complex, and provides a forum for those who want to know and want to share. (P.O. Box 176, Peterborough, NH 03458–0176; (603)924–9464.)

Chapter 6
THE TECHNICAL REFERENCE MANUAL

INTRODUCTION

Our subject is the *technical reference manual*, a fairly expensive but extremely valuable book published by (or for) the manufacturer of your computer. While not explicitly concerned with repair and mainte-nance, the tech manual typically contains a wealth of hardware infor-mation that can be put to good use by a troubleshooter. Because I consider the tech manual as another tool in your collection, I urge you to (rush out and) buy one. The next time you buy a computer, insist that the dealer throw the tech manual in with the deal.

The purpose of this chapter is to introduce you to the tech manual and to give you a short course in reading technical diagrams.

A Note to the Nontechnically Oriented

Please be assured that (1) you can do most of the troubleshooting out-lined in Chapter 2 without knowing about schematic diagrams and the other matters dealt with below, and (2) the material presented herein isn't as forbidding as it may look at first glance. I urge you to give it a go, but it really isn't required reading.

Just as all microcomputers are siblings under the lid, so are all tech manuals, although some are more useful—*i.e.*, more explicit, more clearly written, more "user friendly" than others. By and large, all com-puter systems are comprised of the same functional blocks, and tech manuals cover the same types of technical information. The principal differences lie in cosmetics, and in the specifics of hardware and of machine-level software. What follows, therefore, is a summary sketch of the *"Any System" Technical Reference Manual*.

TECH MANUAL CONTENTS

Hardware Information

This is an illustrated review of the hardware, from the outside in, from the enclosure to the system and expansion boards. You may be shown how to open the enclosure and how to disassemble the computer into major subsections. There will be pictures and descriptions of the I/O (input/output) ports, disk drives, keyboard, power supply, and the various circuit boards, as well as schematic and block diagrams for the main system board and any boards normally or commonly supplied by the original manufacturer.

The manual accompanies its description of each piece of hardware with explanatory material concerning the operation of key components. For example, a drawing of the system board will include a general explanation of the board that covers certain fairly technical points regarding the operation of the central processing unit (CPU, the microprocessor). There will also be a *memory map* showing how the main system memory is partitioned among the principle functions: user memory, video memory, ROM (the internal *system monitor*, not to be confused with the video display monitor), disk drive control, and so on.

Much of this information will be of little or no use to you, unless you decide to write low-level (*i.e.,* assembly language) software for your computer. So don't worry if it doesn't make much sense. Scattered here and there in the welter of technical jargon, however, you'll find lots of clear and useful information, like pin assignments for I/O port pins, voltage values for interboard and power supply connector pins, and switch settings for memory and other configuration options.

Some of this information may be included in the computer *user's manual*. Unfortunately, these manuals too often tell you too little. Thus, the tech manual can be thought of as the thinking person's user's manual.

Firmware

Firmware is *software* that has been "burned" into one or more *Read-Only Memory* chips. In principle, such a program is no different from any other computer program, whether on disk or cassette tape, or written directly from the keyboard into memory. The ROM, called the *monitor ROM*, is plugged into a socket on the system board and acts as a kind of mediator between the CPU and the rest of the computer system—and you.

The program material in ROM is called the BIOS (basic input/output system) and is used to "organize" the logic of the computer when you turn it on or reset it. The video character set may also be in ROM, and, in some computers, there may be a ROM-based programming language—most commonly, BASIC.

The tech manual will describe the basic ROM monitor functions, list their memory locations ("addresses"), and tell how to control certain computer operations using them. There may also be an actual program listing of the contents of the ROM BIOS. Careful study of this listing will reveal a lot of interesting information about the operation of your computer. To fully appreciate these riches, however, you need to learn the elements of assembly language programming—not such a formidable task, actually.

A lot of this material is beyond the troubleshooter's need to know, but it's there against the day when you are overcome by the desire to take control of your computer beyond simply loading in a program.

Codes, Colors, Keystrokes, and Other Odds and Ends

Every computer is set up by the manufacturer to respond to certain codes entered from the keyboard, or *via* a program on disk or tape. Likewise, every keyboard is set up to transmit a distinctive code for each keyboard character. All manufacturers have agreed to use ASCII (American Standard Code for Information Interchange) for coding the letters, numbers, and standard punctuation marks. (This is more properly designated, USASCII, the USA Standard Code, etc.) But many keyboards allow access to other characters—various graphics symbols—which have no universally accepted coding standard. Your tech manual will tell you all about the codes, standardized and otherwise, for your particular computer. I've included the ASCII code set in Chapter 10 because no computer book is complete without one!

Your manual may also contain the following:

bus pinouts
cable configurations
glossary
integrated-circuit pinouts

microprocessor *instruction set*
parts lists
system diagnostic and error messages
theory of operation
timing diagrams
troubleshooting charts

DIAGRAMS

For the serious troubleshooter, diagrams are perhaps the most useful inclusions in a tech manual. Broadly, there are four types: *pictorial*, *X-ray*, *block*, and *schematic*.

The Pictorial Diagram

The pictorial is a simplified drawing of the actual object. For example, the pictorial for the main circuit board will show the location of the integrated circuits, the power connections, the I/O connections, the expansion slots, and the switch blocks (dual-inline-package or DIP switches, small blocks containing several actual switches). The resistors, capacitors, and other electronic components will not usually appear in this type of drawing. (Figure 9-22, the "homebrew transient suppressor, found in Chapter 9, exemplifies the pictorial).

The Circuit Board X-Ray Diagram

X-ray diagrams can be thought of as specialized pictorials. In this case, however, you are shown each board as though made of clear glass, with—on both sides of the board simultaneously—every trace, solder pad, and component precisely located and identified. With such a diagram, you can "look through" a board whose underside may not be readily accessible. This will aid you in tracing a connection hither and yon, for on many circuit boards a trace will pass through to the other side, and pass back again at another location. It can get mighty confusing without the special kind of roadmapping the X-ray drawings provide. Unfortunately, many tech manuals don't include them. By far, the best I've seen come with Heathkit products.

Circuit boards are themselves often made of a glass composite called *glass-epoxy* (fiberglass-reinforced with epoxy). This material acts as a substrate for a copper coating, which is then acid-etched in accordance with the board designer's layout. Etching removes the unwanted copper, leaving behind traces ("wiring") and solder pads. The board is then drilled to receive component pins and leads. Finally, the board is silk-screened (painted) with the outlines and numbers of the parts.

The Block Diagram

Block diagrams define the functional units of a system and their inter-relationships. Block diagrams can be devised for every "layer" of the computer system, from the whole system down to any circuit board, board circuit, or integrated circuit.

Figure 6-1 is a representative block diagram of the CPU, memory, and I/O interface.

When you attempt to decipher such a diagram, the first step is to identify the major elements, in this case: CPU, system clock, memory, I/O block(s), and so on. Next, identify the bus lines: address, data, and control. (Power is understood to be routed to every chip). Then trace

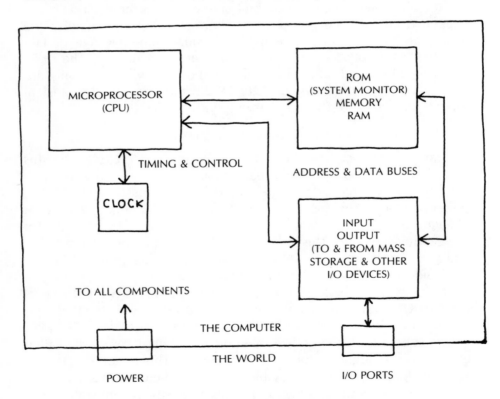

Figure 6–1. Computer Block Diagram.

the interconnects in the direction of the arrows, which show the movement of *signals*. Signals are the nerve impulses of the computer, whose operation depends on their presence and proper movement. To keep all the signals moving in an orderly fashion, the clock must be running correctly. A clock (timing) failure will scramble signals and produce a variety of unwanted results.

A careful examination of block diagrams, from the most general to the most particular, will give you a good idea of what's going on in your computer. But the block diagrams are, after all, highly abstract. They establish the general logic of the system, not the detailed patterns of electrical interrelationship. So while the block diagrams can show you where you may find the cause of the trouble, you'll have to move to the *schematic* diagram to find the actual connections from chip to chip.

If the block diagrams are road maps of the overall system logic, the schematics are road maps of the electrical pathways. In neither case, however, will the diagram match in a literal way what you'll find when you look at, say, a given circuit board. For that kind of map, you need the pictorial, which, though it does give you the lay of the land, omits a great deal of detail. But since most circuit boards are silk screened with component identifiers that match those given on the schematic, you should have no difficulty in finding what you're looking for.

Schematic Diagrams

In some tech manuals, you're given a set of hybrid diagrams that may be thought of as "logic schematics," the purpose of which is to show all of the interconnecting lines, those carrying data, address, and control signals, but omitting a number of the resistors, capacitors, and other support components. IBM calls these *logic diagrams,* which can be thought of as the melding of block diagram and schematic—more detailed than the block, less than the full schematic.

Note, however, that the term *logic diagram* is also used to designate the tables that show the *Boolean logic* characteristics of individual integrated circuits or elements within those circuits. This type of logic diagram is discussed and explained. *Boolean logic* (named for George Boole, mathematician) refers to the "on/off" logic that is at the heart of computer operations.

For the amateur troubleshooter, there is little meaningful difference between the two types of schematics. In fact, you'll find fully detailed schematics in relatively few technical reference manuals. From such schematics, one could reproduce the circuitry and, theoretically, end up with a working, if possibly crude-looking, version of the schematized computer.

As I've been insisting, it's not the intent of this book to train you to become a computer technician. On the other hand, it won't hurt to familiarize yourself with the schematics. Why? After all, this stuff can get a bit thick. And lacking a solid grounding in the theory that underlies these diagrams, you are not well placed to really wade into the hardware. That's true enough. Yet little problems can crop up that can be overcome by someone who who has taken the trouble to study these diagrams and follow their logic.

Table 6-1 identifies the common schematic symbols. Each of the electronic components is defined and explained in the **Glossary,** which also "translates" most of the abbreviations commonly used in schematics.

Since most schematics use gate symbols as a way of helping you visualize the logical operations, here are the symbols and their *truth tables* (logic diagrams of the other type). Although a given gate will ordinarily have two inputs (shown here as A and B), there are gates with multiple inputs. But let's not complicate matters.

Gates.   The term *gate* here refers to a *node* in the logical pathway of a computer circuit. These days, these gates exist almost exclusively as minute regions within integrated circuits (though prior to the advent of the IC, they were created with discrete transistors; prior to the transistor by electron tubes; and prior to that by electromechanical relays). We're really talking about *switches*. Anyway, these gates or nodes are *decision points*, the decision in each case dictated (1) locally by the immediate input values and (2) globally by the design of the system and the particular values being generated by the system at the moment.

In the final analysis, gate logic operates under control of two voltage values, one representing binary 0 and one representing binary 1. These values constitute digital data, the electrical behavior of the various gates emulating Boolean logic.

The *yes* and *not* gates are not, strictly speaking, Boolean. The yes gate or *buffer,* acts as a temporary storage depot, delaying the transmission of data bits until they are needed by the next circuit. The not gate inverts the binary value of the input as required by the next circuit.

Table 6–1.   Schematic Diagram Symbols.

SYMBOL   PART

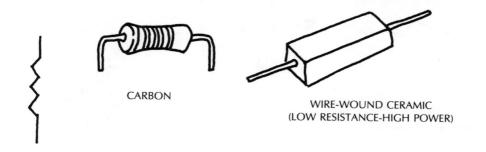

CARBON

WIRE-WOUND CERAMIC
(LOW RESISTANCE-HIGH POWER)

FIXED RESISTOR

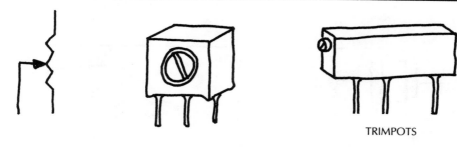

TRIMPOTS

VARIABLE RESISTOR

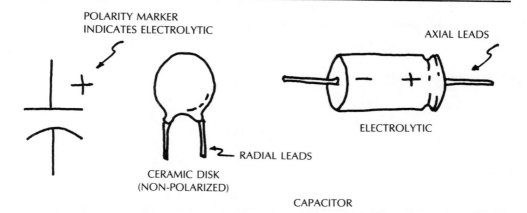

POLARITY MARKER
INDICATES ELECTROLYTIC

AXIAL LEADS

RADIAL LEADS

ELECTROLYTIC

CERAMIC DISK
(NON-POLARIZED)

CAPACITOR

Table 6–1. continued

SYMBOL	PART
	NORMALLY-OPEN SPST PUSH BUTTON
	PUSH BUTTON
	TOGGLE
	TOGGLE SWITCH (ON/OFF) SINGLE POLE SINGLE THROW (SPST) SWITCHES
	CRYSTAL
NO CONNECTION	
CONNECTION	
GROUND (EARTH)	
GROUND (CHASSIS)	
+5V CIRCUIT POWER SOURCE	

Table 6–1. continued

SYMBOL   PART

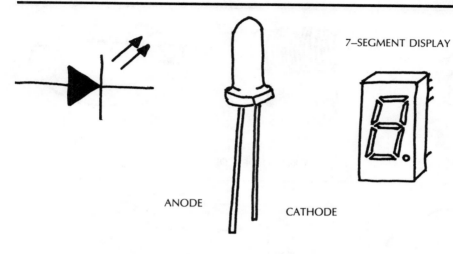

7–SEGMENT DISPLAY

ANODE   CATHODE

LIGHT-EMITTING DIODE (LED)

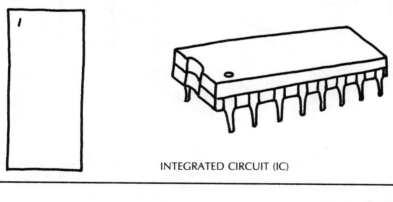

INTEGRATED CIRCUIT (IC)

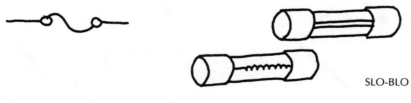

SLO-BLO

FUSE

Table 6–1. continued

SYMBOL	PART

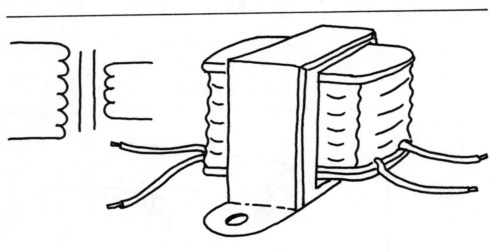

TOROID

INDUCTOR (COIL)

TRANSFORMER

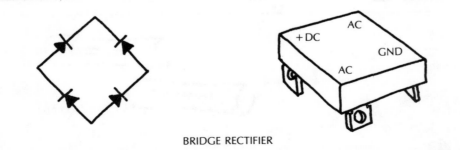

BRIDGE RECTIFIER

Table 6–1. continued

SYMBOL   PART

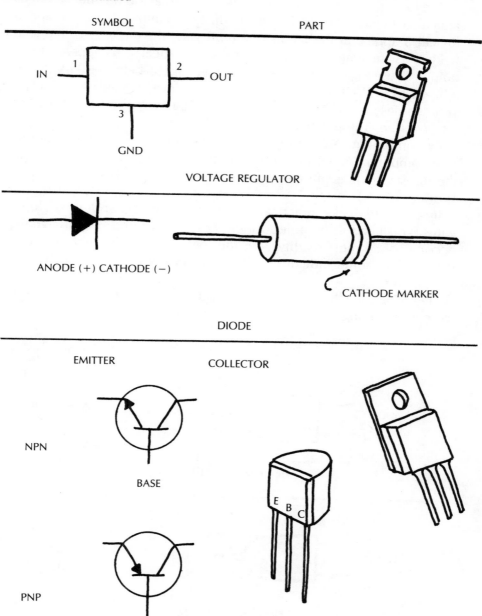

IN   1 ┌──────┐ 2   OUT
        │   │
        3 └──────┘
        GND

VOLTAGE REGULATOR

ANODE (+) CATHODE (−)

CATHODE MARKER

DIODE

EMITTER   COLLECTOR

NPN

BASE

E B C

PNP

TRANSISTORS

The logic gates shown in the following tables are to be understood as logical pathways for digital signals. If, for example, logical 1 and a logical 0 appear at the inputs of an OR gate, the circuitry of the gate (within its integrated circuit) will cause a logical 1 to appear at the output. These logical values are, in fact, voltages—below +0.8VDC for a 0, +2 to +5VDC for a 1. (NOTE: Since voltage can also be negative, you can design a system in which the logic is *negative true* instead of *positive true*. The practical results are the same).

By combining gates in various patterns, all of the many operations of a computer can be performed. We'll take an "over-easy" look at the inner workings of digital systems in Chapter 7, **How Computers Work**.

In order to make practical use of your understanding of logic gates, you need to be able to identify the input and output signals, accomplished most readily with the logic probe, although you can usually find some indication of life (if not correct logic) with your multimeter.

Here, then, are the Boolean logic diagrams (*truth tables*) for the basic logic gates, along with the schematic symbols for each:

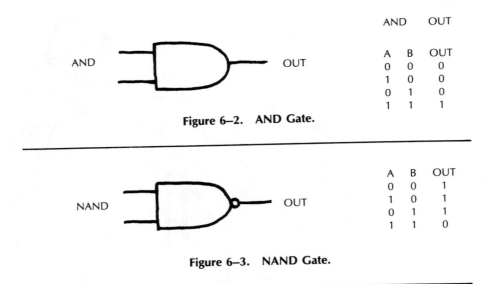

AND   OUT

A	B	OUT
0	0	0
1	0	0
0	1	0
1	1	1

Figure 6–2.   AND Gate.

A	B	OUT
0	0	1
1	0	1
0	1	1
1	1	0

Figure 6–3.   NAND Gate.

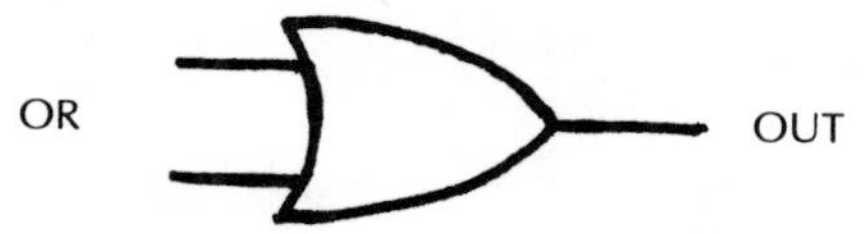

A	B	OUT
0	0	0
1	0	1
0	1	1
1	1	1

Figure 6–4. OR Gate.

A	B	OUT
0	0	1
1	0	0
0	1	0
1	1	0

Figure 6–5. NOR Gate.

A	B	OUT
0	0	0
1	0	1
0	1	1
1	1	0

Figure 6–6. XOR Gate.

A	B	OUT
0	0	1
1	0	0
0	1	0
1	1	1

Figure 6–7. XNOR Gate.

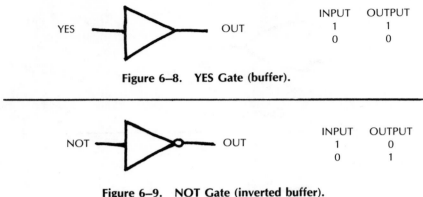

Figure 6–8. YES Gate (buffer).

Figure 6–9. NOT Gate (inverted buffer).

Reading and Interpreting Schematics

Some manuals chop up the schematics to fit the page size of the manual. Others give you schematics as fold-outs, to avoid segmenting the diagram for a particular board or circuit. Still others provide schematics as large, discrete sheets, each containing a complete circuit or circuit board. Irrespective of the physical disposition of the drawings, they are generally read from left to right, top to bottom. Of course, these drawings are not comparable to printed text, and you'll end up doing a lot of "back-and-forthing" and "up-and-downing" as you track signals here and there. Indeed, a standard technique in troubleshooting is to work from the manifestation point of the problem backward to the various downstream points that could be the source(s) of the problem. This routine echoes the approach you should take when looking at the hardware itself.

The block diagrams should be considered keys to the schematics. With the block diagram you get an overall picture. The schematic leads you to the specific details.

A good way to learn the art of schematic reading and interpretation is to spend some time tracing CPU signals—back and forth. There should be enough information on the schematic itself to give you a fairly clear—if simplified—picture of what's happening. The narrative discussion in the manual will fill out the picture.

It would fill more pages than we can spare to take you on a walking tour through the CPU circuitry of a typical computer, but we can do it for a simple linear power supply. The drawing in Figure 6-10 shows you what it looks like. The list below explains the drawing.

(1) 117VAC (nominal) from the mains passes through the fuse (on one side of circuit) and enters primary winding of power transformer.

(2) The transformer drops the voltage from 117VAC to about 24VAC. What started out as 117VAC at, say, 1AMP, is now 24VAC at 4.88A. If you multiply either pair of volts and amps (117 x 1 or 24 x 4.88), you end up with the same number, namely, 117. This is the *power* rating or *wattage*. Because electricity is governed by *Ohm's Law*—the algebraic relationships among voltage, current, resistance, and power—a change in any one value will force a corresponding change in the other values.

(3) Since AC is, in fact, *alternating*, that is, swinging from a positive peak to a negative peak—producing as it does so a simple *sine wave* 60 times a second (the *line frequency*)—what goes into the transformer at 117VAC and comes out at 24VAC is nonetheless 60-cycle (more properly, 60-hertz) AC. As such, it cannot be used by the computer circuitry, which requires DC power. The AC must, therefore, be *rectified* or turned into DC.

(4) Rectification blocks half of the AC cycle, producing DC with "bumps," that is, *rippling DC*. It's in the nature of diodes to allow current to flow one way and not the other, so the positive half of the cycle is allowed through and the negative half is blocked. Doing that alternately with each half of the sine wave—possible with a bridge rectifier—results in an output waveform with "bumps" close together instead of spaced apart. The spacing results from the loss of the negative half of the cycle. The bridge rescues those missing halves and "plugs" them into the gaps on the positive half of the cycle.

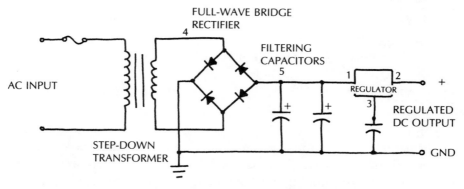

Figure 6–10. Linear Power Supply Schematic.

(5) Rippling DC may be okay for some people, but computers hate it. So it must be smoothed out. The large-value capacitors shown in the schematic are used to *filter* the voltage, reducing the ripple to acceptable limits. Capacitors accomplish this action by storing electrical charges at peak voltages and releasing the charges as the voltage drops, thereby "filling in" the dips (that is, minimizing ripple). Of course, the only way to get truly ripple-free DC is with a battery.

The cleaned up voltage is now passed to the *voltage regulator,* an integrated circuit designed to accept voltages over a fairly wide range of values, but to output only the rated value—in this case, +5VDC. The main's voltage is nominally 117VAC, but at any given moment, it may be higher or lower than the nominal value. This means that the stepped-down voltage will also vary, as will the recitified voltage. The regulator keeps the voltage being sent to the *load* (the computer circuitry) honest.

Below are the Ohm's Law formulas covering voltage (E), current (I), resistance (R), and power (W). In case you're wondering, **E** stands for *electromotive force*, a measure of electrical pressure expressed as *volts*. **I** stands for *intensity*, the current or number of electrons passing a given point in a given time expressed as *amperes*. **R** is electrical resistance expressed as *ohms*; and **W** (or **P**) is power expressed as *watts*. This topic will be dealt with in more detail in Chapter 7.

Unknown	Formulas	Formulas	Formulas
I (current) =	E/R	P/E	$\sqrt{P/R}$
E (voltage) =	$\sqrt{I \bullet R}$	P/I	P$\bullet$R
R (resistance =	E/I	E^2/P	P/I^2
P (power) =	E$\bullet$I	$I^2 \bullet R$	E^2/R

Note: These are the formulas for *DC* circuits.

Figure 6–11.   Ohm's Law Formulas for E, I, R, and P.

SUMMARY

This chapter is actually a kind of extended footnote. You don't absolutely *need* a tech manual in order to do basic troubleshooting and repair. For those brave and inquisitive folk who want to tear away some of the mystery surrounding the computer, however, this could prove a valuable footnote. It has introduced you to (1) the resources of the tech manual, (2) technical diagrams (pictorial, block, and schematic) and their symbols, and (3) some of the elements of digital logic.

SOURCE LISTING

Technical Reference Manuals

The official dealers of the various computer systems can provide you with the official tech manuals for your computer(s). For example, IBM's is called, simply, *Technical Reference*, Part Number 6025005. This book is part of the company's "Personal Computer Reference Library," which includes the (very expensive) books that factory-trained service personnel use to repair and service your equipment.

Other examples of official manuals are (1) Radio Shack's *TRS-80 Color Computer Reference Manual*, and Texas Instruments' *Texas Instruments Professional Computer Technical Reference Manual*, Part Number 2223216-0001. TI also offers the *Texas Instruments Professional Computer Maintenance Handbook*, Part Number 2223200-0001. Perhaps the best of the official manuals are the tech and assembly manuals provided with Heath/Zenith kits. For those who may have bought used Heath computer equipment, take heart—the manuals can be purchased separately.

Unofficial and "published for" manuals are available "through booksellers everywhere." An example is the *Apple IIc Technical Reference Manual*, published by Addsion-Wesley.

Suggestions for Further Reading

John Douglas-Young, *Complete Guide to Reading Schematic Diagrams*, Parker Publishing Co., Rte. 59 at Brookhill Drive, West Nyack, NY 10995. This should turn you into a schematic-diagram maven.

Forest Mims, *Engineer's Notebook*, published by and available from Radio Shack. This is really a kind of electronic cookbook, but it reprises the basics of digital logic in a variety of easy to understand circuits.

Chapter 7

HOW COMPUTERS WORK

INTRODUCTION

We've already started this—in the preceding chapter. The motive is the same, namely, to put you far enough into the picture to raise your troubleshooting, repair, maintenance, and tinkering efforts above the level of cookbook exercises. After all, if you do nothing but follow the instructions in a cookbook, you may succeed in concocting the particular dish, but you'll have little, if any, understanding of the principles involved and will be become just another ho-hum, cook-by-the-numbers food assembler. On the other hand, with a feel for the behavior of ingredients, the effects of various cooking methods, and knowledge of the other arcana of cooking, you'll soon take flight into the world of creative cookery.

"Creative *troubleshooting*?" While this isn't exactly the aim, it's an intriguing concept. Having in mind the general nature of the various functional blocks of the computer and their relationship one to the other, and knowing something of logic, signals, and power, you can be creative in the sense of being able to "synthesize" the probable cause(s) of the problem as well as possible solutions. Have no fear! The **Troubleshooting Guides** are your cookbook. And they'll help you through the common problems.

At any rate, what we'll do in this chapter is poke around inside the computer for an understanding of the basics of computer logic and computer electricity. We'll look again at *truth tables*, this time to apply them to computer operations. And we'll look at how electricity is used to create computer logic as well as computer power (not to be confused with "the power of the computer").

Your technical reference manual and this chapter should get along well together. Suggestion: While reading about the "Any Brand" computer that is the centerpiece of this chapter, leaf through the tech manual for your brand.

This chapter moves from electrons (the fundamental building blocks of electricity) to the complete computer. At any level, you may feel that you're getting more information than you need or even want to know. For example, you may be curious about the general operations of a microprocessor and its supporting circuitry, but haven't the slightest desire to know about electrons and their behavior. Skip to the point of interest and carry on from there.

Instant Big Picture

To bypass the heavy technical stuff, turn immediately to the section of this chapter called **Putting It All Together**. This gives you all you need for a broad idea of what's happening under the hood.

ELECTRONS AND OTHER SMALL THINGS

The visible and outward parts of your computer hide a universe of invisible activity dependent on one of the smallest entities known: the electron, the quantum of electrical energy. So what's an electron? As long as electrons obey their own laws, who cares? I can live with that, but I'd rather not. (*Quantum*—a properly serious-sounding word—specifies the smallest measurable particle of energy associated with a particular physical event or phenomenon. An electron is a quantum, as is, for another example, a *photon*, or "particle" of light.)

Electrons—The Basis of It All

Let's put the electron under an impossible microscope, one that can show us individual electrons. What will we see? What we probably won't see are little balls or clearly outlined pieces of matter. In all likelihood, electrons are *vortices* or mini-cyclones—little bundles of energy—each exhibiting either clockwise or counterclockwise spin, the direction determining the *charge*. The positive version is called a *positron*; the negative version, a *negatron*. It's the negatron that commonly goes by the name of *electron*. This means that in most discussions of electricity, the electron is considered a negatively charged particle.

Since the circumference of an electron is ill-defined, again like a cyclone or a tornado, it hasn't a rigidly fixed size. However, scientists tend to shun indefiniteness and have determined that the radius of an electron at rest is 2.8×10^{13} centimeters, with a weight of 9.1×10^{-28} grams. Are these imaginable dimensions? Don't even try to picture them. Satisfy yourself with "mighty small!" Furthermore, because electrons are smaller than the shortest light wave, they cannot emit light. In fact, there's no way that electrons can be seen, though their *effects* certainly can.

Among the interesting (and frustrating) things about the behavior of electrons is that we know so little about this behavior despite the vast amount of work it accomplishes for us. At the very core of your computer, truly mysterious things are happening.

Atoms, Ions, Conductivity

From the standpoint of electron flow (*current*), there are three kinds of substances: *insulators*, *semi-conductors*, and *conductors*. An insulator resists the flow of electricity, a conductor allows it, and a semiconductor can do either, depending on its role in a given circuit.

Insulators

Wood, paper, most plastics, various liquids (even water), and air all exhibit greater or lesser degrees of nonconductivity, making at least some of them useful as *dielectrics*. A dielectric is an insulator used in an electrical device such as a capacitor, the plates of which may be isolated electrically by air, mica, certain plastics, oil-impregnated paper, and various kinds of glop. Although water isn't used as an electrical insulator, it can be made electrically inert by distillation. The chemicals dissolved in ordinary water make it conductive by providing the free electrons needed for the propagation of an electrical current. Since household water **is** conductive, keep it and electricity **far** apart!

Conductors

Your classic conductor is copper wire, which, because it **is** an excellent conductor, is loaded with what are termed "free electrons." (In reality, of course, it's the other way around: The free electrons make for good conductivity.) These are electrons that have been knocked out of their normal orbits around the parent atomic nuclei—in this case, copper atoms. (Picture the atom as a structure similar to Saturn and its rings, with the rings, however, lying in a number of planes, not merely around the "middle," that is, equitorially.)

Many metals are conductors, though most are not as good as copper. Electrons are freed by energy, commonly heat or light or a combination of the two. The unit of thermal energy at this level of reality is called a *phonon*, which sounds as if it should refer to sound rather than heat. (The term truly is *phonon*, not *photon*, as some might think.) Anyway, in the case of copper, it's heat that gets the electrons running around loose.

With the electrons free to wander, we are ready for *electricity*, which can be thought of as the controlled flow of electrons. But what about lightning? you ask. That's electricity and it doesn't look in the least controlled! But it is—by physical laws acting in the framework of the ambient circumstances at the time of discharge. The electrons are thus being discharged in a manner and along a path following all the rules of the game. The storm cloud and the earth are two plates of a *capacitor*, or electrical storage device, and the air between is an insulator—up to a point. If the quantity of electrons (amperage) and the pressure (voltage, or *electromotive force*) are sufficient, even the least conductive of materials will conduct. It's like punching a hole through a board. The board may resist your fist, but a nail struck with a few smart hammer blows will probably do it. A rifle shot certainly will. Anyway, since lightning usually strikes under humid conditions, the insulating property of air is compromised by water, a relatively good conductor (unless distilled, not the case in natural circumstances).

The failure of a dielectric is a common cause for the failure of a capacitor. A jolt of juice in excess of the rated voltage of a capacitor will do the job. This doesn't happen often in a computer, but it happens. The most frequent failures are the big can-like capacitors called *electrolytics*. These are found mostly (but not exclusively) in power supplies. We'll look at capacitors in greater detail later on.

The Crystal Lattice

Most substances (copper wire, for instance) are made of atoms arranged into basic structures called *crystal lattices*, which can be thought of as bundles of atoms linked to form a three-dimensional structure, perhaps a cube or a prism of some sort. The crystalline structure of table salt is made of sodium and chlorine atoms arranged in an alternate pattern three atoms high by three wide by three deep. Actually, they're not *atoms* but *ions*.

An ion is an atom in which the outer shell of electrons is either lacking one or more electrons (positive ion) or has picked up one or more electrons (negative ion). This lack or overabundance causes the atom (now called an ion) to become especially energetic, either anxious to lose the extra electrons or grab what it considers rightly its own. When an ion on the prowl for one or more electrons to complete its shell meets one with an excess of electrons, a lattice is formed.

Some lattices are electrically stable, some are less so. The more readily the ions in the lattice can lose electrons, letting them wander around in the substance, the more conductive, (electrically active) the substance is. In the case of copper, since we're not talking about a compound but an element, the lattice contains nothing but copper atoms with easily dislodged electrons.

Incidentally, the characteristic crystals of various materials (salt, quartz, and the rest) are, at bottom, the result of the crystal-lattice structure. It's hard to imagine that all the invisible activity I've been describing can produce the special beauty of crystalline forms, but there you have it.

Semiconductors

In the case of semiconductors—the "miraculous" *silicon*-based materials that made transistors, then integrated circuits, then microcomputers possible—we have a material that can be made to encourage the flow of electricity or inhibit it, as circumstances require. By *biasing* one element of a semiconductor, that is, by "goosing" it with a small voltage, we can turn it on, allowing it to conduct a large quantity of electricity. Removing the bias voltage will shut it down again. This describes the action of a *transistor*, which is functionally an electronic switch, the fundamental building block of computer electronics. Integrated circuits consist mainly of miniaturized transistors etched into the silicon material of the IC and *doped* or implanted with carefully selected, electrically active materials.

These itty-bitty transistors are arranged in the IC to form the *binary logic gates* you met in the preceding chapter. Electricity (as *signals*, not *power* in this instance) moves in rigidly controlled pathways through the circuitry of a gate, the transistors conducting or not as required, with each transistor thus producing the voltage value needed to turn on or turn off the next one in line. The sum of the switching actions for a given input result in the desired output.

Silicon, a member of the carbon family of elements, is the second most commmon element on the planet. By happy circumstance, it provides an ideal crystal lattice for the controlled migration of electrical energy. This energy—electrons and domains called *holes* (positive charges or missing electrons)—is what makes all the good stuff happen. Electrons move in one direction, holes move in the opposite direction.

In a "native" or *intrinsic* semiconductor, for each electron, there's a potential hole. There is always a balance of *electron current* and *hole current*. If a region of semiconductor has an excess of electrons (a negative charge), there is another region with an equal number of holes (a positive charge).

Such a balance, while it may appeal to one's sense of justice, has little utility. Hence, the doped semiconductor mentioned earlier, which is material with an excess of either electrons or holes, gives the semiconductor especially useful electrical properties. It is this *extrinsic* type of semiconductor that the ICs in your computer are made of.

Practical Electricity

If you understand the simple algebra of *Ohm's Law*, you'll know more than enough about practical electricity, which consists of three primary electrical values: current, voltage, and resistance, and one derived value—power. I oversimplify the case, but in the context of basic troubleshooting, there's no harm in it.

Current

Electrical current, as the term suggests, refers to the *flow* of electricity, that is, the movement of electrical-charge carriers in, on, or through a conductor. These carriers may be positive ions, negative ions, holes, or just plain electrons. Let's stick with the term *electron* as the quantum of electricity, and we'll think of an electron as always having a negative charge. Therefore, where there is a depletion of electrons, there will be a positive charge.

Current, commonly symbolized by I, an abbreviation for *Intensity*, is measured in *amperes* or parts thereof. One ampere (or "amp") will be moved through one ohm of resistance by one volt of electrical pressure.

Prefixes

milliampere   = one thousandth (1/1,000) of an ampere
microampere = one millionth (1/1,000,000) of an ampere

Your entire computer may not use more than five or so amps, with disk drives drawing a sizable portion of the total—perhaps as much as 1.5A while *writing*, that is, recording. Individual ICs draw miniscule amounts of current, though in aggregrate they add up to an appreciable load for your power supply. In a fully packed computer system, one with, say, two floppy drives, a hard drive, and eight filled expansion slots, the "native" power supply may be marginal at best. If you've added a number of boards and whatnot to your computer, you might be wise to upgrade your power supply. An IBM PC-type of computer should have a power supply fully capable of putting out at least 150W (volts times amps = watts). In Chapter 9, I'll show you how to upgrade your computer's power supply.

Power consumption.   Since computer components are designed to use fixed voltages, and since the resistance of most circuits is likewise a fixed value, current is the variable. Adding more electrical components results, therefore, in an increasing demand for current. Hence, changes in *current*, not changes in *voltage* or *resistance*, produce changes in the *power consumption* of the computer.

You may wonder why the power supply fuse is rated at, perhaps, no more than 2A. This fuse is on the AC (mains) side of the supply, where the nominal voltage is, say, 117VAC. Two amps times 117V equals 234 watts. The total power value will remain the same inside the computer, but since the voltage will be much lower (computers commonly using 12VDC and 5VDC), the amperage available increases in proportion.

Current is measured in *series* with a circuit, which means that you have to actually open the circuit and put the meter into the breach, as it were. Voltage, on the other hand, is measured *across* a circuit, that is, in *parallel* with it.

The lockstep relationship among the voltage, current, resistance, and power is captured in *Ohm's Law,* of which more later. (See **Source Listing** at the end of the chapter for the whole set of formulas.)

Voltage

If the current is the *amount* of electricity in the pipe (wire), the voltage is the pressure driving it through. That's why voltage goes by the "official" name of *electromotive force, EMF,* abbreviated E in electrical formulas. (Other terms for voltage are *potential* and *potential difference.*) It is possible to have a little bit of electricity under a great deal of "pressure," resulting in the hair-raising but harmless fun of the general science class Wimshurst machine (static electricity generator). Indeed, the static electricity you generate walking across the rug in the wintertime produces a pretty hefty spark made from a relatively small number of electrons under considerable EMF. Be warned that this high-voltage, low-current blast can send sensitive electronic components to instant oblivion.

In a closed system such as that implied by Ohm's Law, if one value remains constant—let's say, power or wattage—then an increase in voltage will mean a decrease in current, and, of course, *vice versa.* Thus, 10V at 10A equals 100W. But if the EMF is raised to 50V, the current must drop to 2A.

Polarity.   This is an important quality of voltage. AC (*alternating current,* which probably should be called *alternating electricity*) is considered to be nonpolarized. And on the average of any given cycle, it is. But since AC is actually a *sine wave,* each cycle (or *herz, Hz*) moves from the starting point, 0VAC to the positive (+) peak, down through 0 to the negative (−) peak (or trough, if you prefer).

American household electrical frequency is nominally 60Hz. During any 24-hour period, then, an average of the line frequency will be 60 alternations between positive and negative per second. At any given moment, however, there may very well be deviations. The occasional ripples that beset your TV screen or video monitor could be reflecting these deviations. (In Europe, the mains frequency is 50Hz, the nominal voltage 240VAC.)

Polarity, as noted in the discussion of electrons, has to do with the electron spin. And while AC can be said, in the strictest sense, to be polarized, its polarity changes often enough to trick us into thinking of it as nonpolarized—that is to say, it is *on the average* nonpolarized. DC (*direct current* or my term, *direct electricity,* is another matter.

DC.   Direct current is what you get from a battery—and from the output of a computer power supply. The electricity flows steadily from one *pole* of the battery, through a circuit, and back to the other pole. One pole (*anode*) is always positive, one always negative (*cathode*.) The *electron* flow is from negative to positive; the *hole flow* is from positive to negative. Remember, we've settled on the electron as a negative-charge carrier. Conventionally, DC flows from positive to negative, but physicists, and now you, know better!

Battery DC can be converted to AC. There are electrical devices that will do this to enable you to run AC devices from DC sources. The uninterruptable power supply I mentioned in the **Chapter 1** is such a device. The unit's battery takes over as a power source when there is a mains failure. But the DC must be converted to AC in order to be usable by the computer's own power supply. This newly made AC must in turn be converted to DC in order to be usable by the computer circuitry. Rapidly swapping the positive and negative leads to a battery will give you a short-term experimental emulation of AC.

Prefixes

kilovolt = 1,000 volts
millivolt = 1 thousandth (1/1,000) of a volt
microvolt = 1 millionth (1/1,000,000) of a volt

Resistance

Every conductor exhibits some resistance to the flow of electricity. Resistance is measured in *ohms* and symbolized in formulas by **R**. The Greek letter *omega* (Ω) is commonly used to symbolize ohms in schematic drawings and so on. Every material exhibits a given conductance value. As a rule, for a given material the resistance will decrease with the size of the cross section. This is a cumbersome way of saying that, all else being equal, thick wires conduct better than thin ones. Where the voltage and current are small, the small conductor is suitable. But as the power increases, so must the conductor size. (I know about the effect of high frequency on the behavior of current in conductors, but at 60Hz, or with DC, this is irrelevant.)

You can determine the resistance of a circuit by the Ohm's Law formula, resistance equals voltage divided by current. By this formula, a circuit carrying 24VDC at 5A has a resistance of 4.8 ohms. Or if you know that overall circuit resistance is 4.8 ohms, and the current measures 5A, you can discover the voltage by the Ohm's Law formula: E = R × I. To determine the current if R and V are known: divide R into V. Except for power (watts), these formulas constitute Ohm's Law. (See **Formulas** at the end of the chapter.)

While everything in your computer displays some resistance, the typical resistance device is the *resistor*, a homely little thing, but one of critical importance to the operation of most electronic circuits. There are even resistors buried inside of integrated circuits. And being simple gadgets, only passively involved in their circuits, resistors tend to be among the most reliable of electronic components.

By and large, the resistor's function is to convert current to voltage or voltage to current. How can an essentially passive device do these things? Consider this: If a given circuit is carrying 24VDC at 5A, and we add a resistor of 100 ohms, what happens to the current and voltage? If we calculate for voltage, we discover that we now have 500 volts! If we calculate for current, we have only 240 milliamperes. Actually, there's a whole lot more to this, but let this explanation suffice.

Power

The fourth element of Ohm's Law is *power*, measured in *watts* and symbolized with either a **P** or a **W** in formulas. The value of the power being used, or dissipated, by a circuit or a device can be derived if you have any two of the other three Ohm's Law terms: E, I, R. The quickest and simplest measure is made by multiplying E by I (volts by amps). The resultant number is labeled in watts, but sometimes, in AC devices like transformers, it is labeled in *voltamperes* (*VA*), which specifies, if properly calculated, a different value than that resulting from simply multiplying volts times amps (see page 176). A disk drive, for example, running on 12VDC and requiring .6A (600 milliamps), dissipates or demands 7.2W of power. Wattage is actually a measure of work, one horsepower equalling 746 watts. The disk drive in question is thus working at a rate of .0096HP (more or less!).

Technical Note

Strictly speaking, voltamperes (VA) cannot be correctly measured by using straight-up DC Ohm's Law. AC Ohm's Law is more complex and must be used for precise AC calculations, which are beyond the scope of our needs in this book. At any rate, transformers, as well as certain other AC devices, are on the average only about 80% efficient. The power loss results from *hysteresis*, the frictional effect of electrons in a constantly changing electromagnetic field.

Prefixes

Megawatt = 1,000,000 watts
Kilowatt = 1,000 watts
Milliwatt = one thousandth (1/1,000) of a watt
Microwatt = one millionth (1/1,000,000) of a watt

Each electrical/electronic part in your computer is capable of dissipating a certain amount of power. If that amount is exceeded, the part will probably be destroyed. Such things happen. For example, if a diode fails and turns itself into a wire, the components downstream from the diode will be left unprotected and will tend to draw more current than they are designed to handle. Result: smoke and aggravation. Or suppose that a certain resistor has gone bad. The marking on the original tells you that you need a 10W, 20-ohm power resistor. You have a 20-ohm resistor all right, but it's one of those little 1/4W jobs. Will it work? Not by a country mile. The first time you turn on the equipment, the wimpy replacement resistor will give off a brief, bright light and turn to charcoal.

Basically, we're saying that big wires carry big loads; little wires little loads. Everything in a circuit is a kind of wire, after all, for everything is carrying current.

Figure 7–1 shows some illustrations of the Ohm's Law formulas in action.

(See **Source Listing** at the end of the chapter for all the DC Ohm's Law formulas.)

$P = E \cdot I$	$P = I^2 \cdot I$	$P = E^2/R$

Examples

$$P = I^2 \cdot R$$

I = 2 amps
R = 270 ohms
I x I = 4 amps
4 x 270 = 1080 watts

$$P = E^2/R$$

E = 24 volts
R = 330 ohms
576 volts/330 ohms = 1.75 watts

Figure 7–1. Ohm's Law-Power Calculations.

Some Basic Electronic Components

Reminder: The schematic-diagram symbols for these components are shown in Chapter 6, **The Technical Reference Manual.**

Resistors, capacitors, and inductors are electronically *passive* devices that, despite their so-called passivity, make electronic circuitry possible. Passivity here, of course, means that the devices in question add nothing electrically to a circuit beyond what is supplied by the active devices (e.g., transistors or ICs). Capacitors and the rest cause certain desirable effects and make certain useful changes in the electricity, but these actions result in no *net gain* in electrons.

Resistors.   These can be fixed or variable, and are made of a variety of materials. The little fellows that populate the boards in your computer are mostly made of carbon composition or carbon film. They can usually be identified by their colorful bands, a coding system for telling you the value of the resistance and its degree of precision (commonly 5% tolerance). Here's the way the code works.

You read from left to right, starting at the end opposite the tolerance band, either gold (5%) or silver (10%). The first two bands stand for the first two digits of the value, the last one for the number of zeros you need to add. Thus, brown (1) + red (2) + red (x 100) = 1,200 ohms, sometimes expressed as 1.2K ohms (K standing for 1,000).

Table 7-1 shows a few additional examples, with 5% tolerance assumed.

Table 7-1. Resistor Color Code Examples.

Value in Ohms	Color Code
2.7	red-violet-gold
47	yellow-violet-black
100	brown-black-brown
2,200	red-red-red
6,800	blue-grey-red
47,000	yellow-violet-orange
390,000	orange-white-yellow
1,000,000	brown-black-green
3,300,000	orange-orange-green

Prefixes

Kohm = 1,000 ohms
Mohm = 1,000,000 ohms

Should the occasion arise when you need to replace a resistor, you would ideally replace it with one of the exact resistance value and power-handling capability. (On most computer boards, ¼-watt resistors are the rule.) But let's suppose that you have to replace a 200-ohm resistor and all you have are 100-ohm resistors in your junk box. There's a simple solution, for resistors in series are *additive*. Solder one lead of one 100-ohm resistor to one lead of the other, and now you have a 200-ohm resistor.

On the other hand, suppose you need to replace a 150-ohm resistor, and all you have is a pair of 300-ohmers. Nothing to it. Solder the "left hand" leads of the two resistors together, and the "right hand" leads the same way. You've just placed the resistors in parallel. Two resistors of the same value in parallel exhibit the same resistance as half of one of the two. That makes 150 ohms in the present case. Your meter will prove it. (The value won't be exact because of the combined effect of tolerance values, unless you start with two that are **exactly** the same).

COLOR	1st & 2nd DIGITS	MULTIPLIER	TOLERANCE
Black	0	1	—
Brown	1	10	—
Red	2	100	—
Orange	3	1,000	—
Yellow	4	10,000	—
Green	5	100,000	—
Blue	6	1,000,000	—
Violet	7	—	—
Grey	8	—	—
White	9	—	—
Silver	—	.01	10%
Gold	—	.1	5%

Figure 7–2a.   Resistor Color Codes.

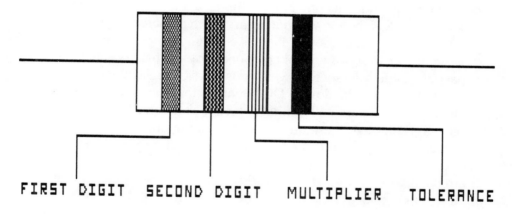

FIRST DIGIT   SECOND DIGIT   MULTIPLIER   TOLERANCE

Figure 7–2b.   Resistor Color Code Interpretation.

When you are using more than two resistors in parallel, or resistors of different values, the formula is more complex. See the **Formulas** listing at the end of the chapter for resistor and capacitor formulas.

A **capacitor** stores an electrical charge. The unit of capacitance is the *farad*, abbreviated **F**. The farad is such a large value, however, that the *microfarad* and the *picofarad* are the common units. If a capacitor can produce 1A of current with a change of 1V per second across its plates, it is said to have a capacitance of 1F. A 1F capacitor can jolt you well into next month, or beyond!

Prefixes

microfarad = 1 millionth (1/1,000,000) of a farad
picofarad = 1 trillionth (1/1,000,000,000,000) of a farad

Capacitors come in a variety of shapes and sizes, both *fixed* and *variable*. The tuner knob on a radio is commonly attached to a variable capacitor. Turning the knob changes the *capacitance* of the capacitor, which in turn changes the frequency of the tuning circuit. Almost without exception, however, the capacitors in your computer are fixed. The differences in appearance among the several kinds derive from the differences in construction. For example, a *ceramic disk* capacitor looks sort of like a button without holes; one type of *electrolytic* capacitor like a small can, another type like a candy drop. The insulating material (*dielectric*) is a critical component of a capacitor, affecting its capacitance and tolerance as well as its physical design.

Capacitors block the flow of DC but allow the flow of AC. Hence, in some circuits they are called *blocking capacitors* and in other *bypass capacitors*. Although these are by no means the only uses for capacitors, many of those found on a typical computer circuit board are either blockers or bypassers. For example, the stray AC that meanders around a circuit board is drained harmlessly away by those little capacitors mounted in memory chip circuits. The AC is passed to ground, but the DC is kept where it belongs.

In case you're wondering how DC blocking and AC passing work, think of DC as a truck running into a wall. It hits the wall and there it stays. Think of AC as a railway engine and the circuit as its track. When the engine reaches one side of the wall, it reverses direction and travels through the circuit to the other side. Thus, AC doesn't literally go *through* the capacitor, it just acts as if the capacitor weren't there. So where there is a place where you want to get rid of AC, you use a capacitor in such a way as to let the AC engine run around and vanish into the ground side of the circuit.

When replacing capacitors, you must match the type, the designated *working voltage*, and, of course, the capacitance. Electrolytic capacitors (the ones most likely to need replacement) are not high-precision components. It's not unusual for a capacitor to test out 50% higher or lower than its marked value. No problem. Furthermore, this gives you some leeway in replacement. It won't hurt, for example, to replace a 33mF electrolytic with a 47mF. On the other hand, the small, non-electrolytic capacitors are made to tighter specifications and should be replaced with exact duplicates.

To substitute, treat capacitors in exactly the opposite manner as resistors. Capacitors in *parallel* are additive in value, but in *series*, their value is calculated like that of resistors in parallel. See **Formulas** at the end of the chapter.

Inductors or coils. Inductors exhibit in an AC circuit a quality termed *impedance*, or resistance to the flow of AC. So while inductors are not actually resistors, the base component of impedance is resistance. Thus, impedance is measured in ohms. As an impeder of AC, the inductor is used in electrical filtering circuits (for example, line filters).

Inductance. The unique characteristic of inductors is *inductance*, symbolized as **L** and measured in *henrys*, abbreviated **H**. A current flowing through a coil (at heart nothing but a hunk of wire) causes a magnetic field to be generated around the coil. Since a magnetic field is basically a bunch of busy electrons, it can be put to work. The more wire, the stronger the field. Place one coil next to another and the field will be transferred to (induced in) the second coil. Two coils in proximity make a *transformer*. Add an iron core and the field is intensified. The coil that gets the juice from an outside source is the *primary*; the other one is the *secondary*. By using a different number of turns in the two coils, you can increase the voltage (while decreasing the current) or decrease the voltage (while increasing the current). In a computer power supply, 117VAC enters the transformer primary and, perhaps, 24VAC exits the transformer secondary. Thus, you drop the voltage and increase the amperage to the levels needed.

The value of the henry is such that when a circuit with a 1A per second change in current results in the induction of 1V, the circuit measures 1H.

Prefixes

millihenry = 1 thousandth (1/1,000) of a henry
microhenry = 1 millionth (1/1,000,000) of a henry

POWER AND SIGNALS

At bottom, there is no meaningful difference between electrical power and electrical signals—signals are just electrically weaker. Ohm's Law rules and that's that. Nevertheless, there are important functional differences with respect to the operation of your computer.

Electricity: Power

At the level of electricity itself, we've examined power in considerable detail. Within the computer, power is the motivating energy. Actually, every movement of electrons carries a certain amount of power—even control and data signals. Unfortunately, these signals are far too weak to turn the wheels, so to speak, and a robust energy source is required. The power supply is such a source. If you don't overtax its capabilities, it'll handle the heavy work, that of turning on and running all of the electrical/electronic components.

Look at the pinouts of an IC, and you'll note that there are always a couple concerned explicitly with electrical power. These power pins are often designated V_{cc} (collector supply voltage) and *GND*. (The collector is one of the electrodes of a transistor. ICs, as we've noted, are mostly transistors.) The power pin of certain ICs will have a different V_{xx} designation, but the principle is the same. The differences arise from the nature of the IC construction. Let's not put too fine a point on it!

Anyway, the parts need electrical power of sufficient wattage to cause them to turn on and do their jobs. If the power system is misbehaving, those components affected cannot work properly. To isolate power problems, you have to identify the *power bus*, that part of, say, a circuit board, handling the power to all chips and other components.

The power bus is traceable to the power supply. Locate the power supply connectors coming out of the supply and note where they're connected. Your tech manual will help, telling you also which connector is carrying what voltage. In all likelihood, there will be a connector for +12VDC and one for +5VDC, as well as a ground line, termed the common or "cold" side. Some computers use other voltage values. You may very well find negative voltages (−12VDC is not uncommon). A negative voltage isn't the same as ground, even though ground is often referred to as "negative." Actually, it's the potential difference between hot and ground that counts. When you measure a voltage point against ground, you're measuring this difference.

From the power connections to the board, you can easily trace the power throughout the board. The ground trace, considerably wider than the other traces, generally runs around the outer perimeter of the board. One or more of the board's mounting holes are often drilled through the ground trace, meaning that the board gets grounded to the chassis of the computer. The ground connections to individual components branch from the main ground trace.

A Note on Grounds

There are, in fact, different approaches to **grounding**. In all likelihood, your computer will use the *chassis ground* described above. A particular piece of equipment, however, may isolate the chassis ground from the *logic ground*, resulting in a small voltage difference between the two grounds. Where such is the case, you would take readings between the hot side and the logic, not the chassis ground. Two pieces of interconnected equipment (computer and printer, for example), may exhibit a difference between chassis ground and *signal ground*. The RS–232–C standard provides for *protective* or chassis ground (pin 1) and signal ground (pin 7). As it happens, these are often tied together because the system relies on chassis ground for all grounding purposes.

In testing for board voltages, you clip the black probe to the ground trace, or to a mounting nut if any are fastened to the ground, and touch the red probe tip to the voltage point you want to measure. On the 8088 CPU found in many PCs, for example, you should get a reading of +5VDC on pin 40. You can use pin 1 or pin 20 for ground, but the ground trace will do nicely, and there is less likelihood of your shorting out anything by using it.

As a rule, the voltages for a nominal +5VDC IC should not fall below about +4.8VDC, nor rise above about +5.25VDC. If you get readings much outside of those values, there's something amiss. A 5V IC will very likely fail above 5.5VDC.

By starting your trace at the point where the power enters the board, you can determine whether the power supply itself is failing to provide the power. If the power is reaching the board, the problem can be tracked down by following the power paths until you note a point where power is interrupted.

Electricity: Control and Data Signals

With everything properly "lighted up," the system is ready to work. Work, in this case, means the propagation and movement of signals containing the information being processed and the signals that control the precedence and timing of operations.

Timing.   Timing signals should be as regular as a clock, which is what they are. Hence the term *system clock*—not to be confused with a *real-time clock*, an onboard version of an ordinary clock. The system clock is generated by a circuit that includes a crystal-controlled oscillator working in concert with a timing signal from the CPU. The 68000 microprocessor clock is found at pin 15. On the 8086 and the 8088, it's pin 19. (The Macintosh computer uses a 68000; the IBM PC group, 8086/8088.) See Chapter 10 for details concerning these CPUs.

Control.   Control signals include clocking signals, and others as well. Interrupts, resets, and chip selects exemplify control signals. On the one hand, they're governed by the clock—as is everything else; on the other they're governed by operational circumstances, usually under the direction of the CPU.

While the power flows in an unbroken stream of electricity at rated voltages, signals are characteristically pulse chains, with the peaks rising abruptly to about 5V and valleys falling abruptly to about 0V. The rise is called the pulse *leading edge*; the fall, its *trailing edge*. Figure 7-3 shows a timing chain and an associated data chain.

The timing chain is completely symmetrical. Should the crystal go bad or some other part of the oscillator circuit fail, the computer will "lose its mind," for the CPU won't know when to do anything. A cold clock circuit means a brain-dead computer.

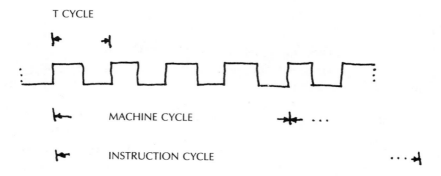

Figure 7–3. Timing and Data Signals.

The sharp edges of all the pulse chains in a computer (clock in-cluded) are critical, for the electronic circuitry is designed to recognize pulse edges as changes of state from high to low or low to high. With-out this edge, (sensitivity), timing precision would be lost. If signals get sloppy enough, perhaps through the aging of electronic parts, the com-puter's mind starts to go.

Data. The data signal is asymmetrical because the data itself is made up of ones and zeros in various patterns. As you can see, the binary digits are really just voltages. A signal voltage held high for two "beats" (clock pulses) equals two ones. Likewise, if it's held low for two beats, the system understands this as two zeros.

In troubleshooting control and data signals, you need to find digital pulses where they're expected. A functioning computer should show digital activity of some sort on all of the data, address, and operational control lines.

Bus. Just as we can identify a *bus* (pathway) for system power, we can identify buses for timing and control, for addressing, and for data. Each grouping of signals has its own pathways through the computer, as some time spent studying tech manual schematics will clearly re-veal. These pathways are not obvious as you look over the circuit boards, but if you locate, say, the address lines emerging from the CPU and follow them along, you'll soon have a picture of the address bus. When we examine the basic operations of a computer, we'll find out more about these buses.

Logic

The ones and zeros that constitute the (a) logic and (b) data of your computer are, as we've learned, nothing but small voltages arranged in strings or chains or strudels, as you wish: 0 to 0.8VDC for binary zeros, 2.0 to 5.0VDC for binary ones.

Remember the *truth tables* in **Chapter 6**? They show the results of sending binary digits to the basic logic gates that all digital logic systems are made of. Thus, an AND gate will generate a one for a pair of ones input, but a NAND gate will generate a zero, for it will invert the expected AND output.

The gates are electronic devices being made to behave as logic manipulators. The logic is Boolean, or binary. George Boole, a nineteenth-century Anglo-Irish mathematician, seemed to have anticipated the age of digital electronics by developing the two-valued way of thinking about events that marks digital operations. He created "switching logic" in advance of the switches, so to speak.

In the digital world, the most fundamental logical operations are AND and OR. The rest are variants and inversions. ANDing, means that two ones are needed to produce a one. ORing means that you need only a single one of two inputs to produce a one.

Picture a water supply, a pump, and piping to carry the water throughout your house. Now add two valves to the pipe, back to back, between the pump and the household. Close both valves. Does water flow to the house? Not a drop. Open one of the new valves. Does water flow to the house? Zilch. Open both valves, and it's shower time, thanks to AND logic. Open valve AND open valve = water on.

Table 7-2. AND/OR Operations

———— VALVE ———— VALVE ————→

⌈ VALVE ⌉
——————————| |——————————→
⌊ VALVE ⌋

Now change the pipe configuration that exits the pump so that the pipe splits into two parallel pipes for a short distance and then rejoins where it joins the household line. Put a valve in each parallel branch.

Turn off both valves: no water. Turn on ONE valve: water. OR logic: Open either one valve OR the other valve = water on.

A Note on Hardware and Software Logic

Patterns of Boolean logic are worked out in hardware as IC gates. But all programming languages provide a set of *software gates* called *logical operators*, software analogs of the hardware. *If A = B AND D = F THEN GOSUB 1000* says that the program should jump to a subroutine if and only if the first pair of variables are equal AND the second pair of variables are equal. Hence, a true is returned if both inputs are true. 1 + 1 = 1, just like an AND gate.

With an idea of how digital logic works, you can make sense of the schematic diagrams that use logic symbols. A given type of gate will be seen to produce a given output for given inputs. If your logic probe tells you otherwise, then you may have located a point in the logical pathway that is experiencing trouble either of its own making or because of problems upstream or downstream.

Bits, Bytes, and Words

Bit.   Each 1 or 0 is a *binary digit* or *bit*. And, as you know, each bit is an electrical value, the only thing your computer really understands.

Byte.   Eight bits as a single string is called a *byte*, which can be thought of as equivalent to a single alphanumeric character. In the coding system understood by the firmware in your computer, a given keyboard character consists of an eight-bit binary number, frequently represented in hexadecimal (base-16). Thus, in the ASCII coding system (the standard), the binary representation of the letter A is 01000001 (hexadecimal 41, octal 101, decimal 65).

Since you're not going to be calculating in base-2, base-8, or base-16 arithmetic, I'll spare you the standard computer-book lecture on the subject. In **Chapter 10**, you'll find a conversion table in case you need to do a quick translation among decimal, binary, octal, or hexadecimal numbers. Sidekick and similar "Computerist's Home Companions'' include a converting calculator in their collection of pop-up utilities.

Word. Computer word size differs among the sizes of computers. In the microcomputer world, two bytes or 16 bits make a word. Microprocessors that can move data and addresses around a word at a time are faster and more efficient than those that can move data only a byte at a time. This is why the trend in microcomputers is toward CPUs able to handle increasingly larger data chunks.

Integrated Circuits

An integrated circuit of whatever type consists of a small piece of electrically active material, usually doped silicon, into which various electronic components like transistors, resistors, and capacitors have been etched and/or deposited in miniature. Their small size suits them for signal, not power, handling. In fact, they act mostly as elaborate switching systems, the different types of transistors turning on and off according to the functions assigned to each IC. The controlled flow of bits through the chips results in a variety of effects, such as that of producing alphamumeric characters on the video display in response to your keyboarding efforts.

Microprocessor (MPU, CPU)

The microprocessor (CPU, central processing unit; MPU, main processing unit) is often called the ''brain'' of the computer. It's more accurate to think of the entire system board as a traffic grid with the microprocessor acting as the traffic cop. The term ''brain'' bothers me because it suggests a similarity to the human brain. If there is any meaningful similarity, it may be between the microprocessor and a single *neuron*. Your computer may do some things super fast, but such narrowly focused brute force can't hold a candle to true brainpower, which computers just don't come close to matching. Anyway, research suggests that the human brain does not operate from a binary orientation at all.

The microprocessor is a generalist among ICs, handling a variety of executive tasks: timing, control, addressing, and data movement. The internal design of the chip determines its capabilities. This design amounts to a permanent program, which you (that is, the software) can use to do all the things you've come to expect from your computer. If you try to use software written for a microprocessor incompatible with the one in your computer, nothing useful will result.

Each microprocessor responds to its own *instruction set*, the code used to write programs for the computer. This code may be written in several forms, from bottom line ones and zeros (*machine code*) up through *assembly language*, and the various *high-level* languages like Pascal, BASIC, and PROLOG. At the machine and assembly language levels, you write using the microprocessor manufacturer's instruction set directly. In a high-level language, you use the instructions of the language, which are later translated into the microprocessor's instruction set.

The CPU is usually a 40-pin socketed IC. Some speed upgrades require that you replace the existing CPU with a faster version. This is easily done, as you'll discover in Chapter 9, **Making Changes**.

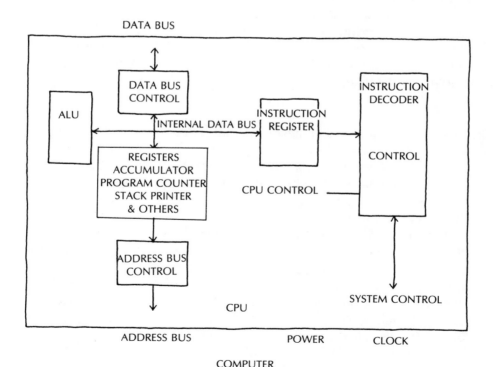

Figure 7–4. CPU Block Diagram.

ROM/Firmware

A ROM *read-only memory* is a support IC containing program material, called *firmware*, "burned" into it by the computer manufacturer. In a typical computer, you'll find a ROM containing a BIOS (basic input/output system) that handles basic "housekeeping" operations for the CPU (microprocessor). You may also find one or more ROMs containing a language, generally a version of BASIC. This means that when you turn on the computer, the computer is able to check its own operations (diagnostics), put an "I'm ready to go to work" message on the screen, and boot up your disk drive. With BASIC-in-ROM, you can write computer programs without having to load in a programming language from an external source like a cassette or disk drive.

There are reprogrammable ROMS called PROMs, EPROMSs, EEP-ROMs and EAROMs, but the reprogramming requires special equipment as well as a fairly sophisticated knowledge of assembly language. So far as the casual computerist/tinkerer is concerned, the ROM is the representative firmware carrier. (PROM = Programmable ROM; EPROM = Erasable PROM; EEPROM = Electrically Erasable PROM; EAROM = Electrically Alterable ROM. They're all different, yet they're fundamentally alike.)

RAM

RAM stands for *random access memory*. But this term doesn't differentiate it from, say, a ROM, in which data is also randomly accessed. Principally, ROMs differ from RAMs in that (1) a ROM can be written to only once, whereas a RAM can be written to innumerable times, and (2) the ROM data is not lost when the computer is turned off, whereas RAM data dies with the power.

There are two general types of RAM: static and dynamic. Virtually all PCs use the dynamic type (DRAM). The differences between the two are irrelevant to the end user, for memory is memory. But if you're curious, static RAMs hang onto their databits without being "refreshed" electrically. This periodic refreshing (refreshment?) is what makes the DRAM "dynamic." The static RAM is fully powered all the time; the DRAM is fully powered only cyclically. DRAMs are cheaper to manufacture and use less power than SRAMs. It's sort of analagous to leaving all the heating registers in all the rooms open all the time, as opposed to opening and closing them according to room usage.

RAMs, of whatever persuasion, come in different memory capacities and operational speeds, the most common these days being 256K at 150 nanoseconds. Translation: 256,000 bits of storage capacity, with an operational speed (officially, *access time*) of 150 billionths of a second.

Miniaturization. The prefix values given below are those commonly used in electronics. All computer chips operate in the nanosecond range. Many capacitors are valued in the picofarad range. As the physical size of ICs shrinks and capacities increase, operational speeds increase and electron density decreases. A startling example of microminiaturization is an experimental IC developed by AT&T containing transistors so small that they can hold no more than **100 electrons** at a time! The internal "wiring" of this chip of the future is capable of carrying electrons only in **single file.**

Prefix Values

giga- billion, 1,000,000,000, (10^9)
mega- million, 1,000,000 (10^6)
kilo- thousand, 1,000 (10^3)
milli- thousandth, (1/1,000) (10^{-3})
micro- millionth, (1/1,000,000) (10^{-6})
nano- billionth, (1/1,000,000,000) (10^{-9})
pico- trillionth, (1/1,000,000,000,000) (10^{-12})

We can expect megabyte, then multimegabyte RAMS in the not-too-distant future. Just imagine the capabilities of such a computer!

A word of explanation regarding memory capacity. You might think that if you are using 256K chips, you'd need only four of them for a 1-megabyte system. Unfortunately, you need four banks of eight 256K chips each, or 32 chips altogether. Why? Because the chips are kilo*bits* not kilo*bytes*. A byte, remember, is eight bits. A computer with 256K of memory has 256 kilobytes, or 2,048 kilobits (2.048 megabits).

To complicate matters, you'll most likely need *nine* chips in each bank because practically all the PCs today include an extra chip per bank for parity (error) checking.

Almost without exception, memory chips are socketed, making them easy to replace. And computers with less than the total allowable amount of memory generally provide empty sockets to enable you to expand memory quickly and easily.

Support Chips

In addition to the CPU, ROM(s), memory chips, and interface chips, the typical computer circuit board contains a number of other chips concerned with moving the data around in an orderly fashion. Unless you're computer has been "zorched" by a natural or unnatural disaster, it's highly unlikely that you'll ever get any grief from the humble, hard-working buffers, gates, and other whatnots. (Zorched is computer-nerd jargon for "wiped out." The etymology of this blend is *zap* + *scorch*.)

A WORKING COMPUTER

Enough of this. Let's find out how a computer works.

The Basic Computer System

We'll start with the computer itself, that is, the computer without any add-ons. This leaves us with the CPU (the microprocessor and its support circuitry), memory, and I/O ports.

In simple terms, the **CPU** executes program instructions and controls the internal operations of the computer, the **memory** stores instructions and data, and the **I/O ports** allow data to get into and out of the computer.

The insides of a microprocessor can be thought of as a whole computer system in ultra-miniature. It has buses for control, data, and addressing, I/O, and memory. In fact there are microprocessors termed *microcomputers-on-a-chip*, such as the Intel 8750H, which are provided with all the elements needed to compute, including both RAM and user-programmable ROM (PROM). See Figure 7-4 (CPU block diagram).

The CPU is the primary system controller, the timing of its control operations governed by a crystal-controlled oscillator, as discussed earlier. These are the operations: (1) timing, (2) instruction fetch, (3) memory read, (4) memory write, (5) wait, (6) I/O, and (7) interrupts.

Timing

CPU instructions are periodic and stereotyped. This means that each takes so many "ticks" of the system clock and each follows a rigid "behaviorial" pattern. First there is a *fetch*, then an *execution*. Some instructions take fewer clock periods than others, but the basic pattern is always the same: fetch, execute, fetch, execute. The fetch-execute pattern is called an *instruction cycle.*

Instruction timing is measured against the absolutely regular tick of the system clock, each tick (called a *T cycle*) consisting of a single peak and trough in the clock pulse chain. Fetching an instruction may take four T cycles, reading from memory three T cycles, and writing to memory three T cycles. The ten T cycles comprise a single instruction cycle. It's easy to see how a disruption in the system clock can send the computer haywire.

Instruction Fetch

When you load a program into the computer, it gets deposited at a number of addresses in RAM. The program contains the instructions that it wants the CPU to carry out. The instruction codes match those built into the CPU, hence "understood" by it. Since the first part of an instruction cycle sets the CPU up to fetch the next instruction, the instructions provided in the program will be acted on automatically once the whole process gets going.

The process is one of reading memory, incrementing, writing back to memory, and so on. Thus, the reads and writes not only cause the events of the program to happen, but cause the CPU to keep track of where everything is.

Memory Read

When the CPU fetches, it actually goes to a location in memory (RAM) and reads what's there. What should be there is a code telling the CPU what to do next. Memory read can be thought of as akin to recalling a fact. To achieve a read, the CPU must start with an address, which is provided by the program being executed. The CPU signals the system that a read is taking place by activating its *read line.*

Memory Write

Instead of recalling a fact, the CPU puts one (actually a byte) into a location in memory. To do this, the CPU's *write line* comes to life and the CPU sends an appropriate address (derived from its internal postal system) out over the address bus to memory, the data following along to that address.

Wait

Sometimes memory may not be able to handle the flow of data as fast as it's being processed. To cover this exigency, the CPU provides *wait states* or idling periods to allow memory to catch up with demand. These wait states can be programmed through software, or even user hard-wired (by setting switches or jumpers).

I/O

Input/output operations differ from memory read/memory write operations in that various external devices (keyboards, printers, disk drives, and the like) play the role of memory. In an I/O operation, you're addressing a device or receiving data from a device, each through its own port.

The CPU's I/O lines talk to the I/O support circuitry, which has its own set of addresses, called port addresses. So when the CPU spots one of these addresses in the program under execution, it knows it has to do some I/O work, perhaps sending data to a printer.

Interrupts

CPUs can manipulate a lot of data in a short time. It may take the CPU only a few instruction cycles to send a whole pile of stored data out to a plotter. But the plotter is a plodder compared to a microprocessor. So while the plotter plods along, drawing a byte's worth of the data, the CPU loafs, awaiting the plotter's call for another byte. An interrupt forces the CPU to stop its loafing or whatever else it's doing and tend to the plotter when the plotter needs tending. In effect, the program being executed, namely, "plot a drawing," is allowed to branch to some other activity temporarily. And return, and branch again, and so on, and so forth. This differs from the *wait state* because the CPU in this instance is being forced to do something other than idle away its time.

There are two general kinds of interrupts in use—hardware and software:

Reset, Non-Maskable Interrupt (NMI), and Interrupt Request (IRQ) typify the hardware-interrupt features built into most microprocessors. Each is accessible through a designated CPU pin. When an interrupt line is pulled low or high, depending on the microprocessor, the CPU interprets the changed electrical state as an interrupt request and acts accordingly—resetting the system, pausing, whatever.

The IBM PC type of computer includes in its design a PIC (Programmable Interrupt Controller), an IC explicitly concerned with prioritizing interrupts. Keyboards and other peripheral devices must be serviced through the interrupt system or else computer activity would be chaotic.

The software interrupt (SWI or some such term) is a specific instruction available directly to the programmer. Its purpose is to force the CPU to accept an interrupt at various points of the programmer's choosing. Often, an interrupt will be called in a program as the result of a test of some sort. "If X is happening, then suspend the present activity, branch off, and do Y."

Microprocessor Instruction Set

Since this isn't a book on assembly language (or any other kind of) programming, there's no need to do more than briefly review the nature of the *Any Chip* instruction set.

The instruction set is actually a programming language. If you can write a program in BASIC or some other high-level language, you can write a program in the native assembly language of your computer. Not immediately, of course, because assembly language requires detailed knowledge of how the microprocessor "thinks." With Pascal, as an example, you can cause a line of text to be displayed on the screen simply by using the Pascal statement, WRITELN. In order to achieve the same result using your CPU's instruction set, you would have to write many lines of programming code.

The characteristic form of assembly language is the *mnemonic*, a memory-jogging abbreviation. Each mnemonic stands for the binary value assigned to the instruction as it appears inside the CPU itself. The assembler knows these values and can translate the mnemonics accordingly. Incidentally, it is possible to program without mnemonics by using the *hexadecimal*, or in some systems, the *octal* values for the mnemonics. In this case, you are working directly with the system's ROM monitor, skipping the assembler altogether.

To clarify what I've just said, here is an example of a 6809 mnemonic and its hexadecimal value:

Mnemonic: BSR (Branch to Subroutine)
Hex value: 8D

Microprocessor instructions can be subtended under headings like data transfer, arithmetic, logic, branching, stack operations, I/O, and control. There are also addressing modes to consider and flags to be set and tested for. When you add up all the permutations and combinations of instructions, addressing modes (immediate, extended, relative, implied, and whatnot), and tests, you end up with a sizable bag of goodies, allowing you to make your computer do anything it is theoretically capable of doing.

A representative data-transfer instruction (from the 8088/8086 set) is *MOVB x,y*. This instruction tells the CPU to move a byte from here (e.g., a register) to there (e.g., memory). Registers are temporary data "storage bins." Every CPU has 'em. In fact, most of what goes on inside of a CPU involves the moving bits, bytes and words in, through, and out of registers.

The assembly language program as written by the programmer is called *source code*. In order to turn the program into something the computer can deal with, it must be *assembled* by a program called an *assembler*. The result is *object code*, the strings of ones and zeros that constitute the computer's "native language."

Regardless of the particular instruction set, assembly language programs all follow the same coding conventions. From left to right, a typical line of code will contain a LABEL, an OPCODE, an OPERAND, and a COMMENT.

Label.   In practice, not every line will have all of these. The *label*, for example, will name a subroutine on the first line of the subroutine. It need not be repeated on each succeeding line. The label identifies the subroutine so that it can be called on later in the program. Thus, you might need a looping routine for counting. You could call it COUNT. In successive parts of the program, every time you want the kind of count you've defined, you need only enter the label.

Opcode. The opcode is the actual instruction in *mnemonic* form: MOV (mov), LD (load), ADD (add), BRA (branch), and so on.

Operand. In most, though not all cases, the opcode takes an argument called the *operand*. This may be as simple as a couple of letters representing two registers, one the source of a chunk of data, the other the destination. The type of addressing you want to use for a given instruction is captured in the operand.

Here's a line of code (from a program I wrote to act as a *software UART* for an RS-232 communication channel) illustrating all the elements of a typical line of assembly language coding. It contains LABEL, OPCODE, ADDRESS, and COMMENT.

```
STARTBIT    LDAA    $C2A0    ; This begins a subroutine labeled
                             ; STARTBIT by loading Accumulator A
                             ; from hex address C2A0, an input port.
```

Addressing. This is one of the more arcane aspects of assembly language programming. An addressing mode is a rule for putting an opcode into or taking it out of memory. Some CPUs provide for a couple of dozen or more such rules. Here's one example to give you a sense of the concept of addressing. In the Z80, a popular 8-bit CPU, there's an addressing mode called *Extended Addressing,* a means of addressing memory directly (instead of addressing registers). In order to use it, you must start with an opcode capable of this kind of addressing. The information with the instruction set tells you what opcodes are capable of which kinds of addressing. By using appropriate opcode with a two-byte operand, the CPU knows that you want to jump from one location in memory to another or to store data in or retrieve data from memory.

Comments. These are optional, but good programmers load their programs with them. Believe me, if you don't, you'll soon forget why you did what you did! You can include explanatory text for every line of code if you wish. The assembler will ignore the comments when the program is turned into object code, but when you print out the source code, the comments will appear. Without them, you'll have a hard time figuring just what you did.

If you're intrigued by the possibilities of assembly language programming, you'll find some **Suggestions for Further Reading** at the end of the chapter. Be prepared for some intense study, but don't just read about it. The only way to get a real grip on assembly language is through practice. Be prepared to pick nits. Every bit and T cycle must be accounted for!

Putting It All Together

Your computer system runs on *power* and *logic*. The power from the wall outlet is converted by the computer's power supply into the voltages needed by digital equipment. Once powered up, the system clock starts its inexorable beat and the logic provided in the hardware design is acted on by the firmware and the software to cause the computer to perform in predictable and useful ways.

Other than the power supply, the principal functional elements in a computer are the CPU, memory (both ROM and RAM), I/O facilities, and buses for addressing, data movement, and control. The I/O channels interface CPU operations to external storage devices (disk and tape drives), peripherals (printers, plotters, sensors), and you (keyboard, video display). Here's the barebones picture:

```
INPUTS━━━▶CPU━━━▶OUTPUTS
             ↕
          MEMORY
```

CPU. Computers can be rated according to the type of CPU, the potential size of memory, and the speed of the system clock. Today's microcomputers use 8-bit, 8/16-bit, and 16-bit CPUs. The Apple IIc (6502) and the KayPro II (Z80) exemplify 8-bit micros. An 8-bit micro is capable of addressing up to a 16-bit number (65,536), but its data bus (internal and external) is only eight bits wide. The IBM PC and most of its clones use the 8088 CPU, a 8/16-bit CPU, capable of addressing over a megabyte (1,048,576 bytes), but, even though it has a 16-bit internal data bus, it uses the same old 8-bit external data bus. The related 8086, used in some of the clones, is a full 16-bit CPU, with a data bus 16 bits wide, internally and externally. (The 8 in 8088 means "eight bits"; the 6 in 8086 means "16 bits.")

The more data a CPU can move at one time, the more efficiently, hence, faster, the computer will work. Or at least that's the theory. Obviously, a poorly written 16-bit program may execute more slowly than a well-written 8-bit program. Since there is a high-degree of coding compatibility between certain 8-bit and 16-bit CPUs, it is not extraordinarily difficult to adapt software running on the smaller chip to run on the larger. But if the adaption is "quick and dirty," it usually falls out that the program runs more slowly on the bigger chip!

Clock. Clock speed is also an important consideration. A Z80 (eight bits) running at a clock frequency of 12MHz (12 million cycles per second) will outperform an 8088 running at 4.77MHz. (IBM settled on 4.77MHz, and many of the cloners followed suit). One of the modifications you make to your 4.77MHz computer is to speed up the processor by the addition of an inexpensive, easy-to-install module. See Chapter 9.

Firmware. Firmware in ROM provides for internal operations independent of the user, operations such as system self-testing (diagnostics) and system bootup. Some computers included a programming language in ROM, as well as a user-accessible ROM *monitor* program for performing extended diagnostics, and even writing machine-level programs directly into the machine.

RAM. RAM memory allows the system to store and use programs and data from any interfaced source: keyboard, external storage, digitizing pads, joysticks, voice, sensing apparatus, instrumentation, and so on. Every bit of data has its own address in the allotted memory space. Some of this memory space, however, is reserved for system use exclusively. Thus, the firmware has its own assigned block(s), memory you can read from but cannot write to. The *memory map* provided with your computer documentation will tell you exactly how the memory is allocated.

Software. Although you can do some things with the computer just as it comes out of the box, it really pays its way only when it's programmed. Most computer users buy the programs they need and let it go at that. All you need do is learn how to load the word processor or spreadsheet or database manager into the computer and how to use the software itself. With each succeeding generation of software, the learning curve grows shorter.

Despite the availability of software for all occasions, however, you may want to try your hand at programming. You can do it with any one of many "high-level" languages like BASIC, Pascal, Modula-2, C, LISP, Forth, PROLOG, and more. Or you may want to take more-or-less direct control of the computer through its native language, accessible through the CPU's instruction set and assembly language programming. It is only by this means that you will *truly* understand what happens every time you press a key. All else being equal, a well-written assembly language program will probably execute faster and use less memory than a program with the same intended outcome written in any other language.

The value to the troubleshooter of this broad view of computer operations should be obvious.

SUMMARY

We've taken the "Grand Tour," albeit at a breathtaking pace and with few stops for a close look at anything. That's okay, because it's the computer landscape panorama we're interested in, not the fine details. Indeed, you may feel that even this superficial view is overly technical and overly detailed. But, as was pointed out, you really don't need this information for basic troubleshooting, yet it's here when you feel that you'd like to do a bit of digging into computer electronics and operations.

If you've strolled along with me, you're no longer a stranger to computer technolingo, and should have a fairly clear picture of the general computer operations and interrelationships, especially if you've read directly along from Chapter 6.

SOURCE LISTING

Formulas

Ohm's Law

The term *Ohm's Law* as used throughout this book should be understood as *DC Ohm's Law*, for there is also an *AC Ohm's Law* that differs in some detail though not in principle. For any calculations offered here or that you may do, DC Ohm's law will give adequately accurate results.

Here, once again, are the DC Ohm's Law formulas for voltage, current, resistance, and power:

E	$\sqrt{I \cdot R}$	P/I	$P \cdot R$
I	E/R	P/E	$\sqrt{P/R}$
R	E/I	E^2/P	P/I^2
P	$E \cdot I$	$I^2 \cdot R$	E^2/R

Resistors and Capacitors

Resistors in Series:

R = R1 + R2 + R3 + ...

Two Resistors of Same Value in Parallel:

$$R = \frac{R}{2}$$

Two Resistors in Parallel

$$R = \frac{R1 \times R2}{R1 + R2}$$

Three or More Resistors in Parallel:

$$R = \frac{1}{\dfrac{1}{R1} + \dfrac{1}{R2} + \dfrac{1}{R3} + \cdots}$$

Capacitors in Series:

Same as resistors in parallel.

Capacitors in Parallel:

Same as resistors in series.

Figure 7–5. **Resistance and Capacitance Formulas.**

Suggestions for Further Reading

This sampling covers the material presented in the chapter. If you're super serious about any or all of the topics, look over the Heathkit's home-study courses on digital electronics and computer programming.

W.H. Buchsbaum and G. Weissenberg, *Microprocessor and Micro-computer Data Digest*, Reston, VA: Reston Publishing Company, 1983.

D.L. Cannon and G. Luecke, *Understanding Microprocessors*, Radio Shack, 1979. Pretty technical, but thorough. Written by technical training personnel at Texas Instruments.

C.A. Crayne and D. Girard, *The Serious Assembler*, New York, NY: Baen Enterprises, 1985 (distributed by Simon & Schuster). Assembly language programming and sample programs for the 8086/8088 microprocessors.

Don Lancaster, *Micro Cookbook, Vols. 1 and 2*, Indianapolis, IN: Howard W. Sams & Co., 1982, 1983. An excellent course on the basics of hardware, logic, and machine level programming. Deals primarily with the 6502 CPU (Apple, Commodore, Atari, and others).

Forest Mims, *Getting Started In Electronics*, Ft. Worth, TX: Radio Shack, 1983. For the absolute beginner. Aimed at electronics in general more than at computers in particular.

E.C. Poe, *The Microprocessor Handbook*, Indianapolis, IN: Howard W. Sams & Co, 1983. Instruction sets for all the popular CPUs. Explanatory comments. Basically just a "look-it-up" book.

Chapter 8

HOW COMPUTERS COMMUNICATE

INTRODUCTION

Since the basic operations of a computer—as sketched in the preceding chapter—would serve no purpose without the computer's ability to move data here, there, and about, let's see how it's done.

Selectivity is Okay

Suppose that your exclusive interest for the present is in hooking up your new serial printer. To learn about serial interfacing, you really needn't spend time on other matters. Turn, therefore, directly to the section on serial communication.

On the other hand, if the general topic of data communication intrigues you, start right here.

Communication in this context means *data transfer*, without which the computer is nothing but an electrical paperweight. *Data* refers to streams of *binary digits*, that is, *bits*, any one of which is either a 1 (high) or 0 (low). You can visualize such a stream this way.

So we'll look in this chapter at signal movement within the computer and between the computer and other people and things. The communication categories we'll explore are (1) parallel communication, (2) serial communication, (3) parallel-to-serial conversion (and *vice versa*), and (4) digital-to-analog and analog-to-digital communication, that is, communication to and from nondigital devices (e.g., telephones, digitizers, and environmental sensors). As for networks, we'll take a quick look at them.

Figure 8–1. Digital Pulse Chain.

This chapter—indeed, the entire book—aims to contribute to your troubleshooting, maintenance, and tinkering skills by giving you not a profound technical education in the subject, but a feel for the subject, a *gestalt*, if you will. Any one of the topics skimmed over here is the basis for an entire book. My reasoning is that if you grasp the general flow of things, you're well placed to diagnose and perhaps even cure a wide range of computer ills. You needn't be a technician in the formal sense of the word, merely a technophile with a broad view.

COMMUNICATION TYPES

In a single conductor, data travels in a serial stream of electrical pulses. *Serial* communication systems use a single path or wire for the movement of data in a single direction. And while there must be a "return-trip" wire to complete the electrical circuit, the bits of information are really traveling down just one of the wires. *Parallel* communication systems send their bundles of data along several pathways at once, in parallel. Each approach has its strengths and weaknesses. Both are used—ideally, each for its strengths—in a typical computer system.

In the diagram below, each asterisk (*) represents one data bit. You can see that in the time it takes eight data bits to travel serially, you could send 64 data bits in parallel.

```
              Serial
—* * * * * * * *⁙→


             Parallel
—* * * * * * * *→
—* * * * * * * *→
—* * * * * * * *→
—* * * * * * * *→
—* * * * * * * *→
—* * * * * * * *→
—* * * * * * * *→
—* * * * * * * *→
```

Parallel Communication

Although data may be isolable as *discrete bits*, most of the data running around your computer is useful as *coherent packages* of bits. To be sure, each bit has to be in its proper place for everything to behave properly. But to make even a single alphabetic character, your computer needs a *byte* (eight bits) not merely a *bit*. To move a character from here to there, then, requires the transfer of eight bits of information. (I'm simplifying, as you'll see later.) This transfer over a single-conductor pathway requires that the bits be lined up in a row. Over a multiconductor pathway, however, all eight bits can be shipped out at the same instant.

Parallel communication can be thought of as a species of serial communication, because the data traveling down *each* line in a parallel system must, after all, travel one bit after another. In other words, one parallel channel is actually carrying eight simultaneous serial channels.

All else being equal, data moving a byte at a time achieves an eight-fold advantage in speed over a serial system. It is not surprising that most of the internal data movement in a computer is done in parallel. The term "8-bit data bus," for example, refers to the fact that the CPU can talk to itself in 8-bit-wide chunks. A computer with a 16-bit data bus can double this data transfer rate, even if the clock rate (the system's operational speed) remains unchanged. Look at the CPU section of your tech manual schematics. Note the CPU pins marked AD and D, that is, the *address* and *data* lines. The pathways are clearly parallel.

Standards

For various pieces of equipment made by various manufacturers to communicate with each other, there has to be some agreement about communication protocols. Within a particular computer, such universal agreement isn't really necessary, but the internal communication system tends to be fairly simple and straightforward; indeed, all computers are pretty much alike with respect to data movement from functional block to functional block within the computer's native circuitry. This means that a computer with an 8-bit data bus ships data a byte at a time down parallel paths from, say, CPU to memory. Control signals generated within the computer keep everything running on time. (Hence the *clock*, mentioned above.)

But when the computer wants to talk to another device like a printer, there must be compatibility in both the physical interface (connectors and circuitry) and the software interface (program controls over data transfer). The least mismatch will result in some degree of communication failure.

Centronics

The *de facto* parallel communication standard in the microcomputer industry derives from an interface designed by one of the early microcomputer printer manufacturers, Centronics. Almost without exception, a peripheral device with a parallel interface uses the "Centronics standard." And even though IBM and its clones have (foolishly) abandoned the distinctive Centronics type of connector at the computer end, the line assignments are the same, and all of the peripheral devices using a Centronics parallel interface have (wisely) kept the Centronics connector. The connector and the pin assignments are illustrated in Figure 8-2.

I downgraded IBM for its abandonment of the Centronics connector (despite whatever miniscule savings in cost) because the replacement connector, the DB-25, is the common *serial interface* connector. If one should accidentally connect a serial device to a parallel device, physical (electrical) damage to one or the other (or both) devices is the likely result. Such a mistake is easily made when the connectors for both systems are interchangeable. The damage is caused by the fact that there are voltages present in both systems that must be properly matched. Sending, for example, 15V to a line that is supposed to be receiving nothing but a control pulse is "reckless endangerment."

Cautionary Note

Make certain that you ALWAYS connect a parallel device to a parallel computer port and a serial device to a serial computer port. Don't be fooled by the fact that your computer may use similar port connectors for both interface types.

The DATA lines and their circuit-completing return lines constitute the heart of the interface, but more than a flow of data bits is needed to make the thing work.

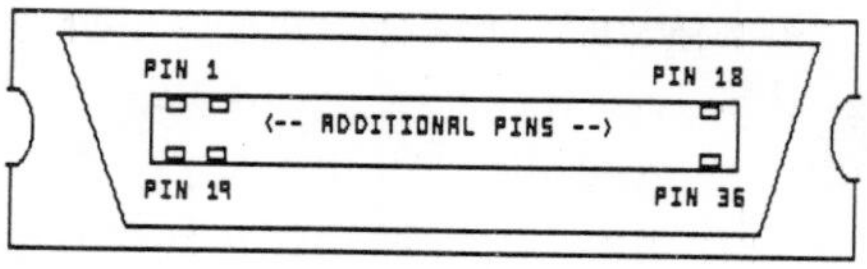

CENTRONICS CHASSIS-MOUNT (FEMALE) CONNECTOR

Pin # (Return)	Designation	⊡to ⊡from Peripheral
1 (19)	Data strobe	→
2 (20)	Data bit 1	→
3 (21)	Data bit 2	→
4 (22)	Data bit 3	→
5 (23)	Data bit 4	→
6 (24)	Data bit 5	→
7 (25)	Data bit 6	→
8 (26)	Data bit 7	→
9 (27)	Data bit 8	→
10 (28)	Acknowledge	←
11 (29)	Busy	←
12	Paper end	←
13	Select	←
14	Supply ground	•
15	OCSXT (100KHz signal)	→
16	Logic ground	←→
17	Chassis ground	•
18	+5V source	•
31 (30)	Input prime (initialize)	→
32	Fault (error)	←
33	Undefined	○
34	Undefined	○
35	Undefined	○
36	Undefined	○

Note: Not all lines are invariably used.

Figure 8–2. Centronics Connector and Pinouts.

In any communication system, the movement of data must be precisely organized and tightly controlled, and the integrity of the data must be ensured. Thus, in a parallel system, eight data and return lines are insufficient to do a proper job. So let's see what the additional commonly used lines actually do.

Handshaking. In a Centronics interface, three lines are used for basic monitoring and control: 1, 19, and 21 (respectively, *DATA STROBE, ACKNOWLEDGE,* and *BUSY*). These constitute the *handshaking* signals. *Handshaking* in data communication signifies agreement to send and receive data.

The data strobe is under computer control; ACK and BUSY are under peripheral control. The strobe is a pulse sent to the peripheral when the computer has dumped a packet of valid data into the data lines. Upon receipt of this telegram, the peripheral issues an ACKnowledgement, which tells the computer that it's okay to keeping transmitting. Inevitably, the peripheral's buffer will fill up because the mechanics of printing or plotting (or whatever) are much slower than the transfer of data. In order to keep the computer from behaving like the broom conjured into brainless life by the Sorcerer's Apprentice, the peripheral issues a BUSY signal, and the computer knows to halt until it gets the go-ahead (another ACK).

ON-LINE lets the computer know whether the peripheral is conscious, so to speak. The other lines are not universally used. The computer and peripheral tech manuals will discuss—or at least identify—all the active lines in any interface.

What happens at the computer end of a typical parallel interface? The wiring on the inside of the parallel interface connector will find its way to a circuit that can be blocked out, as shown in Figure 8-3.

There are other ways of setting up a parallel output circuit, but one such as this, built around a PIA (Peripheral Interface Adapter) is popular and illustrates the principle as well as any.

Even though your PC may be rated as a "16-bit" computer, it will have an 8-bit parallel port. This is appropriate because most transmitted data can be neatly packaged as bytes (8-bit slices). Furthermore, the peripheral device tends to be "I/O bound" anyway. This means that it can deal with only so much data before it runs out of buffer space and must tell the host (computer) to stop transmitting for a while.

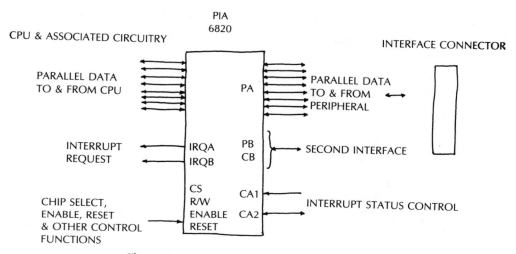

Figure 8–3. PIA and Associated Circuitry.

Software and hardware *spoolers* (data buffers) added to your system can be helpful if, for example, you're doing a lot of printing and don't want to give up the use of the computer while the printer is working. The spooler, either as a reserved section of computer memory or as a "black box" containing a chunk of its own memory (RAM), accepts data from the computer as fast as the computer can dish it out. It then dribbles the data to the peripheral at whatever speed the peripheral requires it. Meanwhile, you get your keyboard back for new work. Of course, if you're not a workaholic, you may be happy just to let the printer have the computer while you contemplate the mysteries of the universe or dream about lazy days at the seashore.

PIA. The Peripheral Interface Adapter is representative of the integrated circuits used for parallel interfacing. It can be thought of as a specialized microprocessor, for it can, indeed must, be programmed if the interface is to function. The programming is taken care of by the software that drives the port. When you install a new piece of software, perhaps FrameWork or Symphony, the installation routine asks you what printer(s) and what port(s) will be used. What you select will govern the operation of the port(s). The program will then install the correct *driver*(s). A driver is the programming routine for the interface microprocessor. A widely used PIA is the Motorola 6821 (part of the 6800 family).

PPI. Another popular parallel interface chip is the Programmable Peripheral Interface. As noted, the PIA is also programmable, so what's the difference? In essentials, not much. So let's not worry about it. Intel's 8255 is the representative PPI. It belongs to the 8080 family of microprocessors, the family from which arose the currently dominant 8086/8088 CPUs.

If you are interested in a detailed discussion of the programming and operations of a PIA or similar ICs, you can find the information in the technical data books published by the various interface chip manufacturers (Intel, National Semiconductor, Motorola, and others). Unless you're ready for some heavy going, however, pass for now.

PIA signals. The PIA and the CPU talk to each other over an 8- bit, bidirectional (two-way) data bus. Control functions between CPU and PIA are exerted over several additional lines (CHIP SELECT, and so on). In turn, the PIA can handle two 8-bit, two-way data buses and several control lines for communication between it and a pair of I/O ports, the gateways to the peripherals. So the PIA acts as an intermediary between the CPU, which is to say, the computer, and the peripherals. The data lines transmit the information you wish to transmit. The control lines manage the system so that data are transmitted at the right time to the right place.

IEEE-488. The Institute of Electrical and Electronics Engineers adopted as a standard the parallel bus designed originally by Hewlett-Packard not for microcomputers but for operational control and information exchange in instrumentation systems (laboratory instruments, and so on). Known first at the GPIB (or HPIB), that is *General-Purpose Interface Bus (Hewlett-Packard Interface Bus)*, it is known officially as the IEEE-488 Standard.

The IEEE-488 Standard actually encompasses a group of standards for computer and instrument bus management. It is basically an 8-bit parallel communication system with special functions that are not part of the Centronics system, as you will note from the diagram in Figure 8-4 on page 211.

As you can see, IEEE-488 is more than just an interface. It is a bus system around which an entire computer system can be built. In fact,

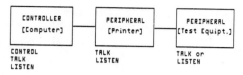

Pin # (Return)	Signal Type	Designation
1-4, 13-16 (24)	Data	Data input/output (DIO)
9 (21)	Control	Interface clear (IFC)
11 (23	"	Attention (ATN)
5	"	End or identify (EOI)
17	"	Remote enable (REN)
10 (22)	"	Service request (SRQ)
6 (12)	Handshaking	Data valid (DAV)
7 (19)	"	Not ready for data (NRFD)
8 (20)	"	Not data accepted (NDRC)
12	Shield	Chassis ground

Figure 8–4. IEEE-488 Parallel Bus System.

the Commodore PET line of personal computers used a slightly modified version of the IEEE-488 bus for all of its input/output operations, including disk drive I/O. This bus structure hasn't survived competition in the general personal computer marketplace, but it can be added to the IBM PC type of computer through an expansion board, allowing the PC to act as a controller for a variety of laboratory instruments. The GPIB is by no means dead. Rather, it has returned, so to speak, to its origins. Most of the manufacturers of electronic instrumentation for laboratory and industrial use use the GPIB interface.

The "philosophy" behind the IEEE-488 bus is suggested by the terms *talker*, *listener*, and *controller*. This nomenclature contrasts with terms like *master* and *slave*, used in certain other communication protocols. The significance is that in the IEEE-488 system, any device can play any role, depending on the nature of current operations. Hence, the notion of the "smart peripheral," which acts as a kind of subsidiary computer. Normally, but not inevitably, the host computer will play the role of controller.

In a typical IEEE-488 setup, the computer is the principal controller, the disk drive system will both talk and listen, as will a printer, and a laboratory instrument may simply talk or simply listen. The devices are all hooked up in "daisy chain" fashion, each cable connector provided with a male element and a female element to allow for stacking. The input to the computer is thus through a single port with one or more cables stacked onto the one actually making the computer connection.

Disk Drive Interfacing

Disk drives use a hybrid interface, part serial (for read/write operations), part parallel (for disk drive control operations). The diagram shows a representative 5¼-inch disk drive interface.

Since the data must be read from and written to a disk one bit at a time, it makes sense that a serial channel is used for read/write operations. On the other hand, the several control operations required to run a disk drive are best handled on separate (parallel) lines.

The disk system consists of three blocks: (1) the disk controller circuitry, usually inside the computer; (2) the disk drive itself, which may or may not be physically inside the computer; and (3) the disk drive

Floppy Disk Controller	[→] [←] Disk Drive
Drive Select	[→]
Side Select	[→]
Motor On	[→]
Direction	[→]
Head Step	[→]
Track 0 Detect	[←]
Index Detect	[←]
Write Protect Detect	[←]
Write Enable	[→]
Write Data	[→]
Read Data	[←]
Signal Return (Ground)	•

Figure 8–5. Typical Floppy Disk Interface Lines.

electronics, mounted on a circuit board attached to the disk drive itself. The disk drive electronics manages the electromechanical operations of the drive—the motors, the production of the magnetic flux required for writing and erasing, and so on. The data and control signals are shipped to the drive electronic from the controller circuitry.

General Considerations in Parallel Communication

Parallel advantages.   For fast and efficient data transfer over short distances, it makes sense to use a parallel system. Most printers, for example, come set up as parallel devices. From a design point of view, this makes sense, because the basic mode of data transfer within most computer-related equipment is parallel. It stands to reason, then, that it's easier to ship the data straight out in its native form. To output serial data requires another step in the data-managing process—that of parallel-to-serial conversion (which we'll check out further along in this chapter).

Parallel disadvantages.   But there are no unalloyed blessings, after all. Parallel data maintains its integrity only over a short haul. The longer the cable, the flakier the outcome. The limit is fairly stringent. Parallel cables longer than about ten feet are definitely not recommended. Serial systems have no trouble with cable runs as long as 100 feet, even more.

Another consideration is conductor count. Whereas parallel communication requires a whole bunch of wires, serial can get by with as few as two, three, or four, depending on data transfer rate and the need for two-way communication.

And, finally, some devices will accept serial interfacing, only—modems, for example.

Serial Communication

In its simplest form, serial data transfer takes place as a single pulse chain of bits moving in a single wire. To complete the electrical circuit, a second wire, the *return* line, is needed. A two-wire telephone system is a real-world example. Or the old railroad telegraph system.

As simple as it may be in principle, serial communication can be complex in practice. Happily, once you have a serial system working properly, it tends to be reliable, even over long distances.

A comprehensive picture of serial communication requires we look at (1) transmission modes (-*plexing*), (2) the EIA RS–232–C Standard, (3) transmission protocols, and (4) practical interfacing problems.

Transmission modes

There are three transmission modes: (1) simplex, (2) half duplex, and (3) full duplex.

Simplex communication. Simplex is strictly a one-way street, a transmitter at one end and a receiver at the other. If your video monitor is hooked up to your computer with a two-wire cable, you're looking at an example of simplex communication. Many of those clattering teleprinters so important to the ambience of a newsroom are at the receiving end of a simplex loop.

Half duplex communication. In this arrangement, two-way traffic is allowed over the two wires, but one end must listen while the other talks. Data can travel only in one direction at a time. A teleprinter with a keyboard can send as well as receive, but while it's receiving data, it cannot send data, hence, *half*-duplex.

Full duplex communication. By adding a second set of wires (or using some fairly sophisticated electronic techniques), you can communicate in both directions (more or less) simultaneously. Thus, an ordinary telephone conversation exemplifies *full duplex* transmission.

-Plexing is of consequence primarily to the *modem* user, and in a special way. *Simplex* has no relevance here because there must be two-way communication when you compute over a telephone line—even if you've programmed your computer to send a file to another computer at 3:00 a.m., long after bedtime. So we're talking about a form of either *half-duplex* or *full-duplex* communication.

The main thing you have to be concerned about is that your modem software is configured to conform with the software at the other end, and that the appropriate switches on the modems themselves are set accordingly. In the section of this chapter on practical interfacing, we'll hook up a modem.

EIA RS–232–C Standard

The Electronic Industries Association, a trade association, is an "official" organization that, among other activities, establishes various standards that its members are encouraged to follow. The most widely known of these standards is RS-232-C, a set of rules concerning the serial exchange of digital (binary) information between the two general types of equipment defined under the standard: *data terminal equipment* (DTE) and *data communication equipment* (DCE).

DTE and DCE. In a "pure" RS-232-C system, the computer terminal is a DTE device and a modem is a DCE device. The package of data to be transmitted begins at one terminal, moves to a modem (which turns the digital signals into the analog "beeps" and "boops" usable by the telephone company), travels over the telephone line to a modem at the other end, where it is converted from tones back to digital signals, and ends the journey at the receiving terminal. Thus, two DTEs, two DCEs, and a telephone line constitute the full communication loop.

Concerning Modems

Note that the *modem*, which stands for *modulator/demodulator*, is alternately a digital-to-analog, analog-to-digital converter. (DAC and ADC are discussed toward the end of the chapter.) When you're transmitting, the modem's task is to convert the ones and zeros produced by the computer into tones representing ones and zeros so that the signal can be sent over a telephone line. This is the *modulator* half of the operation. Telephone transmission must be done within the auditory spectrum of sounds. Hence, the modem emulates, if you will, talking, except that the sounds of this kind of talking are nothing more than the alternation of two tones. When the modem is receiving, it *demodulates* these strings of tones, turning them into strings of binary digits, the only "speech" that the computer can understand. The terms *modulator* and *demodulator* refer, then, to the production, respectively, of audio tones and binary digits.

Now all of this seems straightforward enough. Plug in a cable and away you go. Not so! Let's find out why.

EIA RS–232–C. This standard includes (1) electrical characteristics, (2) mechanical characteristics (hardware), and (3) pin/line definitions. If every manufacturer were to use every aspect of the system exactly as defined, perhaps you would need do nothing more than plug and go.

But (1) many manufacturers seem more concerned with proving their uniqueness than with conforming to a standard, and (2) the principle of RS-232-C interfacing has spread beyond terminals and modems. These realities, coupled with riches provided within the standard, can turn the interfacer's task into a large headache.

To confound the serial interfacing madness, EIA has promulgated a new serial interfacing standard called RS-449, designed to take advantage of the latest developments in communication and computer technology. And while there is a high degree of compatibility between RS–232–C and RS–449, a good deal of the terminology differs. The good news is that, for the present, RS–232–C will continue as the dominant serial interfacing standard in the microcomputer world.

Let's start with the pin/line definitions shown in Figure 8-6.

Although the RS–232–C standard doesn't specify a particular type of connector, the *DB-25* 25-pin subminiature connector has become something of a tradition for serial interfacing.

RS-232-C lines can be grouped for (1) direction of signal flow and (2) signal type (data, control, timing). Note that certain lines are designated as *secondary*. These secondary lines duplicate some of the primary lines, allowing you to set up two fully functional interfaces from the same cable. Of course, the secondary lines must be internally active in order to achieve this result. As it happens, most RS-232-C interfaces use no more than a few of the primary lines, the rest being, for all practical purposes, nonexistent.

Several lines are concerned explicitly with modem hookups, among them *ring indicator* and *received line signal detector*. If you're interfacing, say, a printer, these lines will be irrelevant.

Lines 2 and 3 are the critical ones, for they carry the mail. And they illustrate the important difference between a DTE and DCE device. In order for communication to take place, data must move out from a DTE on line 2 (*transmitted data*) to a DCE. The DTE is the generator and user of data. The DCE is the communicator of data. In the classic setup discussed earlier (terminal/modem/modem/terminal), no difficulty arises because DTE and DCE configurations are properly mated. But when manufacturers chose to design RS-232-C peripherals that were themselves DTE devices, things got confused. The fact is that you can-

Type	⊡to ⊡from DTE	RS-232C	DB-25 Pin #	RS-449
Data	⊡	Transmitted data	2	Send data
"	⊡	Received data	3	Receive data
"	⊡⊡	Signal ground (return)	7	Signal ground
"	⊡	Secondary transmitted data	14	Secondary send data
"	⊡	Secondary received data	16	Secondary receive data
Timing	⊡	Transmitter clock-DCE	15	Send timing
"	⊡	Receiver clock	17	Receive timing
"	⊡	Transmitter clock-DTE	24	Terminal timing
Control	⊡	Request to send (RTS)	4	Request to send
"	⊡	Clear to send (CTS)	5	Clear to send
"	⊡	Data set ready (DSR)	6	Data mode
"	⊡	Carrier detector	8	Receiver ready
"	⊡	Data terminal ready (DTR)	20	Terminal ready
"	⊡	Signal quality detector	21	Signal quality
"	⊡	Ring indicator	22	Incoming call
"	⊡	Signal rate selector	23	Signaling rate selector
"	⊡	Secondary carrier detector	12	Secondary receiver ready
"	⊡	Secondary CTS	13	Secondary CTS
"	⊡	Secondary RTS	19	Secondary RTS
Chassis Ground	•	Protective ground	1	—

Figure 8–6.   EIA RS-232C and RS-449 Equivalents.

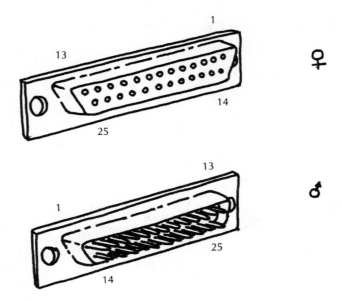

Figure 8–7. DB-25 Chassis-Mount Connectors.

not directly hook a DTE to a DTE. You can, but not with straight cabling.

Think about it: DTE to DTE means that line 2 in each device is trying to transmit, that is, the data bits are trying to scrimmage. It can't possibly work. So a straight-through cable is suitable only where you have a DTE matched with a DCE. To get around the problem of interfacing to either kind of port, you can cross wire lines 2 and 3 (transmitted data to received data, and *vice versa*).

The confusing part of all this is the terminology, *transmitted* and *received*. You have to think of the terms this way: in DTE, TxD is outgoing and RxD is incoming; in DCE, on the other hand, TxD is incoming and RxD is outgoing. A cross-wired arrangement to achieve the desired mating is called a *null modem*. If you wanted to transfer files between two computers in physical proximity, you could do so by connecting the two serial ports with a null modem cable, forcing one of the computers to act as DCE to the other's DTE.

Serial handshaking. With the data moving correctly, you need to turn your attention to the *handshaking* signals. In a representative

DTE/DCE configuration, straight wires between CTS (clear to send, pin 5 on each) and DTR (data terminal ready, pin 20 on each) provide the handshaking. But if you're mating a pair of DTE ports, you'll have to cross wires, perhaps hooking line 5 to line 20.

Another complication arises from the issue of whether handshaking signals are positive or negative. Some operating system configuration utilities allow you to specify the correct choice for the device you're interfacing. For example, a given plotter may respond to a DTR signal only when it's negative. If your system hasn't been set to transmit a negative DTR, then proper handshaking won't be established between the computer and the plotter.

Some interfaces allow for either *hardware* or *software* handshaking. The former, discussed above, is generally preferable because it requires its own dedicated pair of signal lines (DTR, CTS, RTS, or whatever the manufacturer has chosen) and operates clear of the data transmission line. In a software handshaking setup, the same lines that handle data (2 and 3) also carry the handshaking codes. Under the XON/XOFF protocol (ASCII designation: DC1/DC3), when the printer buffer is full, the printer sends an XOFF signal (CTL-S or hexadecimal 13) to the computer on line 3 telling it to stop transmitting. As soon as the printer has caught up with itself, it sends XON (CTL-Q or hexadecimal 11).

The advantage of this type of handshaking is the elimination of separate handshaking lines. The disadvantage arises from the fact that the handshaking signals can corrupt graphics data, which requires an 8-bit word. Straight ASCII text can live happily with XON/XOFF, but with some graphics programs you will run into glitches. The Hewlett-Packard LaserJet printer will allow either hardware or software handshaking, but the manual (without saying why) urges the former. Now you know why.

The manual accompanying the peripheral device will usually give you the common configurations. The least stressful approach to solving the problem of interconnection is to demand that the dealer from whom you bought the peripheral provide you with the proper cable and the proper computer and peripheral switch settings.

The ground lines are universally the same, and even if the interfacing instructions for your new peripheral don't require it, you should use *both* grounds, pins 1 and 7.

Transmission Protocols

Although serial data is transmitted a bit at a time, these bits are useful to the receiving device only as larger blocks, usually bytes (8-bit chunks). A single alphanumeric character, for example, is packaged in the ASCII system as a byte. So when you press a given key on your computer keyboard, the code for that character starts on its way, eventually ending up as a printed or displayed number or letter. The issue here is how the transmitting/receiving system "knows" where a given character begins and ends.

Part of the answer lies in the method of data transmission. If the system depends primarily on a rigidly controlled *clock* or *sync* signal, it is called *synchronous*, that is, "timed" transmission. Most microcomputer systems do not use synchronous data transmission, opting instead for *asynchronous* transmission.

Baud Rate

In an asynchronous or "untimed" system, there is, of course, some kind of timing. Instead of a sync signal (and other stuff), however, the two communication devices must match *baud* rates. The baud rate is the transmit/receive speed measured in bits per second. Thus, if your computer is dishing out data to your printer at 9,600 baud, the printer should be set to receive data at 9,600 baud. Failure to assure this matchup will result in garbage or system lockup.

Word Size

In addition to baud rate, you also need to match *word size*, *start bits*, *stop bits*, and *parity*. For most peripherals, these parameters are set *via* hardware configuration switches, which usually take the form of dual-in-line-package (DIP) blocks with multiple switches.

The "full" word size is eight bits, but if your peripheral isn't using graphics or any kind of fancy printing, then a 7-bit word will be suitable. Daisywheel printers and older dot matrix printers generally use 7-bit words. Regardless of which word size you're using, both computer and peripheral must be matched. "Word" in this context has nothing to do with ordinary words—it is strictly a technical term. With a 7-bit word, you can use a *parity* bit. As a rule, with an 8-bit word, no parity is possible. See page 221 for a discussion of parity.

Framing Bits

As the illustration reveals, each data byte ("word") is framed by start and stop bits. These bits (which again must be matched on both side of the transmission) serve to delineate the actual data, indicating where each new byte begins and ends. The baud rate moves the data along at a fixed speed, but the receiver must know how to deal with the flow of bits, otherwise how would a printer, for example, know which particular group of bits should be turned into the printed character you requested? When the baud rates are not matched, the printer grabs the wrong chunks and prints gibberish (or nothing, if there's too great a discrepancy). When the start and stop bits are not matched, the receiver will confuse the framing bits with the data bits, and, once again, gibberish will be the outcome.

Parity

To further insure the integrity and accuracy of the data being trans-mitted/received, most serial interfacing schemes provide for the addi-tion of *parity* bits to the data stream. Each data byte, then, may have both one or two start bits, one or two stop bits, and a parity bit. In practice, however, the pattern is to use one start bit, one stop bit, and (perhaps) a parity bit, which may be either *odd* or *even*.

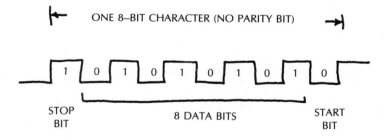

SERIAL BIT STREAM FOR ASSUMED

CHARACTER $1 0 1 0 1 0 1 0_2$

Figure 8–8. Data Bits.

The parity bit works like this. Suppose that you've opted for odd parity. If the transmitted byte contains an even number of ones ("high" or "on" bits), an additional high bit would be added to produce an odd number of ones. At the receiving end, this would appear to be correct, because the receiver is looking for a package containing an odd number of ones. In the event that an even number shows up, it would assume that there has been an error in transmission and you'd get some kind of message to that effect. The transmitter (e.g., the computer) adds the parity bit and the receiver (e.g., the printer) strips it.

Many peripherals don't require that parity be used. The only rule is that the choice must be matched on both ends: odd, even, or none. As pointed out under the discussion of *word size*, when you're using 8-bit words, you must give up parity.

Where Serial Data Comes From

Serial data, as noted earlier, arises in a parallel world. By this I mean that data moves around the inside of a computer on parallel paths. (The term *data* refers to those signals that carry the freight, as opposed to *timing* and other digital signals concerned with internal operations.)

How, then, does parallel data inside the computer end up as serial data outside the computer? Enter the communication interface adapter, a general name for a class of specialized microprocessors whose function it is to convert parallel data to serial data, and with the help of a little support circuitry, ship the data out to a port for transmission to whatever peripheral device is plugged into the port. The conversion works in reverse as well, for serially transmitted data from the outside world enters the port and is converted into parallel data.

Parallel/Serial conversion chips.   The IC that does the conversion, the communication interface adapter, goes by several names: ACE (Asynchronous Communication Element), ACIA (Asynchronous Communication Interface Adapter), UART (Universal Asynchronous Receiver Transmitter), and USART (Universal Synchronous/Asynchronous Receiver Transmitter). Each of these devices is a little different from the other, but they all perform basically the same functions, that of serial/parallel parallel/serial data conversion and the production of RS-232-C control and timing signals.

For convenience, let's refer to the serial communications IC as ACE. The drawing, in Figure 8-9 is that of an 8250, a widely used communications adapter.

The parallel data bus is bidirectional (data can enter the ACE from or leave the ACE for the CPU circuitry). Serial data leaves through SOUT (serial out) and enters through SIN (serial in). The incoming 8-bit chunks of parallel data are "squeezed" into a single stream and sent to the *transmitter holding register*. When their time comes, they enter the *transmitter shift register*, and from there are tossed out into the world. When you see the printer grinding out your wordprocessed text, you know that the ACE (and everything else) is doing its job.

Registers can be thought of as temporary storage bins for data bits. They may merely accumulate data until it's ready to be sent to the next "station," or they may perform some change on the data (e.g., shifting each bit to the right, in order to set up the data in the correct order). Our serial out shift register takes in parallel data bytewise (in 8-bit slices), dumping it out bitwise (a bit at a time). The "dumps" occur every time the register gets a full byte for transmission.

Serial-to-parallel conversion in the ACE simply reverses the process, with the data moving from the outside through the receiver elements of the ACE.

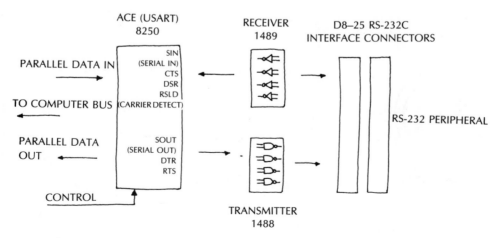

Figure 8–9. Serial Interface Using 8250 ACE.

To match the baud rate of the printer or other RS-232 devices, the ACE's baud rate generator is programmed by the computer (through the DOS and, for example, your word processing software). The baud rate circuitry of the ACE sees to it that the data gets shipped out at the correct transmission rate. Likewise, it reads the incoming data at its predetermined rate, accepting the data if it matches, getting confused if it doesn't match.

Another function of the ACE is to generate standard RS-232-C handshaking and modem signals. So, when you're using your RS-232 port, the ACE (or equivalent IC) is mighty busy.

Because the communication interface adapter is almost as complex as a CPU, hence susceptible to a greater failure rate than many of the support chips in your computer, it is often socketed for easy replacement. Should your serial device suddenly start acting peculiar, it may very well be the device itself that's at fault. But don't overlook the ACE (ACIA, UART, USART) as a likely culprit.

Non-Standard Serial Interfaces

Some of the older game-oriented computers (Commodore 64) provided a serial port, but one that did not follow the RS-232-C standard. The result of this non-standardization is the inability to interface the computer directly with RS-232-C devices. Since neither the cabling nor the voltage values match, it is necessary to interpose an "inter-interface."

The Commodore serial pinouts are shown in Figure 8-10.

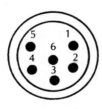

DIN SOCKET

1 SERIAL SERVICE REQUEST (SRQ) IN

2 GROUND

3 SERIAL ATTENTION (ATN) IN/OUT

4 SERIAL CLOCK (CLK) IN/OUT

5 SERIAL DATA IN/OUT

6 NOT USED

Figure 8–10. Commodore 64 Serial Interface Connector Pinouts.

Because most microcomputers and serial interface expansion boards currently in production use the RS-232-C standard in some form or another, you'll probably never be faced with this special kind of interfacing problem.

Digital/Analog Conversion

Digital/analog data conversion is a big, complicated subject that, for the purposes of this book, we needn't dwell on at length.

We are analog creatures living in a mostly analog environment, yet we depend increasingly on digital computers and expect these wonderboxes to relate somehow to our analog existence. So we must provide ways of converting digital and analog information back and forth and transmitting the converted data. This is the rationale for our inclusion of a brief consideration of the topic in a chapter on data communication.

Our world is one of continually changing values on an infinitely graded scale, that is, it's an analog world. Even the picture on your TV picture is painted by analog signals. That's why the TV pictures (unless they've been computer-generated at the station) look so natural—no "stair steps" on what should be smoothly drawn curved and angled lines.

And while there are such things as analog computers (various kinds of laboratory instruments and control devices, for example), your computer and mine are digital machines. But what if you want your computer to play a tune you've programmed in BASIC, or do something useful with information picked up by various kinds of sensors (temperature, sound, light, stress, moisture), or communicate data over a telephone line?

DAC and ADC devices are integrated circuits whose job it is to establish equivalents between digital and analog data.

Digital-to-Analog Conversion

If you think of a digital system as a series of on/off switches, it's not hard to picture a setup where a byte is represented by eight switches, each of which will be either on or off. If each switch is hooked through a resistor to a point in a voltage-divider network—nothing more than a string of resistors hooked up in series (elephant-walk fashion)—then the voltage value of the resistor chain can be varied by which and how many switches are opened and closed. The voltage is thus continuously variable as the digital input varies bitwise. The varying voltage, now purely analog, but under digital control, can be applied to any appropriate analog device, including audio and video systems.

Of concern to the user of a DAC are such parameters as (1) conversion rate or resolution in bits (8, 12, 16, etc.), (2) precision (generally, more bits, more accuracy), (3) conversion period (the time it takes to convert a defined unit), and (4) range of operation (min/max).

Analog-to-Digital Conversion

ADC—or *data acquisition*, as it is often termed—turns signals that are commonly in the form of varying voltages into the patterns of ones and zeros your computer can cope with. The varying voltages may be produced, for example, by a *transducer*, a sensor that can convert one kind of energy into another. Your household thermostat is a good example. As the ambient temperature changes, the bimetal coil in the thermostat unit moves, typically causing a mercury switch to shift its position. When it has shifted enough, the blob of mercury moves to the end of the switch containing the contacts. The contacts are then closed by the mercury (a conductive metal), and the furnace turns on.

Nothing digital here, right? Wrong. The switch is digital—it's either on or off. So a thermostat is a simple, noncomputer example of ADC.

Digitizing pad.   This device may be as inexpensive as a Koala Pad or as costly as a Textronix digitizer. When you use a digitizing pad, your drawings are being converted from analog (continually varying) values in the form of curves, shadings, and whatnot, to digital values. Each point on the pad is given a digital value, and when you hit a given point with your stylus or drawing cursor, that digital value is sent to the computer. On a smoothly changing waveform, the ADC performs a technique known as *sampling*, that is, picking off a value every so often and assigning to that value a binary number. The higher the sampling rate, the smoother the appearance of the converted output.

If your drawing of an absolutely smooth diagonal line shows up on your screen as a kind of staircase, an important part of the reason is the sampling rate. There are other reasons as well, of course.

Joystick.   A joystick is another ADC device. In one type of joystick, the movement of the handle changes the values of two variable resistors. A variable resistor, or *potentiometer,* is very much the same kind of gadget used to control the volume of your radio. Anyway, the varying resistance results in a varying voltage. Each change in voltage is converted by the ADC circuitry into a specific digital value. The *mouse* and the *game paddle* belong in this department. In basic operation, these and the digitizing pads are very much alike.

Speech synthesis.   Perhaps a more telling example (pardon the pun) can be found in computer speech synthesis. Inexpensive speech digitizers take relatively few samples, missing, perforce, many of the subtleties of speech. But if you're willing to pay the price, you can get computer-generated speech (made from samples of actual speech) that is virtually indistinguishable in sound from that produced by a high-quality tape recording.

Music synthesis.   Digital sampling has become a major force in the realm of music synthesis. Much of the apparently live music you hear these days is actually pieced together from music sampling/synthesis systems. Again, the higher the sampling rate, the more finely polished the outcome (at least from the standpoint of the raw sound!). Some microcomputers have music synthesizers built in. Nearly any micro can be interfaced through a relatively new interfacing standard called MIDI (Musical Instrument Digital Interface) to external music synthesizers.

ADC/DAC expansion boards.   Where the computer is used to process real-world signals, the actual values are "read" by a device (a thermometer, for example) converted by a *transducer* to electrical values (voltages) and fed into an ADC, which may be located on a multichannel ADC/DAC expansion board. The conversion from voltage to binary data is made on the board, these data then being acquired by the software running the system. This software, for example, may be set up to trigger an alarm when the acquired temperature hits a predetermined value. At the trigger point, the software sends a digital signal to the DAC channel on the ADC/DAC board to which the alarm system is connected. The binary code is converted to an analog voltage capable of tripping the alarm switch.

The parameters critical to ADC (acquisition time, aperture time, decay rate, feedthrough, and the rest) require more space for discussion than we have space to give. Don't feel cheated. Knowing this stuff at this stage of the game is next to useless.

ADC/DAC Considerations

The quality of output will depend on a number of factors. But given the best in eyes, ears, video display capability, audio capability, and printing capability, you'll want your ADC/DAC equipment and circuitry to produce the best possible output. But you'll pay for it. A CAD workstation, one able to produce ultra-high-resolution drawings with all the detail you're capable of creating, will cost several pretty pennies. On the other hand, a low-cost setup may be entirely adequate.

As for troubleshooting, you've just been introduced to yet another area of your computer system susceptible to gremlins. When, for example, your computer-controlled climate control system goes weird, you've entered the ADC zone.

Practical Interfacing

Parallel-to-Parallel Interfacing

Almost without exception, parallel-to-parallel interfacing (Centronics-to-Centronics or IEEE-488-to-IEEE-488) amounts to nothing more than plugging in the cables and, possibly, setting a switch on the peripheral for parity and for either 7-bit or 8-bit words, a choice that depends on the program you're configuring for. (Straight text usually needs only seven bits; graphics and access to special characters need eight bits). Then, of course, you need to install your software, a routine that includes *configuration* or *setup* for the peripheral(s) you'll be using. Once it's done, you can forget it—unless you change your hardware.

Serial/Parallel Interfacing

Let's assume that you have a plotter with a parallel interface, but the software for running the plotter is provided with a serial device driver only. I ran into just such a gloom-inducing situation recently! But gloom wasn't needed after all, for I dug around in my collection of doodads and came up with a serial-to-parallel converter that dumb foresight prompted me to buy at a computer flea market.

To harmonize the software and the plotter, here's what I had to do. (Remember, we're sending serial signals out of the computer and converting them to parallel signals for the plotter.)

(1) Set the switches on the converter to match the serial signals for baud rate, handshaking, word size, and parity.

(2) Connect the converter to the serial port of the computer with a straight-through RS–232–C type of cable. There will probably be a female DB–25 connector on board the converter.

(3) Connect the converter to the plotter (or whatever) through a parallel cable (generally supplied with the converters).

(4) Configure the computer software to talk to the *serial* port. In the IBM PC type of computer, this will be either COM1 or COM2.

(5) In the IBM and related computers, you will also have to use the MS-DOS (PC-DOS) *Mode* command to redirect printer output from the default parallel port (LPT1) to the selected serial port. The mode change requires two simple steps, the first to set the serial values (assuming here, 9,600 baud, no parity, eight-bit word, one stop bit); the second to direct parallel output to a serial port. Thus: (1) MODE COM1:9600,N,8,1,P RETURN, (2) MODE LPT1:=COM1: RETURN. *Mode* must reside on the current disk or current directory. (Some, but not all, applications software will make the port change automatically. No harm is done, however, by you're doing it, too.)

Serial-to-Serial Interfacing

A look at two interfacing problems will give you an insight into how it's done. In the real world, the permutations and combinations are legion, but once you have a grasp of the principles, the key to a particular lock should be easily found.

Texas Instruments TI-855 printer. This is an interesting case because the printer can be interfaced to either a serial or a parallel port, through the *same* Centronics type of connector. You **cannot**, however, use the *same* cable for either interface!

The printer comes with a single DIP switch block containing eight switches, allowing for 24 selections covering baud rate, parity, word size, print quality, automatic line feed option, and interface type (serial or parallel). The switch and the choices are shown in Figure 8-11. Here's the way to set up the system:

(1) First we must make a cable. Since the printer has a Centronics connector doing double service, we need to identify the correct serial lines. The printer tech manual tells us that lines 15, 16, 17, 19, 33, 34, and 35 are the relevant ones for a serial interface. We don't need them all, of

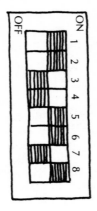

1 } 8–BIT WORD, NO PARITY
2 }

3 SOFTWARE-GENERATED LINEFEED AFTER CARRIAGE RETURN

4 EPSON-TYPE PRINTER CONTROL-CODE SET

5)
6 } 9600 BAUD, HARDWARE HANDSHAKING (READY/BUSY)
7 }
8)

Figure 8–11.   TI-855 Configuration Switch-Typical Settings.

course, but we do need TxD (35, transmitted data), RxD (16, received data), grounds (17, 19), DSR (33) and DTR (34). In a "standard" RS–232–C arrangement, the pinouts are, respectively, 2 (TxD), 3 (RxD), 1 and 7 (grounds), 6 (DSR), and 20 (DTR).

(2) The cable will have a Centronics connector at the printer end and a DB-25 connector of the correct gender at the other end. Before connecting the wires at the computer (DB–25) end of the cable, you need to determine what kind of handshaking is provided for and whether the communication port is configured as a DTE or DCE. In the event that the computer COM port is emulating a DCE, you won't have to crisscross lines 2 and 3. If it is a DTE, you will. Likewise, if you're connecting a DCE to a DTE, the handshaking lines (DSR and DTR) can be wired straight, not crossed.

(3) In the **Source Listing** for this chapter you'll learn about the *breakout box*, a gizmo for identifying the active signals in a serial interface and for allowing you to experiment with the various lines until you get a successful combination. Unless you expect to be doing a lot of serial interfacing of a lot of different devices, it would be extravagant to buy a "full-service" breakout box. There are relatively inexpensive versions

that will do nicely for occasional setups. Another do-it-yourself interfacing gimmick, the "intelligent cable," is also discussed in this chapter's **Source Listing**.

(4) Because the TI-855 printer is a DTE, as are most computer COM ports, crisscross we must (see Figure 8-12.).

(5) Next we'll set the printer switches as follows:

    (a) Eight-bit data, no parity (enables dot-addressable graphics): switches 1 and 2 ON.

    (b) No automatic line feed (software takes care of it): switch 3 OFF.

    (c) Data processing mode (*Epson* type) printer codes: switch 4 OFF.

    (d) Baud rate 9,600 (faster is better): switches 5-8, ON, ON, ON, OFF.

    (e) Interface (preceding selection forces serial interface).

(6) Since parity requires a bit of its own and since we've opted for an 8-bit word, we must abandon parity. No great loss. Most systems today do without parity.

(7) With the electrical power to both computer and printer turned off, you now plug the cable in at each end.

(8) Finally, we need to configure the software, a task amounting to no more than choosing the same values as you set with the printer DIP switch.

Modem Interfacing

To physically interface an internally mounted modem, you need only plug in an extension telephone cable (one with a *modular* connector). A stand-alone modem requires a regular RS-232-C cable. Since your computer COM port is probably DTE and modems are always DCE, the cable needs no cross-wiring. Most modems of either type provide for switch settings to default the modem to various conditions, such as that of answering the telephone automatically.

The software interfacing part of the job asks for setting COM port, baud rate, parity, stop bits, dialing mode (touch tone or pulse), and establishing whether you're operating at full or half-duplex. All communication software comes with a menu of choices, which may include a lot of fancy business concerning the behavior of your communication system (automatic dialing, and so on). Let the manual and the menu help screens guide you through the maze.

A 300/1200 baud modem is currently the best choice, for practically every bulletin board and online service supports one or the other of these baud rates. Just be certain that you've set your system to talk to

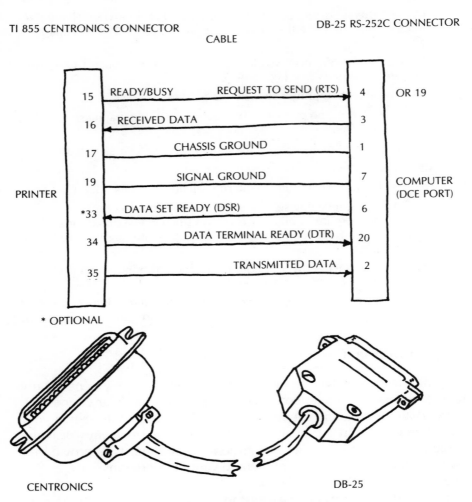

Figure 8–12. TI-855 Serial Cable.

the system at the other end at a baud rate it can read. Although modems operating at 2,400 and 4,800 baud are growing in popularity, relatively few telecommunications services are supporting them at this time. The picture is bound to change soon. Be advised, however, that the higher the data transmission rate, the higher the data-service user fee.

RS-232C INTERFACE CABLE

TO TELEPHONE JACK

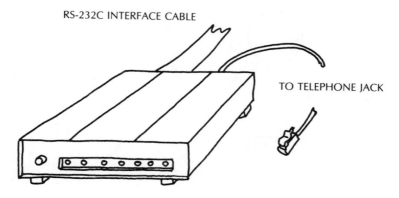

Figure 8–13.   External Modem.

For a complete, easy-to-assimilate course in modem-based communication, see Alfred Glossbrenner's book, listed in the **Suggestions for Further Reading** at the end of the chapter.

Networks

Microcomputer timesharing *via* a LAN (Local Area Network) is a rapidly growing branch of microcomputer data communications. It's also in an advanced state of confusion. There are no hardware, performance, interfacing, or software standards, and costs are all over the lot.

In essence, a network allows two or more computers to share hardware and/or software resources, and even communicate directly with one another. In a small business, an arrangement whereby two or three microcomputers can use a single large-capacity hard disk drive on a time-sharing basis might prove far more efficient in terms of inventory control, client-file access, accounting system access, and so forth, than efforts to use the three micros as independent devices. The mere avoidance of disk swapping among the computers is a big gain.

In any event, LAN (Local Area Network) is a hot ticket. Several *topologies* (pathway configurations) are in use, as are several interfacing systems, no universal standard having yet been settled on. Most of the patterns do use some sort of serial data transfer methods, at kilobit and megabit rates.

Star, ring, and *bus* are the current topologies. In a star configuration, outlying *nodes* (terminals) each communicate with a central node that acts like a switchboard. Where all the nodes are daisychained in a

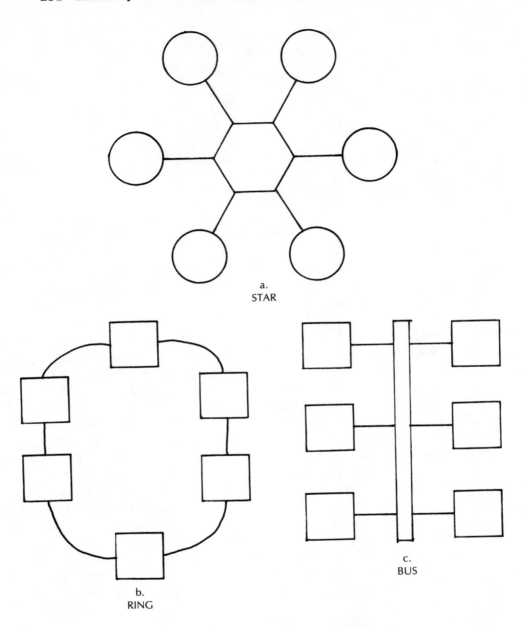

Figure 8–14a,b,c.   LAN Configurations.

circle, it is called a ring, in which data run around and around to be picked off as needed by whatever node. The bus provides a central common pathway for each of its nodes.

In order for the nodes in each topology to work harmoniously, data handling must be arbitrated by the system software, each system using its own set of communication protocols.

A point to consider: Since tinkering with a network can affect other members of the network, it might be best to call in an expert when your network goes crazy. Of course, it won't hurt to check cables for integrity. That's always a good early move in times of disaster.

SUMMARY

This chapter has attempted to give you a comprehensive (if not exhaustive) view of the communication landscape. We've touched on the basic communication types (parallel and serial), the question of standards, communication protocols, interfacing problems, and data conversion. We slighted networks because of the extent and complexity of the topic, reminding you that because networks involve several users, it's probably best for the casual tinkerer/troubleshooter to turn network problems over to trained technicians.

SOURCE LISTING

Interfacing Gadgetry

IEE–488

To turn your PC into an IEEE-488 controller able to run any device with an IEEE-488 bus interface, plug a National Instruments' Lab Boss card into a spare expansion slot and go to it.

National Instruments
1209 Technology Blvd.
Austin, TX 78727
(512)250–9119

Serial/Parallel Converters

Several companies make external devices that will convert serial signals to parallel, or parallel signals to serial. These can be had with or without data buffers. A buffered unit has its own complement of memory, commonly from 16K RAM up, and can act as a spooler as well as a converter. This means that you can, for example, ship serial data out of the computer through the converter to a parallel printer and continue your keyboard work without having to wait for the printer to do its job, the converter/buffer having made the communication changeover while at the same time accumulating the data in its own memory.

Quadram's *Microfazer* line is perhaps the most well known of the buffer converters:

Quadram
One Quad Way
Norcross, GA 30093–2919
(404)923–6666

The intraComputer *Turbo Transmit* buffer/converters are notable for their ultracompact size (2 1/4 x 3 x 3 3/4).

intraComputer
101 West 31st Street
New York, NY 10001
(212)947–5533

For straight conversion (no buffering), use the serial‹›parallel bi-directional converter:

Intectra Inc.
2629 Terminal Blvd.
Mountain View, CA 94043
(415)967–8818

Tigertronics Incorporated
2734-C Johnson Drive
Ventura, CA 93006
(805)658–7466

RS–232–C Gender Changers

To match connecting elements (cable/cable or cable/chassis connector) of the *same* gender, you need to interpose a union fitted with a pair of connectors of the opposite gender. This union can be easily made by fitting a pair of appropriate connectors to a short piece of 25-conductor ribbon cable. Or you can buy ready-mades. B&B Electronics sells a complete line of interfacing gadgets, including gender changers:

B&B Electronics Manufacturing Co.
P. O. Box 1008B
Ottawa, IL 61350
(815)434–0846

Breakout Boxes

By plugging the serial cable from the computer and the serial cable from the peripheral into the two connectors of a *breakout box*, you have effectively "broken out" the serial lines so they can be examined and experimentally cross wired to achieve a successful serial interface. The expensive breakout boxes come with individual switches and status lights for every RS–232–C line. To enable crosswriting, they come with jumper cables. Figure 8-14 makes all of this plain.

Several companies make breakout boxes of varying complexity, the more elaborate, the more costly. Expect to pay $150 and $200 for full-blown versions. Basic models can be had in the $30-$50 range. Try B&B Electronics (see above) and Black Box.

Intelligent Cables

Smart Cable is the brand name of a kind of automatic breakout box that you can just leave in line, or that you can use as a "template" for making your own RS–232 cable. You start by plugging one end of the Smart Cable into the serial port and the other end into the serial connector of the peripheral. One switch controls the data lines and one the handshaking lines. Four LEDs tell you which lines are active. By experimenting with switch settings, you'll find a combination that works.

IQ Technologies, Inc.
11811 NE First Street, Suite 308
Bellevue, WA 98005
(206)541–0232

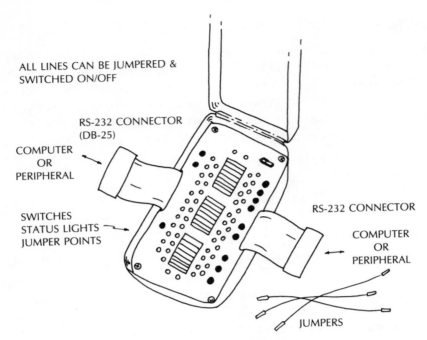

ALL LINES CAN BE JUMPERED &
SWITCHED ON/OFF

RS-232 CONNECTOR
(DB-25)

COMPUTER
OR
PERIPHERAL

SWITCHES
STATUS LIGHTS
JUMPER POINTS

RS-232 CONNECTOR

COMPUTER
OR
PERIPHERAL

JUMPERS

Figure 8–15.   RS-237–C Breakout Box.

A slightly more complex intelligent cable is called Easy-Cabler, available from many computer supply houses, such as Priority One Electronics, 21622 Plummer Street, Chatsworth, CA 91311–4194; 1–(800)423–5922.

Either one of these can greatly simplify RS-232 cabling, but each costs close to $100, rather a lot if you plan to leave it in place once you've got your interfacing problem solved.

Null Modems

To avoid making a cable with lines 2 and 3 crisscrossed (to enable you, for example, to transfer files between two computers in physical proximity), you can use ordinary straight RS-232-C cables and a *null modem*, which you can make or buy. A simple homemade model consists of straight wires for grounds (1 and 7) and crossed wires for TxD and RxD (2 and 3). At each end, use a DB-25 connector of appropriate gender for your interface. A store-bought version will be a little more elaborate and made on a small circuit board instead of a flexible cable. B&B Electronics sells these for about $25.

Suggestions for Further Reading

The reader interested in building an entire library of books on data communications and local area networks should write or call the Telecom Library, a bookseller specializing in these topics. Telecom Library Inc., 12 West 21st Street, NY, NY 10010; 1–(800)LIBRARY; (212)691–8215 (in NY).

A few specific recommendations:

T.J. Byers, *Guide to Local Area Networks*, New York, NY: Brady Books, 1985. A good general introduction to LANs.

Alfred Glossbrenner, *The Complete Handbook of Personal Computer Communications*, New York, NY: St. Martin's Press, 1985. Over 500 highly informative, clearly (and entertainingly) written pages.

Stevanne Lehrman, *Local Area Networking with Microcomputers*, New York, NY: Brady Books, 1986.

Martin D. Seyer, *RS–232 Made Easy*, Englewood Cliffs, NJ: Prentice Hall, 1984. Covers this aggravating topic about as well as anything I've read. Lots of practical interfacing examples.

Chapter 9
MAKING CHANGES

INTRODUCTION

What is this chapter doing in a book on *troubleshooting and mainte-nance*? Here's a thought: Modifying your computer system to make it work better, faster, more to your heart's desire can be thought of as *system maintenance*. Let's put a finer point on it. Suppose that in the process of troubleshooting a problem, you decide to substitute a bor-rowed memory board for one that seems to be malfunctioning. You don't need to substitute a board of **exactly** the same type and capacity. To your computer, memory is memory, and so long as the substitute board is *compatible* with your computer, go ahead and use it. Now suppose further that the borrowed board has twice the memory of the old board, and a few other goodies beside.

Okay, you turn on your computer, which is now provided with a substitute board, and it works fine. So there you are, looking longingly at the borrowed "troubleshooting" board, wishing you had one of your very own. So why not get one (as soon as the cash is available)? Thus has troubleshooting melded with modifying!

Because you may feel some reluctance to tear into an expensive, complicated gadget that's working just fine as it stands, I won't press you to make any but the safest and easiest of changes. This chapter, then, amounts to an annotated catalog of "safe" add-ons, each of which will enhance the capabilities of your computer, as well as your ability to manage it for your purposes.

For the most part, the enhancements, expansions, and whatnots are available "off the shelf," often requiring little more mechanical skill than the ability to plug tab A into slot A.

It's worth remembering that hardware is nothing without software, and that there's a lot of specialized software around for helping you make the most of your hardware. Printer utilities, both commercial and public domain, are just one type of hardware-enhancing software.

WISH LIST

First off, let's agree that the terms *modification* and *enhancement* are in this context synonymous. Surely you wouldn't modify something to **un**enhance it! And since *modification* denotes *change*, any change is a modification, whether you shove a board into an expansion slot or homebrew a circuit.

Hardware additions to your computer can drive the total cost of your computer to undreamed of heights. Indeed, some individual expansion boards cost more than an entire system. Think of your present system, therefore, as the kernel of something potentially much larger and more powerful than you imagined when you walked out of the computer store, carrying your computer, monitor, and printer. A couple of book-length treatments of computer-system expansion are listed in the **Suggestions for Further Reading** at the end of the chapter.

Here are some of the ways you can modify a computer system:

- Adding disk drives, floppy or hard or both.
- Adding a tape drive.
- Adding exotic mass storage (e.g., EAROM disk).
- Adding memory.
- Adding a coprocessor.
- Changing the CPU.
- Adding an expansion box.
- Adding expansion boards, for example: (1) memory, (2) communication ports, (3) modem, (4) game port(s), (5) video display enhancement, (6) data acquisition (analog/digital), and (7) real-time clock/calendar.
- Speeding up the system ("turbo mode")
- Upgrading power supply
- Adding or changing data-entry devices, for example: (1) keyboard, (2) mouse, (3) joystick, (4) digitizing pad, (5) light pen, (6) voice command system, (7) numeric keypad, (8) optical text scanner, (9) optical Bar-code reader, and (10) optical digitizer.
- Adding or changing video monitor
- Adding other peripherals: (1) printer (high-density dot matrix, color, formed character or "letter quality" or plotter), (2) print buffer (spooler), (3) external modem, and (4) networking equipment
- Adding electrical protection

- Adding peripheral switch
- Adding a fan

You have my permission to rush out and buy it all. But because many add-ons are added on in the same way, I'll discuss representative examples only.

OFF THE SHELF

It's obvious, yet worth saying: Before you buy any addition for your system, determine the need. Is this something that you truly can no longer compute successfully without (additional memory required to run a new piece of software)? Or is this merely an indulgence (a faster printer, perhaps)? An evaluation of your needs will help you to spend your computer dollars wisely. If the choice must be made, upgrading from a 10- to a 20-megabyte hard disk will probably be a better move than upgrading from a 20-character-per-second to a 40-character-per-second daisywheel printer. You really can live with the slower printer, but your hard disk may be reaching its limit. Anyway, think about it.

Sources

You can buy computer add-ons from (1) specialized computer stores, (2) department stores, (3) mail order businesses (which may not be actual walk-in stores), (4) amateur radio/computer flea market vendors, (5) fellow computer club members, and (6) friends. What's your best move?

You need to consider (1) cost; (2) vendor reputation for customer satisfaction, which includes knowledgeable "handholding," and hassle-free repair, replacement, or refund as appropriate; (3) service and repair facilities, and ease of access thereto; and (4) product depth (range of models, availability of optional features).

Not all of these considerations will be relevant to every potential purchase. A computer club member may offer his not very old Zippy printer for sale, and you may be ready to move up from your Pokey printer. If the price is in the ballpark, and you can see the Zippy actually working, haggle over the price and make a deal.

Specialty Stores

Even if part of a chain, the store is a local enterprise and if it has been around for a while, will probably still be there when your newly purchased *microDigilator* has quit digilating. You can get a feeling for the solidity of the company by comparison shopping. A store that has relatively little merchandise on hand may not be on a solid financial footing. Besides, purely from the standpoint of emptorial gratification, a bare store is a downer.

You can usually bargain the price down—aim for a 25% discount, settle for 10%, but don't pay "list price" for anything but inexpensive items. If you go for a system, insist on a meaningful discount or walk. There are other stores! The store markup averages 40% on undiscounted items. It doesn't hurt to go into your bargaining session with some mail order prices in mind. You can't expect a local retail store to necessarily match those prices, but don't be shy about asking! Just remember that "list prices" are an advertising gimmick, not a "truth." You see a piece of software advertised by the manufacturer at $695, and then spot it in mail order ads at $285. Manufacturers and vendors can justify this sort of thing. Why argue? Just look for the best deal.

The salespersons probably know a bit more about their products than department store clerks. Still, as a general rule of the marketplace, approach any purchase with a healthy measure of skepticism. If you're uncertain about computer products, do some homework about the product(s) you wish to buy, and bring a knowledgeable friend to the store with you. So long as they're more than mere puff pieces, product reviews in computer publications can help.

There is usually a service facility on the premises. But if the speciality store is nothing but a large vending machine (like many "electronic boutiques" in shopping malls), you're better off looking further—unless, once again, the store is selling a particular item at an unbeatable price and you are satisfied with the reliability of the place.

Product depth is generally greater in a specialty store than in a department store, and it will carry a selection of pertinent books and periodicals. Have you ever noticed how department stores seem to sell nothing but the "big pieces," and how nobody knows anything about the little optional goodies described in the manual? How you can buy a printer, for example, but no ribbons? There oughta be a law!

Computer periodicals are filled with ads offering all kinds of stuff that nobody in your neighborhood carries. It doesn't seem fair—what you want is always somewhere else. This need not be a big problem.

Mail Order

The majority of mail order houses are as honest and reliable as the retailers at home. Play it safe, however, by ordering from companies whose ads have been appearing regularly in major magazines over a reasonable period. Generally, the bad apples don't last long.

Be prepared for delays. Many mail order houses have nothing in-house. You order and then they order. If you order by phone, ask them for a firm delivery date. If they hedge, bid them adieu and try another company.

Repair, replacement, and other customer service issues are not conveniently handled by long distance. A mail order store will, on balance, serve you better than what amounts to a catalog buying service. In any case, before you buy, find out what you can about the company's service policy—and don't believe all they tell you.

Since mail order houses sell principally on the basis of heavy discounts, the advertised price will be firm on most items. However, the integrated circuit market is almost like the stock market; so the price at the time of your order may be higher or lower from the advertised price. Shop around for your best deal. On the purchase of a whole system, you should be able to cut a better deal on a package than you'd pay for the individual pieces in sum.

Perhaps your best dollar values can be had at "hamfests," "computerfests," and business expos, held at hotels, motels, exposition halls, and public institutions (armories, schools, colleges). Many of these shows will include a mix of new product vendors and flea-marketers. Bring money. Bargains abound. But be canny, wary, and skeptical. Always: **Caveat emptor.**

Flea Markets

Come armed with specific product information. There are lots of brand-new, name-brand items out there that may look "normal" but are obsolete or designed for special purposes that will not suit your needs at all. For example, there's the case of the super-high-resolution color video monitor, manufactured by one of the leading companies in the field, being sold (in a factory-sealed carton) at an absolute "steal."

Just what you've been looking for, at a price you can afford. Wrong. The monitor was made for an industrial application and is unusable for computer systems without extensive internal modification. If you're up for the modification and are willing to take a chance on its actually working, go for it; otherwise, move along.

NEVER accept an asking price. Flea market vendors expect to bargain, and are both amused and gratified by nonhagglers.

Don't accept assertions of "compatibility" with this or that computer system—or with claims about how easy it will be to achieve "complete" compatibility. Try to get a "second opinion." There are plenty of knowledgeable people wandering around at a flea market. Don't be shy about asking for help.

Get receipts and business cards (or names and phone numbers) from everyone you do business with. Pay by check where possible. But if you're up for some heavy haggling, a wad of bills will hasten the appearance of a reasonable bottom line.

If the expo runs for two days, do your buying on the first day to enable you to test the equipment and return unsatisfactory items the next day. If a vendor gives you a hard time about this, make a lot of noise. It never fails.

At the bigger, business-oriented shows, all of the products for sale will be new (if not necessarily current!). At a show-*cum*-flea market, there will be lots of used equipment, a sizable proportion of which will be flat-out junk. The careful, well-informed buyer can pick up some good deals in used equipment. The innocent buyers should steer clear.

You can make especially good deals in the last moments of the show because the overriding aim among flea market vendors seems to be to go home with nothing but money.

WARNING: Something of considerable value priced too low to be true may be either defective or "hot off the back of somebody else's truck." As tempting as such buys may be, don't be tempted.

Personal sales are almost always of used equipment. If you're buying from a fellow club member or a friend, you're not likely to get stung. Still, it's best to take the equipment on approval, or, at the very least, to arrange for a realistic demonstration. "Realistic" means watching a printer print a document, not merely zip through its self-test routine.

What to Add and How to Add It
Adding Disk Drives

Your computer is capable of supporting at least two floppies and a hard disk. Yours has a single floppy. Or, perhaps, a floppy and a hard disk. Here are the options: (1) add a floppy (easy to do, low cost); (2) add a hard disk (more complicated to do, fairly expensive); or (3) add a floppy and a hard drive (most expensive, but most convenient from a computing point of view).

Shopping around for a drive and installing it yourself can save you considerable dollars. There's really nothing about installation that demands the services of an "expert." Just remember to turn off the juice before you open the computer! Let's start with the floppy.

Adding an Inboard Floppy Disk Drive

Buy a new floppy disk compatible with your system. For example, you can't use a Commodore drive in an IBM system. On the other hand, you needn't buy an IBM-labeled drive for your IBM computer. Most of the drives advertised in the magazines are suitable for IBM and clones. If your computer uses full-height drives, be sure to specify this in your order. You needn't spend more than about $100 for a good quality, direct drive floppy. Direct drive units require no drive belt, an advantage.

A note on **density**. IBM PC/XT and clones use double-sided drives capable of writing 40 tracks (48 tracks per inch). This results in a formatted disk with a usable capacity of about 360K bytes. Would you like to put nearly 800K bytes on a 5½- inch floppy disk? You can, but at an increased cost for the drive and at some inconvenience in use. You'll need a 48 track (96 tracks per inch) drive and a formatting program not provided with your operating system. You won't be able to boot from the high-density drive and you won't be able to run your existing software on it directly. You'll have to transfer programs from the standard floppy to the high-density floppy first. Is it worth the trouble? Not for me. Go for a hard disk if you want *really* high-density storage.

Follow these steps when installing a disk drive:

(1) Turn off power to the computer.
(2) Ground yourself briefly to the power supply case or to any sizable metal object outside of the computer.

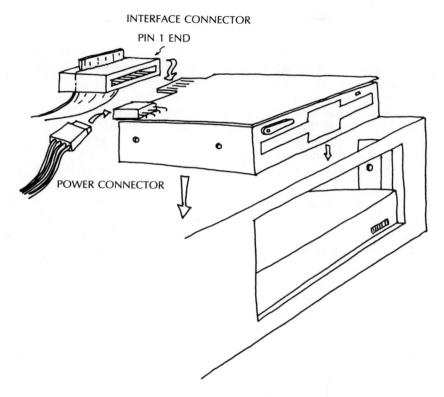

INTERFACE CONNECTOR

PIN 1 END

POWER CONNECTOR

Figure 9–1. Installing a Disk Drive.

(3) A drive being mounted *inboard* requires no additional power supply. A drive being mounted *outboard* requires a power supply and an enclosure. You can buy enclosures with built-in power supplies, which is the best way to go. (See the **Source Listing** at the end of the chapter.

(4) A computer with provision for a second drive will almost invariably have a power connector and a second drive cable connector in place. Check to make sure. It's highly unlikely that the second power connector will be missing, but there may not be a dual-drive interface cable; in this case, you'll need to order one along with the drive. On the off chance that the power supply lacks the second disk-drive power connector, order a Y power cable. The vendor will know what this is.

(5) Disk drives are mounted either stacked or side-by-side. In each case, there is some sort of mounting cage or bracket to which the drives are

screwed. Your user or tech manual will show you the details of your setup.

(6) Likewise, the manual(s) should tell you how to "address" the disk drives. Generally speaking, there is either an *addressing shunt* or a jumper on the disk drive logic board that specifies the address of the drive, as Drive 1 or Drive 2 (Drive A, Drive B). (The addressing legend on the logic board may show 1 as 0 and 2 as 1.) Set the address as required. NOTE: On IBM PCs and certain clones, you needn't worry about the addressing shunt. Addressing in these computers is taken care of automatically by the way the interface cable is wired. Therefore, for these computers, you MUST use the IBM type of interface cable.

(7) As appropriate, change the system board switches to recognize the new drive. Your manual(s) will guide you.

(8) Every new drive comes with a removable resistor pack plugged into a DIP socket (that is, a regular IC socket). This resistor is called a *terminator* and serves to minimize electrical "noise" in the interface. Since no more than one of these should be used, only the terminator on the drive that is "physically" last on the interface cable should be left in place. Whether this is *addressed* as Drive 1 or Drive 2 makes no difference.

(9) Plug in the power connector, which is keyed to fit only one way.

(10) Attach the interface cable to the drive with the pin 1 marker on the cable connector matching pin 1 on the logic board connector. Line 1 is indicated on the cable by a colored stripe; pin 1 on the cable connector (female), by a number or an embossed triangle. The connector fingers on the top of the board begin with pin 2, pin 1 being on the underside. Just consider that the cable connector mark stands for pin 2 and everything will be fine.

(11) Install the screws and tighten just enough for immobility. Don't fasten them for eternity. Too much torquing can (1) mangle the screw head, (2) strip the screw and/or hole threads, and (3) stress the chassis of the drive. I've know cases in which the drive chassis was distorted just enough to misalign the heads.

(12) Before closing the computer box, give the new configuration a test. Boot up on Drive 1, format a disk on Drive 2.

(13) Button up.

In case you're curious about the inner workings of a typical floppy disk drive, Figure 9-5 highlights the main operational components.

This diagram in Figure 9-6 shows a typical disk drive interface cabling arrangement.

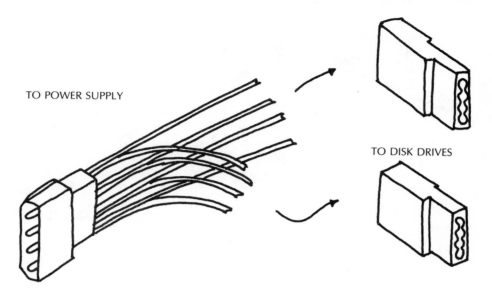

TO POWER SUPPLY

TO DISK DRIVES

Figure 9–2.   Y Connector.

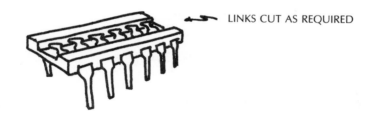

LINKS CUT AS REQUIRED

Figure 9–3.   Addressing Shunt.

Adding an Outboard Floppy Disk Drive

To add an *outboard* disk drive, you need a separate enclosure, an external power supply, and an interface cable long enough to reach the enclosure from the main computer. Disk drive vendors sell enclosures with suitable power supplies already mounted. They will also provide you with cabling. Just measure the length and specify that you need a controller board connector at one end and two disk drive card-edge

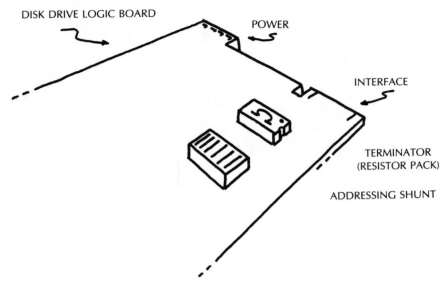

DISK DRIVE LOGIC BOARD

POWER

INTERFACE

TERMINATOR
(RESISTOR PACK)

ADDRESSING SHUNT

Figure 9–4. Terminator

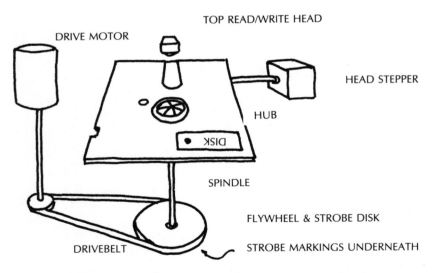

TOP READ/WRITE HEAD

DRIVE MOTOR

HEAD STEPPER

HUB

DISK

SPINDLE

FLYWHEEL & STROBE DISK

STROBE MARKINGS UNDERNEATH

DRIVEBELT

Figure 9–5. Mechanical Essentials of Floppy Disk Drive.

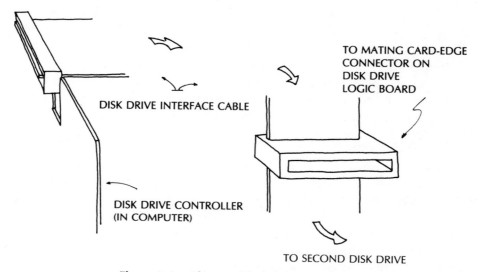

Figure 9–6. Floppy Disk Interface Cabling.

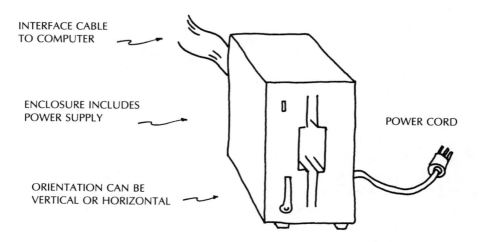

Figure 9–7. External Disk Drive.

connectors spaced *n* inches (your measurement) apart. One connector has to go to the inboard drive, one to the outboard, so leave ample room between the two connectors. "Ample" means including provision for routing the cable from the one drive to the other.

Nothing differs from inboard installation with respect to addressing the drive or to placement of the terminator. The external drive can stand horizontally or vertically, whichever is convenient for you.

Adding an Outboard 3½-inch Drive

Yes, you can add a high density, double-sided microfloppy drive to your IBM-type of system. The vendor from whom you buy the drive can supply you with the correct interface cable. And you'll need either PC-DOS (MS-DOS) 3.2 or a piece of software called Datadisk. (See this chapter's **Source Listing**.) To make the addition, plug in the new interface cable, set the addressing jumper or switches as needed, and install the software. This is a simple procedure that requires the addition of a new line to your CONFIG.SYS file and the copying of the Datadisk device drive to your boot disk.

Datadisk was actually designed for 5¼-inch 80-track floppy disk drives, and you can use one of these rather than the microfloppy if you prefer. But a 3½-inch drive, such as NEC's FD1035, will look electrically just like the larger drive and can be formatted in either "standard" quadruple density (720K) or extended quad (something over 800K). The standard quad formatting is entirely compatible with IBM's 3½-inch drives.

Adding an Inboard Hard Disk Drive

Inboard hard disk drives come in three general types: (1.) the "hard-card" type that plugs into an expansion slot; (2.) the standard "disk-in-a-box" that mounts like a floppy; and (3.) the removable cartridge type that also mounts like a floppy. The standard type comes in *full-height* and *half-height* versions. The half-height drives are the more popular because of their compactness and lower power consumption. Of course, only full-height drives are capable of handling the super high capacities that are rapidly becoming available. There are also hard disk/tape drive combinations for internal as well as external mounting.

Installing a hard-card type of drive involves little more than plugging the drive into a spare slot and setting configuration switches. Although the disk-on-a-card is presently limited to 20 megabytes, drives with greater capacity are undoubtedly in the works. If you have the room, this is a convenient way to add mass storage. It's even possible to install two, but you'd better upgrade your power supply if you intend to do so. Alternatively, you can add a self-powered expansion box for the hard cards and other cards as well. An expansion box (or expansion chassis) is nothing more than an extension of the computer's mother board, that is, the bus system. Since it has its own power supply, the expansion box makes no electrical demands on the computer itself.

Standard hard disks are mounted internally (or externally, for that matter), exactly like floppy drives (see above), with the exception that hard drives require their own *controller card*, a circuit board that plugs into an expansion slot. Two cables (instead of one) link the controller card and the drive. Power can be supplied by the same connector that would otherwise be used for a second floppy. Just plug it in.

In the event that you already have two floppies on board, the hard drive will need power either from the existing power supply (if it's enough) *via* a Y cable that shares power between one of the floppies and the hard drive (see above), or an outboard power supply. Recommendation: Upgrade your power supply to one capable of handling at least 150W. Then you can add boards and whatnot with impunity.

Your computer manuals will guide with respect to configuration switches and hard disk formatting, a process rather more elaborate than that required for floppy disks.

Adding an External Hard Disk Drive

Outboard installation of standard or removable cartridge types is no different from that of a floppy. The controller card must, of course, be mounted inboard in an expansion slot. Outboard mounting of a hard card can be done only in an expansion box, since you need a standard expansion card slot.

Adding a Tape Drive

Tape drives come in a number of formats and capacities. They tend to be pricey and there's no standardization, meaning that no two competing tape systems are compatible with each other. Some require controller boards, some connect to existing serial or parallel ports. Some are packaged with internally mounted hard disk drives. Most are outboard units, with or without hard disk drives. They all need special software drivers. For any configuration, it's mainly a matter of plug and go, insofar as the hardware is concerned. My own preference is for an external unit. Selection from the numerous models available will depend on budget and storage needs. Don't, for example, buy a tape system using tape cartridges or reels with greater storage than your largest-capacity disk. What's the point? Tape is meant only for backing up disks, not for running programs.

Tape advice: Read reviews and test out systems before buying. The hard disk/tape combination is an attraction option.

Exotic Mass Storage

For certain computers you can buy *bubble-memory, ROM disk*, and *battery-powered RAM disk* boards. These lesser-known types of mass storage tend to be fairly expensive, but offer (1) high speed operation coupled with (2) "permanence," that is, retention of data after the computer is turned off. Installing these boards differs in no way from installing any expansion board. The computer itself has to be informed of the presence of the new "drives" in the same manner as for electro-mechanical drives.

Another type of storage is the *CD-ROM*, an optical (laser) disk playback unit capable of storing about a half billion bytes of *read-only* data. That's enough storage for an entire encyclopedia. Like your audio compact disk unit, it cannot accept new data. Several companies are working on optical disk read/write systems, but none are on the market yet.

CD ROM units are plugged into your system pretty much like any ordinary disk drives—using a controller card and an external enclosure. There is no standardization; the disk sizes run from 4½ to 12 inches in diameter. Prices are all over the lot as well.

Adding Memory

Memory can be added to your system in two ways: (1) on an existing board (perhaps the main system board) and (2) as separate cards, either dedicated to memory alone or including other features like additional communication ports, real-time clock, and whatnot (*multi-function* cards). Memory cards may expand system memory to its full capacity or may provide a new range of (extended/ expanded) memory beyond the normal limitation. The latter type is exemplified by Intel's Above Board and Quadram's Liberty Board.

Adding memory to an existing board requires that you buy a set of memory chips of the correct type. These will most likely be either 64K

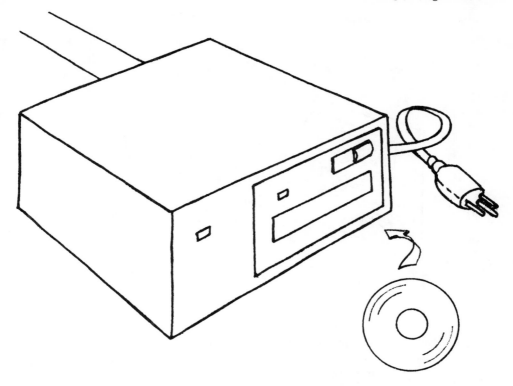

Figure 9–8. CD ROM.

DRAMs (dynamic RAMs) or 256K DRAMs. Your system may use eight, possibly nine, chips to a bank. Check with your computer manuals. The ninth chip, incidentally, is used for error-checking, and must be present in each bank for the system to run.

Don't buy memory chips from your local computer dealer unless prices come close to mail-order prices (no more than about $3.00 per chip). Check the magazines and comparison-shop. You want brand name chips (e.g., Hitachi, NEC, TI, OKI, Motorola) with current dating, rated at 150ns (200ns is acceptable).

Here are the steps for adding memory to an existing board:

(1) Turn off power to the computer.
(2) Ground yourself briefly to the power supply case, or any large metal object outside of the computer.
(3) Open the computer and locate the board to be modified.

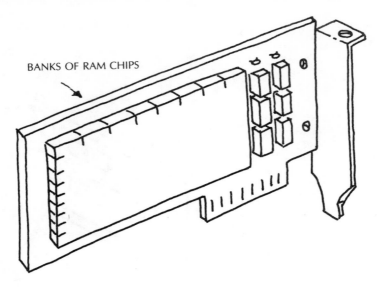

BANKS OF RAM CHIPS

Figure 9–9. Add-on Memory Board.

(4) If the board is removable, remove it, and place it immediately on a piece of aluminum foil (for static protection).

(5) Check your computer manuals for the proper distribution of new memory chips. For example, are the banks arranged horizontally or vertically on the board?

(6) Prepare the chips for insertion by straightening pins as needed. To bend an entire row of pins inward slightly, which may be necessary to socket the chip easily, hold the row against your work surface and press the chip body enough to do the job. In most cases, just a slight inward bend from the new chip's slight outward flair will suffice. Try to concurrently hold all the pins on the chip you are handling.

(7) To socket a chip, align one row of pins with one row of socket holes, then align the other row. When each pin is in place, press the chip gently downward, seating it evenly. Take care not to bend any pins and, especially, don't allow a pin to bend under the chip.

(8) Now, actually insert the new chips, matching pin 1 on each chip to pin 1 on the board. DOUBLE-CHECK. If you mount a chip backwards, it will be destroyed as soon as you turn on the power.

(9) Before replacing the board, check once again for correct orientation of chips and for bent pins.

(10) Replace the board.

(11) Change configuration switches and/or jumpers as required by your system to recognize the added memory.

(12) If chips are to be added to the main system board, check the manual for proper arrangement: (a) follow the chip-insertion instructions given above; (b) double-check for orientation and bent pins; and (c) change configuration switches and/or jumpers as needed.

(13) Test the system before closing up.

PINS ON NEW ICs ARE OFTEN FLARED

PRESS FIRMLY DOWN ON COUNTERTOP

Figure 9–10.   Straightening Flared IC Pins.

DON'T ALLOW ANY PINS TO BEND OUT OR UNDER

ALIGN

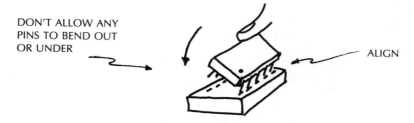

Figure 9–11a.   Socketing an IC.

IC

IC SOCKET

MINIATURE FLAT-BLADED SCREWDRIVER

Figure 9–11b.   De-Socketing an IC.

On computers supposedly limited to 256K on the system board, it is in fact possible to expand memory to 640K without adding a memory board. See the **Source Listing** at the end of the chapter.

Adding a Coprocessor

Many computers come with provision for a coprocessor, an IC that shares some of the processing activities with the CPU, thereby speeding up various operations, especially those requiring a lot of "number crunching." In order to benefit from a coprocessor, of course, you must have software capable of using it.

Computers in the 8086/8088 family use the 8087 coprocessor, which you can buy for about $100 to $150, slower chips costing less than faster ones. The aim is to match the coprocessor speed to CPU clock speed. Thus, if you are running a "turbo" system (8MHz), you'll want an 8MHz coprocessor. Here's how to add a coprocessor:

(1) Turn off power to the computer.
(2) Ground yourself briefly to the power supply case or to a large metal object outside of the computer.
(3) The usual location for the coprocessor is near or right next to the CPU. Look for an empty 40-pin socket. Check with the tech manual.
(4) Prepare the coprocessor pins as required for easy insertion (see above). These ICs are easily destroyed by static electricity, so take care.
(5) Orient pin 1 correctly.
(6) First align one row of pins with the matching row of socket holes, then the other row of pins and holes.
(7) Carefully press the chip straight down, seating it evenly. Watch out for bent pins.
(8) Change configuration switches and/or jumpers as required to allow the CPU and coprocessor to communicate. Your manual will guide you.
(9) Check again for pin 1 orientation and bent pins.
(10) Test the system before closing up. On many computers, the boot-up message will inform you that a coprocessor is installed.

Upgrading the CPU

There are four reasons to replace a working CPU:

(1) It overheats—a potential source of trouble.
(2) It's too slow for the speed-up modification you want to make.
(3) It's "old-fashioned."
(4) It precludes your using software written for the earlier 8-bit members of your CPU family.

If the body of the CPU in your computer is plastic, it is susceptible to overheating. Replace it with a *ceramic* version.

If you're planning to "goose" the clock speed of your computer, you'd best replace the current CPU with one rated at the new speed. The old one *may* work, but it may not work reliably. Speed-up modules, incidentally, are easily added to some computers. For advertisements and helpful articles, check the the magazines that focus on specific computer brands.

"Old-fashioned" may seem an odd choice of terms. Yet think about it. The developmental metabolism of this industry runs so fast that many computer products have become obsolescent (if not obsolete) within a year or two of their introduction. Surely the 8088 CPU, as an example, is already hoary with age. It has been superseded within its own family. Unfortunately, you can't replace an 8088 with 80286 just so. But you can replace it with a NEC V20. (And an 8086 with a V30.)

The V-series chips not only run cooler than the standard 8088/86 chips because they draw very little power, but at equivalent clock speeds they run faster because they handle instructions more efficiently. Furthermore, and this may be the most convincing reason for many computerists, they can run most 8-bit CP/M software.

So why should you care? As it happens, thousands of first-rate programs written for 8-bit CP/M-based computers are available. You may have upgraded from 8-bit CP/M to your present system. And now all of that CP/M software just sits on your shelf, looking historical.

Enter Acceler8/16 (see this chapter's **Source Listing**), hardware/software enhancement that will: (1) speed up your computer (by a little bit to a tad more than a little bit), (2) reduce power consumption, and (3) bring most of your CP/M software back to life. (The current V-series chips won't run Z80 software, but a Z80 emulator is rumored to be under development. See the **Source Listing** for a Z80 expansion board for IBM and compatible computers.)

The V-series CPUs cost about $20 each. The Acceler8/16 package (which includes the the CPU and the necessary software for running CP/M as well as for disk-format swapping among about 100 disk formats) will run you about $100. When you order, get the right chip at the right speed for your system: 8086 (V30); 8088 (V20). Specify the 8MHz version for a "turbo" system.

To replace your CPU with a V-series CPU, follow these steps:

(1) Turn off power to the computer.
(2) Ground yourself briefly to the power supply case or to a large metal object outside of the computer.
(3) Locate the CPU (8086 or 8088). Your manual will point the way.
(4) With a flat-bladed miniature screwdriver, alternately pry up each end of the chip until it comes loose. Press the pins through a piece of aluminum foil and put it away.
(5) Prepare the replacement CPU pins as described above.
(6) Orient pin 1 to match pin 1 of the socket.
(7) First align one row of pins with the matching row of socket holes, then the other row of pins and holes.
(8) Carefully press the chip straight down, seating it evenly. Watch out for bent pins.
(9) **No** changes are required in configuration switches or jumpers.
(10) Test the system before closing. It should run exactly as before. You won't detect the speed improvement unless you run benchmarks. Even then, the difference won't be dramatic. Eight-bit CP/M, however, will run noticeably faster than it does in its native environment.
(11) Button up the computer and install the software as the product manual directs.

Making Other Board-level Changes

There are modifications to circuit boards that require trace cutting and soldering along with chip replacement. Before you buy a product that looks as if it will do something wonderful for your computer, "read the fine print"; talk to a technically knowledgeable person about it. Telephone-order takers generally don't fit the bill! In any event, don't attack your board with blade and soldering iron before you feel fully confident in your ability to work at this level of techno-twiddling.

Adding Expansion Boards

A typical expansion board of whatever purpose is plugged into a spare expansion slot. Some boards on some computers must be plugged into designated slots. Some require internal cabling. Others are cabled to external devices (communication port, game port, mouse, video, and modem boards). For some, you must set or change configuration switches and/or jumpers. And some need special software, which is generally supplied with the board.

If an advertised board promises features that you feel will result in some significant enlargement of your computing power, by all means indulge yourself. Even if you've never lifted the lid of a computer, installing a new board is simplicity itself and will serve nicely to break the tinkering ice.

Complexities may arise, however, when it comes to getting the board to perform as advertised. Don't be put off if it takes a phone call or two to the manufacturer before you get everything organized. Most manuals are the pits when it comes to explaining things for newcomers to the art of computer enhancement!

Multifunction cards such as those popularized by AST and TECMAR generally contain (1) memory, (2) one or more communication ports, (3) a real-time clock and calendar, and, perhaps, (4) a game port or two and a light-pen port. Installation of this type of board is like the installation of any board—just plug the critter into an expansion slot. The manual will guide you through setup and use.

Adding Speed-up Modules

Your computer was manufactured to run at a given clock speed, rated in frequency and *megahertz*. This speed is governed by a circuit that includes a crystal-controlled oscillator and the CPU itself. Merely changing the CPU to one rated at a higher frequency won't do the trick. In other words, if you pulled out your 5MHz 8088 and replaced it with an 8MHz 8088, nothing would change. The typical commercial speed-up module is either a small circuit board that plugs into the main system board or an expansion-card type of board that plugs into an empty expansion slot.

The effect of the small-circuit-board approach is to change the frequency of clock, driving the CPU and other chips to higher operational speed. All well and good, but problems can arise if those chips are just not up to being lashed this way. You'll probably end up changing the CPU and perhaps even the floppy disk controller chip. If you're lucky, the installed memory chips will run fast enough. RAM rated at 150ns will match any currently available speed-up modification.

To install one of these little boards, you have to open the computer, locate and remove a particular IC (as directed by the board manual), insert the board's pins in the now empty IC socket, and insert the IC into the add-on board. The ability to switch between normal speed and high speed is provided by a small switch mounted on an expansion slot

IC REMOVED FROM SYSTEM BOARD &
INSTALLED ON SPEED-UP MODULE

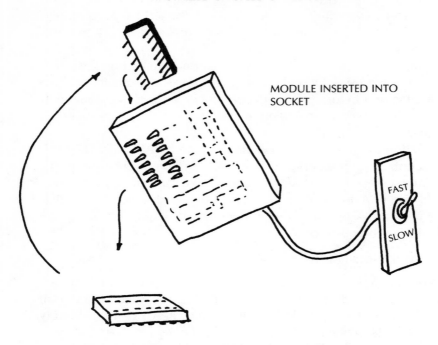

MODULE INSERTED INTO
SOCKET

Figure 9–12.   Small Speed-up Module Installed on System Board.

filler bracket (or whatever bracket or location is suitable for the computer in question).

The expansion board speed-up is more elaborate, and may be far more costly. A small circuit board module may cost as little as $50, an expansion-board turbo module as much as $1000. It depends on what the board is doing. Coprocessor boards—effectively a computer inside a computer—may cost $1000 or more, but not only do you get "blinding" speed, you get a microprocessor of the "next generation"—and 80286, say, or even (in an IBM) a 68000. These boards are plugged into an expansion slot. Some require, additionally, IC removal and simple cabling.

Regardless of which type of supercharging you choose, installation is simple, requiring no special technical skills.

Upgrading the Power Supply

There are basically two kinds of power supply, *linear* and *switching*. Linear power supplies may be fully inboard, or may be all or partially outboard. Any device using a "wall-charger" type of power pack or an external "black box" has a linear power supply. The external parts contain a transformer (wall unit) or an entire supply (free-standing black box). All you can do about these is replace them when they go bad. The wall charger unit usually feeds some internal (board-mounted) power supply components, but fiddling with these is beyond our scope here.

An internally mounted linear power supply can be recognized by the fact that it is either entirely unshielded or only partially shielded, and is built around a fairly hefty transformer. Alongside the transformer you'll find a couple of sizable (often blue) electrolytic capacitors. Once again, messing with power supplies at the component level is not for us.

The most common type of power supply in today's desktop computer is the switcher, a complete, easily replaced module. More often than not, manufacturers provide power supplies that are adequate to run the computer as delivered, but the addition of boards and drives will soon run the original wimpy power supply ragged.

Order a replacement for your type of computer from "your favorite mail order power-supply house." (If you don't have one, see the **Source Listing** at the end of this chapter). For the IBM type of computer, you'll want a supply rated at 150 watts or higher.

Here's how to install a switching power supply:

(1) Turn off power to the computer.
(2) Unplug the power cord and open the computer.
(3) Before disconnecting the old power supply plugs, stick a label on each of the equivalent connectors of the new supply, indicating its mate in the computer.
(4) Unplug power connectors from the system board and disk drive(s).
(5) Remove the screws fastening the power supply case to the computer enclosure.
(6) Take out the old encased supply and drop in the new one.
(7) Install the mounting screws.
(8) Attach the power connectors as per the labels.
(9) Test the computer.
(10) Button it up.

REPLACEMENT POWER SUPPLY

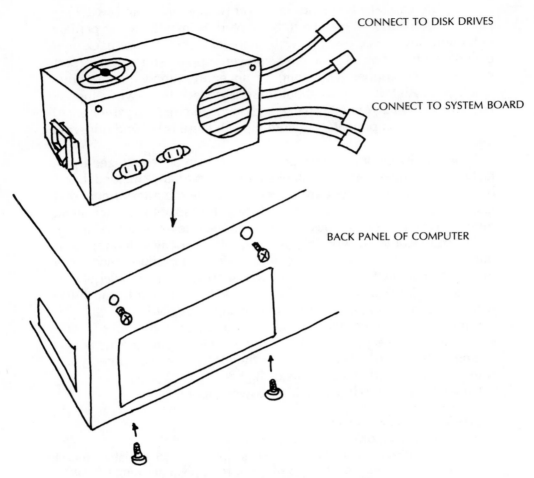

CONNECT TO DISK DRIVES

CONNECT TO SYSTEM BOARD

BACK PANEL OF COMPUTER

Figure 9–13.   Replacing Power Supply.

Adding Data Entry Devices

Keyboard, mouse, joystick, and voice are characteristic data entry devices. Physical installation rarely involves more than plugging in a cable or two. Replacing a keyboard means unplugging the old one and plugging in the new one. Adding a mouse means either (1) plugging the interface cable into a serial or parallel I/O port or (2) plugging the cable into a connector on a special board that you've plugged into an expansion slot.

The biggest irritation comes from trying to get RS–232–C devices communicating successfully with their ports. You'll have to fuss with cables, configuration switches, and software configuration options.

For most of these devices, you also need special software, usually provided with the device, or with the applications software that will use the device. In other words, merely attaching the components to your system won't accomplish anything useful until they've been properly "installed" *via* software. This is usually a simple matter, explained in the software manual and/or prompted through a screen menu.

Mouse.   The mouse, which can be thought of primarily as a *cursor-moving digitizer* needs both a *device driver* and software that "sees" the driver, hence "knows" that the mouse is active. A device driver is a small program that acts as an intermediary between the operating system (in particular, the BIOS) and the device. Once physically present in the system, the data bits are routed through the driver.

Light pen.   A light pen, not a *writing* but a *reading* instrument, will undoubtedly plug into either an RS–232 port or a special light pen port, provided on many multipurpose expansion cards. The driver will activate it and from that point it's up to you how to use it—either through commercially available programs written for it or through programs you concoct yourself in BASIC, Pascal or whatever. The light pen works by responding to lighted locations on the video screen.

Voice Data Entry.   VDE systems allow you to enter a limited range of data via a microphone. I say "limited" because there is as yet no system on the market that will act as a full-fledged "typewriter you talk to." Not only does VDE need a special board (actually, a computer in its own right), a microphone, and special software, but the software must be "trained" to respond to your voice. The board goes into an expansion slot. "Installation" from this point means "software installation."

Voice and Music Synthesis.   These systems may be purely software driven, or may require hardware as well. Hardware devices like Votrax's Personal Speech System and Type 'N Talk are interfaced through a communication port. Likewise MIDI (Musical Instrument Digital Interface products.

Optical digitizer. Optical gadgetry may seem exotic, yet an optical digitizer is really just a kind of camera plus the circuitry needed for turning degrees of light and dark into ones and zeros—analog-to-digital conversion. The data thus created gets dumped into the computer through a normal port and interpreted by the appropriate software, then sent to a video display or printer. Once again, the hardware installation amounts to plugging in a cable or two, and possibly a board.

Replacing a Video Display Monitor

Let's assume that you're tired of monochrome computing. You'll need a color-adapter board and a color monitor. Why not an EGA (Enhanced Graphics Adapter) board and an RGB monitor?

To make full use of the EGA capabilities, you need software written for it. But lacking that, you can run the board in normal color graphics mode. Why get a "fancy" color board instead of a $100 special? Because color resolution is lower than monochrome resolution, and on a marginal board, it's lower still! This is why you should also go for the most expensive color monitor you can afford. It's short of good sense to skimp on something you'll be looking at for hours on end!

The board will either replace the monochrome board or take up a spare slot. It won't hurt to leave both boards in place. Besides, the monochrome probably has a printer port on it. The color board will also have a printer port. If you have a parallel port already, get a color board with a serial port.

The RGB (video) port on the new color board will probably look like Figure 9-14.

Be sure you get the correct video cable. You can make one if need be, but why bother? Follow these steps when replacing the monitor:

(1) Turn off the power.
(2) Ground yourself briefly to the power supply case or to a large piece of metal outside the computer.
(3) Unplug the old monitor and put it away.
(4) Set the configuration switches of the new board according to the manual that comes with the board. Among other things, these switch settings will take into account the presence of another video board.
(5) Install the board in a spare slot.
(6) Plug in the monitor's power and video cables.
(7) Turn on the power and test.
(8) Turn off the system and button it up.

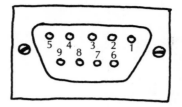

DB-9 CONNECTOR

```
1  GROUND
2  GROUND (OR N/C)
3  RED
4  GREEN
5  BLUE
6  INTENSITY (OR N/C)
7  N/C
8  HORIZONTAL DRIVE
9  VERTICAL DRIVE
```

Figure 9–14.   RGB Video-Interface Connector Pinouts.

Most color video ports put out RGB signals. Suppose, however, you just bought a computer with an RGB output, yet sitting at home is a perfectly good composite video monitor. Well, you can try to sell the monitor to justify your buying an RGB unit. Or you can put your electronic hobbying skills to the test by building the circuit described in Thomas L. Clarke's article, "Easy Color Conversion: Convert RGB Output to Composite Signals," *ComputerSmythe*, Volume 1, Number 1 (January, 1985), pp. 40–44. Don't try this if you're not a budding techno-nerd.

Adding Miscellaneous Peripherals

Printers and plotters, print spoolers, external modems—those sorts of gadgets. You probably already have a printer so you know about peripherals. I mean, what's there to it but cabling and configuration?

Cabling Notes

• Use the best, not the cheapest. "Best" means (1) heavy duty and (2) well shielded. Metal end connectors are better than plastic. Why? Shielding and grounding. Metal *Centronics* type of connectors are more easily latched with the chassis clips than plastic connectors.

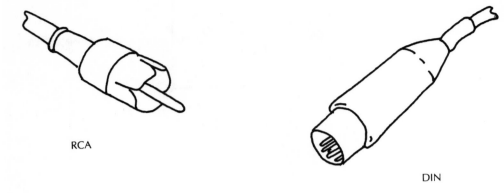

RCA

DIN

(DEUTSCHE INDUSTRIE NORMENAUSSCHUS)

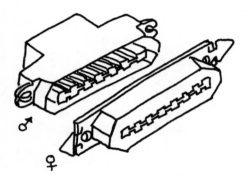

CENTRONICS

Figure 9–15. Cable Connectors.

- Use the shortest cable that will do the job—especially with parallel inter-face devices.
- Route cables to avoid hazards like sharp edges, excessive heat, and being crushed under foot.
- Fasten cables, don't just plug them in. Use the screws on DB-25 connec-tors and the clips on Centronics connectors.

Configuration Notes

- When you have the peripheral configuration switches set so that the de-vice is working satisfactorily, make a drawing of the switch and its set-tings. Stash the drawing with the product manual or with your personal computer operations notebook.
- Likewise, make a note of the software configuration for the operating system and each piece of software. Unfortunately, you can't necessarily

use the same configuration throughout your operations. A given piece of software, for example, may not allow for a baud rate higher than, say 1,200, even though the peripheral is capable of 9,600. Or a piece of software may insist that a given output device (plotter, perhaps) be attached to communication port 1, not communication port 2.

- Tape a small plastic shield over the switch block(s) to prevent tampering.
- Set serial peripherals to run at the highest possible baud rate. This may be limited by the software rather than the hardware. Whatever the case, the hardware rate and the software rate must match.
- In serial devices, wherever the option exists (and it usually does) choose hardware handshaking over software handshaking. That is, RTS, CTS, DTR, or DSR (whichever is provided for) over ETX/ACK or XON/OFF (DC1/DC3). Software handshaking can interfere with graphics data.

Printer Notes

- Parallel interfacing is easier than serial interfacing, and data transfer is faster. In most cases, factory switch settings can be left alone and standard cables can be used.
- With respect to cabling, serial interfacing may be simple (plug in a standard cable) or it may be a large pain. Use of an "intelligent" cable will hasten the task. (See the **Source Listing** for this chapter.)
- Whatever other dot matrix printers your software *may* support, it will *surely* support printers using **Epson** control codes.
- Whatever other formed-character printers your software *may* support, it will *surely* support printers using Diablo control codes.

Plotter Notes

- Whatever other plotter control codes your software *may* support, it will *surely* support Hewlett-Packard HP7475A plotter codes.
- Match your software to your plotter with respect to interfacing. That is, buy a plotter with the interface type (serial or parallel) your software expects to find. Some CAD programs will support *serial* only; some *parallel* only. Data redirection through the operating system may not work. Dual-interface peripherals are ideal, but (1) not all manufacturers make them and (2) they are more expensive than single-interface versions. Of course, if you own, or are willing to buy a serial-to-parallel or parallel-to-serial converter, this presents no problem.

Hardware Spooler Notes

- Meant primarily to act as holding tanks for data being shipped to peripherals, hardware spoolers can also serve as interface swappers (serial to parallel, parallel to serial). If you don't need the latter function, you may

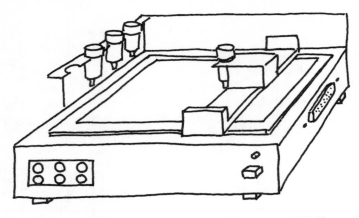

MULTI-PORT PROGRAMMABLE DATA SWITCH/SPOOLER

Figure 9–16. Plotter.

not need a hardware spooler at all. Inexpensive software spoolers allow you to define a chunk of user memory to act as a spooler. Not only are there any number of stand-alone programs for the purpose, but many of the current generation of word processors offer a spooling utility.

● Should you decide to buy a hardware spooler anyway, don't buy one with more memory than your largest anticipated print file. The best move is to buy one with minimal memory and expand the memory yourself. Check to see whether it is thus upgradable.

● Some spoolers offer features like control over special printer capabilities. Decide whether you need such extras before plunking down the money for them.

● Serial spoolers must be configured like any other serial device. The interesting thing about them is that they can accept one set of protocols and translate them into another set so that the software can be configured one way and the peripheral another.

Data Switch Notes

● A data switch allows you to (1) switch between two or more peripherals a single computer port and (2) share one peripheral among two or more computers.

● There are two general types of data switch, mechanical and electronic. The mechanical switch typically uses a rotary switch with two or more positions (A, B, C, etc.) to switch *n*-number of lines (e.g., the 25 lines of an RS–232–C system). The electronic switch typically uses push buttons to select among two or more devices (A, B, C, etc.) to switch the communication lines. I'm using an electronic type of switch to share a printer between two computers. It's never let me down.

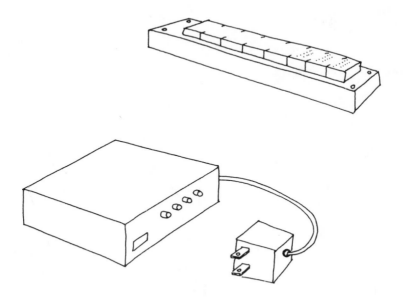

Figure 9–17. Spooler

- Make sure the switch you buy is correctly configured with respect to input/output connectors DB–25 or Centronics).
- Since data switches are simply *feed-through* devices, they come with no configuration switches to set and require no electrical power.
- A good-quality data switch will cost about $75–$100. You may find cheaper ones of acceptable quality, but be warned that a flaky switching mechanism can corrupt transmitted data.

Modem Notes

- Whatever other modems your software *may* support, it will *surely* support Hayes-compatible modems.
- Should you opt for an internal or an external unit? An internal modem is handy because it's out of the way and requires no interfacing other than a standard four-wire telephone cable between the modem and the phone outlet. It can be inconvenient because it takes up an expansion slot, draws power from the computer power supply, adds to the buildup of heat, and is accessible for troubleshooting and reconfiguring only by opening the computer.

INPUT & OUTPUT CONNECTORS
OR REAR PANEL

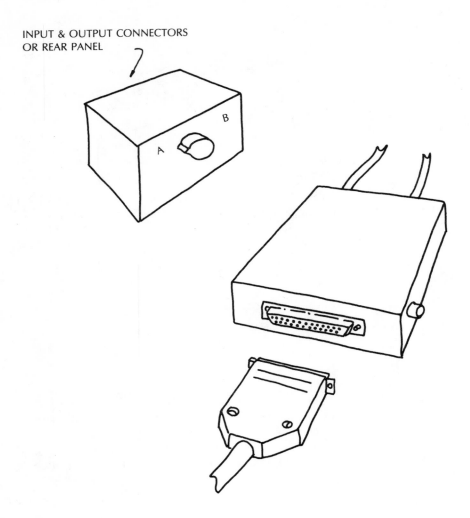

Figure 9–18.   Data Switches.

- An external modem is handy because it can be monitored (through status lights) and, because it is "out in the open," easy to reconfigure and troubleshoot. On the other side of the coin, an external modem requires an external power supply and an interface cable in addition to the phone cable. It takes up space, gathers dust, and adds more wires to your already wire-rich work station.
- Modems are invariably serial devices and must be suitably configured.

- Most online services can handle 300-baud and 1,200-baud transfer rates. You'll pay twice as much to the service for 1,200-baud operation, but you'll gain anyway because 1,200 is four times faster than 300.

- Modems are now on the market that can run at 2,400 and 4,800 baud. Relatively few services are as yet set up to handle these rates, and most common carrier telephone lines are noisy enough to introduce glitches into data being transferred at these rates.

- Before spending extra money on features that you don't need, decide what you expect to be doing with your modem. If you want to do nothing but access online databases, you won't need all kinds of fancy stuff like autodialing, autoanswering, and a bunch of programming capabilities.

- Ditto for the modem software. It's not necessary to spend big bucks for a million wonderful features to perform a handful of simple tasks. Possibly the best all-around communication software available is the family of public domain programs that have grown out of Ward Christensen's Modem program.

- Almost all integrated software (Framework, Symphony, and others) comes with a communication module, obviating the need for a separate program.

- Buy brand-name equipment. Really cheap modems usually give really "cheap" results.

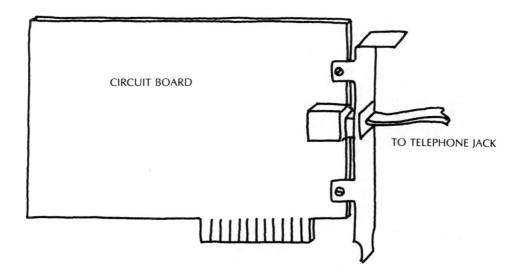

Figure 9–19. Inboard Modem.

Networking Notes

- This is a great can of worms—and not one that you should be anxious to poke into without some professional help.
- A local area network (LAN) typically consists of a software driver, some sort of control box (which may include a large capacity hard disk system), and cabling to link the computers into the network configuration the particular LAN hardware/software package demands.
- With no LAN standard as yet established, each system is unique. My best advice: Examine several systems to determine which will do the best job for you at the most reasonable cost. Stick with name brands to the extent that you can. Several LAN systems manufacturers are already defunct.

For a brief discussion of LANs, see Chapter 8, **How Computers Communicate**. Interfacing requires the familiar issues of proper cabling, and the matching of communication and handshaking signals. LAN software controls the network once you've got it physically organized.

Adding Electrical Protection

This topic has been dealt with in an admonitory way in Chapters 1 and 2. The actual process of adding protective gadgetry involves plugging electrical power cable into outlets. Here are notes for an "ideal" power setup:

- Computer, monitor, printer, and other peripherals are plugged into a circuit breaker and transient protected outlet strip (of good quality).
- The outlet strip should be rated comfortably in excess of the total power demands of the units plugged into it.
- The outlet strip is plugged into an uninterruptable, line-conditioning power supply of sufficient power-handling capacity to comfortably service your whole system.
- If the uninterruptable power supply lacks line voltage regulation, it should be plugged into a voltage regulator (constant voltage transformer).
- The uninterruptable power supply (or voltage regulator) is plugged into an outlet in a circuit that serves no heavy-duty electrical equipment, especially equipment with motors.
- The power equipment should be placed so that the master switch is easy to reach and the unit is protected from heat, dirt, and moisture. Don't stash it in an unventilated cabinet.
- The cables should be routed neatly, not looped, away from the hazard of being stepped on.

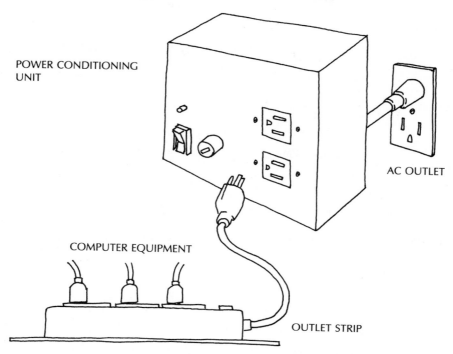

POWER CONDITIONING
UNIT

AC OUTLET

COMPUTER EQUIPMENT

OUTLET STRIP

Figure 9–20. Computer System Power Hook-up.

Making Your Own Transient Suppressor

Let's say that you have a perfectly good, no-frills outlet strip. That is, it's sturdy, breaker-protected, and switched. But it has no transient protection. Here's a little project that will give you a beefy transient suppressing unit and a dollop of tinkering experience.

Figure 9-21 is a schematic diagram of what we'll be doing. These are the parts and equipment you'll need:

(1) Three heavy-duty MOVs (metal-oxide varistors) (RS 276-568 or GE V130LA10A)
(2) Tubing (insulator), which you can strip from a piece of wire
(3) Electronic solder (RS 64-006)
(4) Soldering iron
(5) Hand tools as needed

Figure 9-22 is a pictorial diagram of the suppressor. Here's how to do the job:

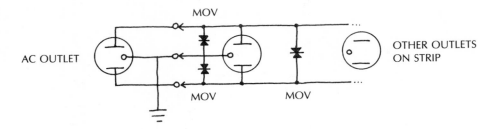

Figure 9–21.   Transient Supressor Schematic.

(1) Disconnect your outlet strip from the wall.
(2) Open the case. If it's riveted, you can clip the rivets and replace self-tapping screws.
(3) Each connector should be electrically sound even before soldering. This means that you should wrap the lead a couple of times around the connecting point and squeeze it.
(4) Slip a piece of tubing over the MOV leads to prevent shorts. Leave enough bare lead to make the connection!
(5) Heat each solder joint to a count of "1,001, 1,002, 1,003," then apply the solder, which should flow smoothly over the joint. As soon as you've made a clean, neatly fused joint, remove the solder, then the iron.
(6) Connect one MOV across the AC lines. These are usually color-coded black (hot) and white (neutral). Solder.
(7) Connect one MOV from hot to ground (color-coded green). Solder.
(8) Connect one MOV from neutral to ground. Solder.
(9) Double-check for shorts, solder globs, and incorrect connections. Correct mistakes as necessary.
(10) Close up the unit and rest assured that you've got good transient protection.

Adding a Fan

There are those who feel that unless your nonfan-equipped computer is really overheating, you shouldn't bother adding one. The reason offered is that because fans suck in dirt, they cause more trouble than they're worth. On the other side of the issue, one can argue that if you provide a reasonably clean environment, such as recommended in this book, and if you subject your computer to regular cleaning, the value of the cooling should overbalance the "dirt effect." After all, heat will kill electronic components faster than dirt will!

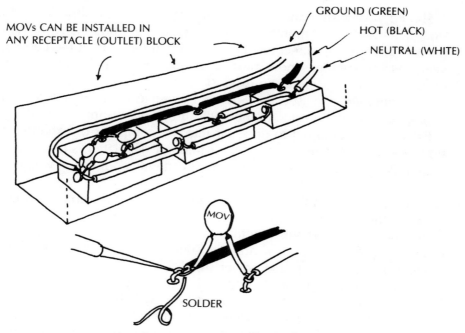

Figure 9–22. Suppressor Project Diagram.

Computers and related equipment prefer cool to warmth. It would be ideal to compute in a room that remains at a constant 68-70°F. Even in such a room, your computer should be accorded some supplementary cooling, and, in fact, we find it in most computers as sold. The inboard fan, mounted inside the power supply case in most IBM PC/XT type of computers, will do the job so long as (1) you don't load up the expansion slots with boards that draw a lot of power, and (2) your computing room doesn't get overly warm and humid.

A note about humidity: As the moisture in the air *increases*, the density of the air *decreases*. The decrease in density lowers the cooling efficiency of the air, hence, of the fan. This may not mean much in most circumstances, though in some it could mean that a marginal cooling effect has been reduced to virtual zilch.

Fans can be added to your system three ways: (1) located conveniently nearby, (2) attached to the outside, and (3) mounted on the inside of the computer enclosure.

Should your computing environment get overheated only on occasion (like the summer months, for instance), an easy but relatively ineffective solution is to direct the air from a small desk fan at the cooling vents of the computer. These must not be the vents that the internal fan (if there is one) is using as an exhaust outlet.

An equipment fan (see the **Source Listing**) can be mounted with contact tape to the outside of the enclosure over existing vents.

Fans can be mounted to drive air into the computer or exhaust air from the computer, that is, to pull air through. The latter is marginally preferable, for it draws off hot air, replacing it with cool. Either way will work.

If you mount with the air directed inward, place a thin foam filter between the fingerguard and the fan.

In either case, make sure that there are other vents in the enclosure to provide a path for the air to follow. There should be a swath of air moving over the boards and power supply.

The fan power cord can be plugged into the system outlet strip, or led inside and wired to the computer power switch (see below).

The same arrangement for external mounting can be followed internally if there is room in the box to mount a fan without its getting in the way of anything inside, and in a location that will provide meaningful air flow. You can lead the power cord out of the computer or wire it to the power switch. Here's a wiring diagram. Don't do this job unless you're comfortable working with wires and a soldering iron.

Fan Notes

- You can mount the fan with screws if you're willing to strip down the computer to allow drilling. Of course, you'll have to strip the computer to cut out a couple of slots—about two inches square—in the event that it lacks adequate venting.
- It's perfectly okay to add a fan to a computer that already has one. As was pointed out, in many computers the existing fan is mounted inside the power supply case. This arrangement helps the power supply but does relatively little for the rest of the computer. A fully packed expansion board area really needs help. So look for a suitable vent fan location in that part of the computer.
- One solution to inadequate cooling in a computer with a cooling fan already in place is to expand the size of the vents. Where the vents are louvered, bend the louvers open as far as you can. It's curious that manu-

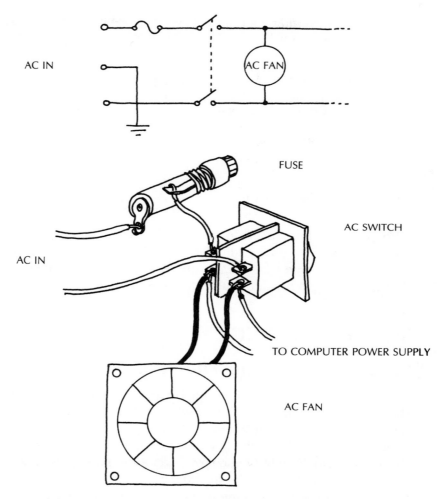

AC IN

AC FAN

FUSE

AC IN

AC SWITCH

TO COMPUTER POWER SUPPLY

AC FAN

Figure 9–23. Wiring an AC Fan to the Computer Switch.

facturers will go to the expense of putting in a splendid little fan and then
impede its work by providing inadequate ventilation!
- When buying an equipment fan, opt for the Whisper type, or you'll soon
  regret the fact that your computer needs cooling. In lieu of actually listen-
  ing to a fan, you can judge the "howl" factor by the fan's electrical rating.
  A discreet (but adequate) fan will come in at around 7–9W watts. That's
  115VAC (nominal) at about 60-100 milliamperes (.06–.10 amps). All else

being equal, the higher the power rating, the more air the fan will pull and the more noise it will make. These are recommended:

3-inch-diameter fan: Rotron Sprite, SU2G1 (9W). Digi-Key catalog number RT100-ND (see **Source Listing**).

4¼-inch-diameter fan: Rotron Whisper, WR2A1 (7W). Digi-Key catalog number RT101-ND (see **Source Listing**).

• Always include a finger guard in a fan installation.

SUMMARY

You've been introduced to some of the ways you can tailor your computer system to your particular computing needs. We've looked at internal changes and external add-ons. And you've been given a simple "hot iron" project to start you on the road to serious tinkering.

SOURCE LISTING

Suppliers and Manufacturers

This is just a brief listing, focusing on less highly advertised products. The computer magazines are filled with ads for memory, multifunction, video, and other popular boards. As a rule, you can get a better price from a retailer than from the manufacturer, who will insist on selling at "list price." On the other hand, you'll get a lot more information about the product directly from the manufacturer than you will from the retailer. So pick the brain of the manufacturer, then shop.

The first company listed below is a kind of national computer equipment "flea market." Perhaps this should be your first call, for the Exchange buys as well as sells. As always in this book, a listing in this book does **NOT** imply endorsement!

Boston Computer Exchange Corporation
Box 1177
Boston, MA 02103
(617)542–4414
Used computer equipment brokerage

Brown and Co., Inc.
P. O. Box 2443
South Hamilton, MA 01982
(617)468–7464
"PC-Pedal" foot data-entry device, IBM and compatibles

BTE Computers, Inc.
14644 N. Cave Creek #6
Phoenix, AZ 85022
(602)867–8962
Apple expansion products

CHORUS Data Systems, Inc.
6 Continental Blvd.
Merrimack, NH 03054
1–(800)624–6787
Optical digitizers

Computer-Age, Inc.
55 Fishfry Street
Hartford, CT 06120
(203)724–5100
80286 high-speed coprocessor board for IBM and compatibles

Controlled Data Recording Systems Inc.
7210 Clairemont Mesa Blvd.
San Diego, CA 92111
(619)560–1272
"ZS100" system-board speed-up module for Zenith Z100/H100

Curtis, Inc.
22 Red Fox Road
St. Paul, MN 55110
(612)484–5064
EPROM and RAM disk drive emulators for IBM and compatibles

Datadisk
Box 15313
Santa Fe, NM 87506
(505)579–4496
High-density disk-formatting software

DECMATION
2065 Martin Avenue, Suite 110
Santa Clara, CA 95050
(408)980–1678
"Blue Thunder" Z80 coprocessor board for IBM and compatibles

Digi-Key Corporation
P.O. Box 677
Thief River Falls, MN 56701
1–(800)DIGI–KEY (1–(800)344–4539)
fans, etc.

Display Telecommunications Corporation
8445 Freeport Parkway, Suite 445
Irving, TX 75063
1–(800)227–8383
Mega-Net LAN system; high-speed automatic switching buffer (data switch/spooler)

ELEXOR
P. O. Box 246
Morris Plains, NJ 07950
(201)299–1615
RS–232–C compatible digital-to-analog/analog-to-digital interface

Exec-PC, Inc.
P. O. Box 11268
Shorwood, WI 53211
(414)242–2173
"PC-Sprint" system board speed-up module for IBM and compatibles

Floppy Disk Services
39 Everett Drive, Building D
Lawrenceville, NJ 08648
1–(800)223–0306
Disk drives, enclosures, power supplies, PC clones

FORTRON
3225 Seldon Court
Freemont, CA 94538
1–(800)821–9771
(415)490–8171 (in CA)
IBM power supplies, boards, expansion chassis, equipment enclosures

Hooleon Corporation
P. O. Box 201
Cornville, AZ 86325
(602)634–7517
Keycap overlays and replacements

HYMCO Technologies, Inc.
5320–D Monterey Highway
San Jose, CA 95111
(408)225–1511
PEX-100 IBM expansion chassis system

Intercomputing Inc.
2100 N. Hwy. 360, Suite 2005
Grand Prairie, TX 75050
(214)988–3500
Amiga expansion products

Intersecting Concepts
4573 Heatherglen Court
Moorpark, CA 93201
(805)529–5073
Acceler8/16; Media Master

IOMEGA Corporation
1821 West 4000 South
Roy, UT 84067
(801)778–3000
"Bernouilli Box" removable cartridge disk systems

Mandrill Corporation
P.O. Box 33848
San Antonio, TX 78265
1–(800)531–5314
1–(800)292–5619 (in Texas)
"Coldblue Ventilation System" for IBM computers

Maynard Electronics
460 E. Somaran Blvd.
Casselberry, FL 32707
(305)331–6402
System board speed-up module for IBM PC/XT, Compaq, NCR

MicroSync
P. O. Box 116302
Carrollton, TX 75011
(214)492–5265
"Screamer" expansion board speed-up module for IBM and
compatibles

Otto Electronics
895 Route 130
East Windsor, NJ 08520
(609)448–9165
NEC V-series CPUs, 8087 coprocessors, most other ICs, modems,
boards, microfloppy drives

PKI Incorporated
2539 W. 237 Street E.
Torrance, CA 90505
(213)539–2123
Add-on microfloppy drive for Macintosh

Source Electronics Corp.
45277 Fremont Blvd., Unit 6
Fremont, CA 94538
1–(800)826–0267
(415)651–3355 (in California)
Expansion chassis subsystems

Tipz
P.O. Box 690
San Francisco, CA 94101-0690
1–(800)–862–7587
(415)567–4067 (in California)
Data switches, tool kits

Versatron Corporation
103 Plaza Street
Healdsburg, CA 95448
1–(800)443–1550
"Footmouse" foot data-entry device, IBM and compatibles

Votan, Inc.
26046 Eden Landing Road, #3
Hayward, CA 94545
(415)846–4973
Voice data-entry systems

Votrax
1394 Rankin
Troy, MI 48083
1–(800)–521–1350
(315)588-0341 (in Michigan)
Speech peripherals

Warp Speed
4357 Chase Avenue
Los Angeles, CA 90066
(213)391–4156
Light pen, IBM and compatibles

Suggestions for Further Reading

Bruce A. Artwick, *Microcomputer Interfacing*, Englewood Cliffs, NJ: Prentice Hall, 1980. Strictly for the serious student of such things.

ComputerSymythe magazine, P.O. Box 176, Peterborough, NH 03458–0176; (603)924–6371. Mainly for hardware hackers, or those who would be.

Linda Gail Christie, *The Simon and Schuster Guide to Computer Peripherals*, New York, NY: Simon and Schuster, 1986. Easy, non-technical.

Daniel Metzger, *22 Microcomputer Projects to Build, Use, and Learn*, Englewood Cliffs, NJ: Prentice Hall, 1985. Want to build an IC tester, logic analyzer, EPROM programmer, and other such entertaining and useful gadgets? Great book for learning how to hardware-hack.

Seth Novogrodsky, *et al.*, *The Complete IBM Personal Computer*, New York, NY: Simon and Schuster, 1986. A detailed guide to IBM expansion.

Chapter 10
TECHNICAL REFERENCES

INTRODUCTION

Contained herein are a few technical references—ASCII codes, numeric conversions, the pinouts (in tabular form) of popular micro-processors—as well as a reprise of principles for computer survival.

ASCII

Although ASCII (American Standard Code for Information In-terchange) is commonly used, the strictly correct term is USASCII (USA Standard Code for Information Interchange), a 256-element, 8-bit cod-ing system representing in binary digits the visible characters of the computer keyboard (upper and lower case) and a number of "invisi-ble" ones as well, that is, control and graphics characters. Various computer manufacturers implement the code differently, but all agree on the 7-bit part, namely the standard *QWERTY* keyboard with its al-phabetic and numeric characters and its punctuation. Among the USASCII control functions, the *escape* key and *control* key are among those invariably implemented.

The table that follows on page 287 covers the "universal" 7-bit part of the code (128 items). Note that 127 (the one-hundred twenty-eighth number, starting with zero, which, in the computer world is a *number*, not a *nothing*) is 01111111, seven bits!

Many "desktop utility" programs such as SideKick include an ASCII reference window.

Table 10-1. USASC11 CODES

Decimal	Octal	Hexadecimal	ASCII	Decimal	Octal	Hexadecimal	ASCII
0	000	00	NUL	64	100	40	@
1	001	01	SOH	65	101	41	A
2	002	02	STX	66	102	42	B
3	003	03	ETX	67	103	43	C
4	004	04	EOT	68	104	44	D
5	005	05	ENQ	69	105	45	E
6	006	06	ACK	70	106	46	F
7	007	07	BEL	71	107	47	G
8	010	08	BS	72	110	48	H
9	011	09	HT	73	111	49	I
10	012	OA	LF	74	112	4A	J
11	013	OB	VT	75	113	4B	K
12	014	OC	FF	76	114	4C	L
13	015	OD	CR	77	115	4D	M
14	016	OE	SO	78	116	4E	N
15	017	OF	SI	79	117	4F	O
16	020	10	DLE	80	120	50	P
17	021	11	DC1	81	121	51	Q
18	022	12	DC2	82	122	52	R
19	023	13	DC3	83	123	53	S
20	024	14	DC4	84	124	54	T
21	025	15	NAK	85	125	55	U
22	026	16	SYN	86	126	56	V
23	027	17	ETB	87	127	57	W
24	030	18	CAN	88	130	58	X
25	031	19	EM	89	131	59	Y
26	032	1A	SUB	90	132	5A	Z
27	033	1B	ESC	91	133	5B	[
28	034	1C	FS	92	134	5C	\
29	035	1D	GS	93	135	5D	]
30	036	1E	RS	94	136	5E	^
31	037	1F	US	95	137	5F	_
32	040	20	SP	96	140	60	`
33	041	21	!	97	141	61	a
34	042	22	"	98	142	62	b
35	043	23	#	99	143	63	c
36	044	24	$	100	144	64	d
37	045	25	%	101	145	65	e
38	046	26	&	102	146	66	f
39	047	27	'	103	147	67	g
40	050	28	(	104	150	68	h
41	051	29	)	105	151	69	i
42	052	2A	*	106	152	6A	j
43	053	2B	+	107	153	6B	k
44	054	2C	,	108	154	6C	l
45	055	2D	-	109	155	6D	m
46	056	2E	.	110	156	6E	n
47	057	2F	/	111	157	6F	o
48	060	30	0	112	160	70	p
49	061	31	1	113	161	71	q
50	062	32	2	114	162	72	r
51	063	33	3	115	163	73	s
52	064	34	4	116	164	74	t
53	065	35	5	117	165	75	u
54	066	36	6	118	166	76	v
55	067	37	7	119	167	77	w
56	070	38	8	120	170	78	x
57	071	39	9	121	171	79	y
58	072	3A	:	122	172	7A	z
59	073	3B	;	123	173	7B	{
60	074	3C	<	124	174	7C		
61	075	3D	=	125	175	7D	}
62	076	3E	>	126	176	7E	~
63	077	3F	?	127	177	7F	DEL

NUMERIC POWERS AND CONVERSION TABLES

Powers

Since computer numeric values are invariably expressed as powers of 2, even though stated in decimal numeration, here are the powers of 2 (2 x 2 x 2, etc.) up to 32^2.

Table 10-2. Powers of Two

2 to power of n	*Value*
2^0	1
2^1	2
2^2	4
2^3	8
2^4	16
2^5	32
2^6	64
2^7	128
2^8	256
2^9	512
2^{10}	1,024
2^{11}	2,048
2^{12}	4,096
2^{13}	8,192
2^{14}	16,384
2^{15}	32,768
2^{16}	65,536
2^{17}	131,072
2^{18}	262,144
2^{19}	524,288
2^{20}	1,048,576
2^{21}	2,097,152
2^{22}	4,194,304
2^{23}	8,388,608
2^{24}	16,777,216
2^{25}	33,554,432
2^{26}	67,108,864
2^{27}	134,217,728
2^{28}	268,435,456

Table 10-2. Powers of Two (continued)

2 to power of n	Value
2^{29}	536,870,912
2^{30}	1,073,741,824
2^{31}	2,147,483,648
2^{32}	4,294,967,296

What are you supposed to do with a table like this? One use is to quickly determine the size of addressing space available to a CPU of a given value. Okay, so you're not intensely interested in this information. But what would a computer book be without tables of numbers? Here are some popular CPUs with their "bit-value" addressing space translated (courtesy of the above table) into the actual numbers:

- 8-bit CPU (6502 family, Apple computers), 16-bit addressing capability, total number of addresses: 65,536.
- 8/16-bit CPU (8088, IBM PC/XT and clones), 20-bit addressing space, total number of addresses: 1,048,576. (Roughly, one megabyte.)
- 16-bit CPU (68000, Macintosh), 24-bit addressing space total number of addresses: 16,777,216. (Roughly, 16 megabytes.) The 68000 can, in fact, address 64 megabytes, but only in segments.

Numeric Conversions

The following table converts among decimal (base-10), binary (base-2), octal (base-8), and hexadecimal (base-16) numbers, up to the value of 255 decimal. You probably won't turn to it very often in your life, but on the off chance that you're curious about what, say, 150 decimal is in binary (10010110), here it is.

Table 10-3. Numeric Conversions to 255

Decimal	Hexa-decimal	Octal	Binary	Decimal	Hexa-decimal	Octal	Binary
000	00	000	00000000	007	07	007	00000111
001	01	001	00000001	008	08	010	00001000
002	02	002	00000010	009	09	011	00001001
003	03	003	00000011	010	0A	012	00001010
004	04	004	00000100	011	0B	013	00001011
005	05	005	00000101	012	0C	014	00001100
006	06	006	00000110	013	0D	015	00001101

Table 10-3. Numeric Conversions to 255 *(continued)*

Decimal	Hexa-decimal	Octal	Binary	Decimal	Hexa-decimal	Octal	Binary
014	0E	016	00001110	054	36	066	00110110
015	0F	017	00001111	055	37	067	00110111
016	10	020	00010000	056	38	070	00111000
017	11	021	00010001	057	39	071	00111001
018	12	022	00010010	058	3A	072	00111010
019	13	023	00010011	059	3B	073	00111011
020	14	024	00010100	060	3C	074	00111100
021	15	025	00010101	061	3D	075	00111101
022	16	026	00010110	062	3E	076	00111110
023	17	027	00010111	063	3F	077	00111111
024	18	030	00011000	064	40	100	01000000
025	19	031	00011001	065	41	101	01000001
026	1A	032	00011010	066	42	102	01000010
027	1B	033	00011011	067	43	103	01000011
028	1C	034	00011100	068	44	104	01000100
029	1D	035	00011101	069	45	105	01000101
030	1E	036	00011110	070	46	106	01000110
031	1F	037	00011111	071	47	107	01000111
032	20	040	00100000	072	48	110	01001000
033	21	041	00100001	073	49	111	01001001
034	22	042	00100010	074	4A	112	01001010
035	23	043	00100011	075	4B	113	01001011
036	24	044	00100100	076	4C	114	01001100
037	25	045	00100101	077	3D	115	01001101
038	26	046	00100110	078	4E	116	01001110
039	27	047	00100111	079	4F	117	01001111
040	28	050	00101000	080	50	120	01010000
041	29	051	00101001	081	51	121	01010001
042	2A	052	00101010	082	52	122	01010010
043	2B	053	00101011	083	53	123	01010011
044	2C	054	00101100	084	54	124	01010100
045	2D	055	00101101	085	55	125	01010101
046	2E	056	00101110	086	56	126	01010110
047	2F	057	00101111	087	57	127	01010111
048	30	060	00110000	088	58	130	01011000
049	31	061	00110001	089	59	131	01011001
050	32	062	00110010	090	5A	132	01011010
051	33	063	00110011	091	5B	133	01011011
052	34	064	00110100	092	5C	134	01011100
053	35	065	00110101	093	5D	135	01011101

Table 10-3. Numeric Conversions to 255 (continued)

Decimal	Hexa-decimal	Octal	Binary	Decimal	Hexa-decimal	Octal	Binary
094	5E	136	01011110	134	86	206	10000110
095	5F	137	01011111	135	87	207	10000111
096	60	140	01100000	136	88	210	10001000
097	61	141	01100001	137	89	211	10001001
098	62	142	01100010	138	8A	212	10001010
099	63	143	01100011	139	8B	213	10001011
100	64	144	01100100	140	8C	214	10001100
101	65	145	01100101	141	8D	215	10001101
102	66	146	01100110	142	8E	216	10001110
103	67	147	01100111	143	8F	217	10001111
104	68	150	01101000	144	90	220	10010000
105	69	151	01101001	145	91	221	10010001
106	6A	152	01101010	146	92	222	10010010
107	6B	153	01101011	147	93	223	10010011
108	6C	154	01101100	148	94	224	10010100
109	6D	155	01101101	149	95	225	10010101
110	6E	156	01101110	150	96	226	10010110
111	6F	157	01101111	151	97	227	10010111
112	70	160	01110000	152	98	230	10011000
113	71	161	01110001	153	99	231	10011001
114	72	162	01110010	154	9A	232	10011010
115	73	163	01110011	155	9B	233	10011011
116	74	164	01110100	156	9C	234	10011100
117	75	165	01110101	157	9D	235	10011101
118	76	166	01110110	158	9E	236	10011110
119	77	167	01110111	159	9F	237	10011111
120	78	170	01111000	160	A0	240	10100000
121	79	171	01111001	161	A1	241	10100001
122	7A	172	01111010	162	A2	242	10100010
123	7B	173	01111011	163	A3	243	10100011
124	7C	174	01111100	164	A4	244	10100100
125	7D	175	01111101	165	A5	245	10100101
126	7E	176	01111110	166	A6	246	10100110
127	7F	177	01111111	167	A7	247	10100111
128	80	200	10000000	168	A8	250	10101000
129	81	201	10000001	169	A9	251	10101001
130	82	202	10000010	170	AA	252	10101010
131	83	203	10000011	171	AB	253	10101011
132	84	204	10000100	172	AC	254	10101100
133	85	205	10000101	173	AD	255	10101101

Table 10-3. Numeric Conversions to 255 *(continued)*

Decimal	Hexa-decimal	Octal	Binary	Decimal	Hexa-decimal	Octal	Binary
174	AE	256	10101110	215	D7	327	11010111
175	AF	257	10101111	216	D8	330	11011000
176	B0	260	10110000	217	D9	331	11011001
177	B1	261	10110001	218	DA	332	11011010
178	B2	262	10110010	219	DB	333	11011011
179	B3	263	10110011	220	DC	334	11011100
180	B4	264	10110100	221	DD	335	11011101
181	B5	265	10110101	222	DE	336	11011110
182	B6	266	10110110	223	DF	337	11011111
183	B7	267	10110111	224	E0	340	11100000
184	B8	270	10111000	225	E1	341	11100001
185	B9	271	10111001	226	E2	342	11100010
186	BA	272	10111010	227	E3	343	11100011
187	BB	273	10111011	228	E4	344	11100100
188	BC	274	10111100	229	E5	345	11100101
189	BD	275	10111101	230	E6	346	11100110
190	BE	276	10111110	231	E7	347	11100111
191	BF	277	10111111	232	E8	350	11101000
192	C0	300	11000000	233	E9	351	11101001
193	C1	301	11000001	234	EA	352	11101010
194	C2	302	11000010	235	EB	353	11101011
195	C3	303	11000011	236	EC	354	11101100
196	C4	304	11000100	237	ED	355	11101101
197	C5	305	11000101	238	EE	356	11101110
198	C6	306	11000110	239	EF	357	11101111
199	C7	307	11000111	240	F0	360	11110000
200	C8	310	11001000	241	F1	361	11110001
201	C9	311	11001001	242	F2	362	11110010
202	CA	312	11001010	243	F3	363	11110011
203	CB	313	11001011	244	F4	364	11110100
204	CC	314	11001100	245	F5	365	11110101
205	CD	315	11001101	246	F6	366	11110110
206	CE	316	11001110	247	F7	367	11110111
207	CF	317	11001111	248	F8	370	11111000
208	D0	320	11010000	249	F9	371	11111001
209	D1	321	11010001	250	FA	372	11111010
210	D2	322	11010010	251	FB	373	11111011
211	D3	323	11010011	252	FC	374	11111100
212	D4	324	11010100	253	FD	375	11111101
213	D5	325	11010101	254	FE	376	11111110
214	D6	326	11010110	255	FF	377	11111111

Binary numerals: 0 1 10 . . .
Octal numerals: 0 1 2 4 5 6 7 10 . . .
Decimal numerals: 0 1 2 3 4 5 6 7 8 9 10 . . .
Hexadecimal numerals: 0 1 2 3 4 5 6 7 8 9 A B C D E F 10 . . .

$$10_2 = 3_{10}$$
$$10_8 = 8_{10}$$
$$10_{16} = 16_{10}$$

Because computers live in a binary world, programs written at the machine level must be written in either binary code or a number system directly resolvable into powers of two, namely octal or hexadecimal. Of course, when you program in a high-level language like BASIC, you can use decimal numbering, so all this other stuff becomes more or less irrelevant. Nevertheless, the more time you spend in the computer world, the more likely it is that you'll run into hexadecimal numbers, and, to a lesser extent, octal numbers. Certainly you'll meet hex numbers in file dump and disassembly programs.

For converting between decimal and hexadecimal numbers, try this table (from *Webster's New World Dictionary of Computer Terms*, Simon and Schuster, 1983, by permission).

Table 10-4. Numeric Conversions

Hexadecimal and Decimal Conversion
Hexadecimal Columns

6 hex	6 dec	5 hex	5 dec	4 hex	4 dec	3 hex	3 dec	2 hex	2 dec	1 hex	1 dec
0	0	0	0	0	0	0	0	0	0	0	0
1	1,048,576	1	65,536	1	4,096	1	256	1	16	1	1
2	2,097,152	2	131,072	2	8,192	2	512	2	32	2	2
3	3,145,728	3	196,608	3	12,288	3	768	3	48	3	3
4	4,194,304	4	262,144	4	16,384	4	1,024	4	64	4	4
5	5,242,880	5	327,680	5	20,480	5	1,280	5	80	5	5
6	6,291,456	6	393,216	6	24,576	6	1,536	6	96	6	6
7	7,340,032	7	458,752	7	28,672	7	1,792	7	112	7	7
8	8,388,608	8	524,288	8	32,768	8	2,048	8	128	8	8
9	9,437,184	9	589,824	9	36,864	9	2,304	9	144	9	9
A	10,485,760	A	655,360	A	40,960	A	2,560	A	160	A	10
B	11,534,336	B	720,896	B	45,056	B	2,816	B	176	B	11
C	12,582,912	C	786,432	C	49,152	C	3,072	C	192	C	12
D	13,631,488	D	851,968	D	53,248	D	3,328	D	208	D	13
E	14,680,064	E	917,504	E	57,344	E	3,584	E	224	E	14
F	15,728,640	F	983,040	F	61,440	F	3,840	F	240	F	15

Each hex column of the table represents a *weight*, the equivalent in hex of *units*, *tens*, *hundreds*, etc.

Suppose you want to convert hex B4EF to its decimal equivalent:

(1) Since the number to be converted has four places, look up the most significant digit in column four of the table. In the present case, the number is **B**. (That doesn't look like a number, but in hex it is.) B translates into 45,056. Write it down.

(2) Move to column three for the next digit, 4. Write down its equivalent, 1,024.

(3) From column two, find the value for E: 224. Write it down.

(4) The least signficant digit is F, from column one: 15.

(5) Add all the equivalents: 45,056 + 1,024 + 224 + 15 = 46,319. Conversion complete.

Now let's convert decimal 146,527 to hex:

(1) Start with the highest decimal number that is smaller than the number you're converting. Write down the hex value from the appropriate column of the table. In this case, it's 131,072, found in the fifth column, with hex 2 as the equivalent.

(2) Subtract this decimal number from the original decimal number. 146,527 − 131,072 = 15,455

(3) Move to the next column, and repeat, marking down the hex equivalent. Closest number is 12,288, hex equivalent 3.

(4) Next: 15,455 − 12,288 = 3,167. Closest: 3,072 = hex C.

(5) Next: 3,167 − 3,072 = 95. Closest: 80 = hex 5.

(6) Last: 95 − 80 = 15. Hex F.

(7) Gather up the hex values: 23C5F

MICROPROCESSORS

Should you reach a point in your computing life when the urge to write assembly language programs becomes irresistible, you will need to buy, at the very least, a book on the particular microprocessor you wish to program. Here are two examples:

Tim King and Brian Knight, *Programming the 68000*, Reading, MA: Addison-Wesley Publishing Co., 1983.

Leo J. Scanlon, *IBM PC & XT Assembly Language*, New York, NY: Brady Books, 1985.

The information that follows barely hints at what's involved in using a microprocessor, but will at least tell you what sort of signal to expect on each pin. To locate a pin on a particular chip, locate pin 1 (see below) and number the pins counterclockwise from pin 1.

Note: In the following descriptions, the term *active high* means that, from a troubleshooter's perspective, a logic probe will show a 1 (red LED) when the line is active. Conversely, *active low* means that a logic probe will show a 0 (green LED) when the line is active. On pinout drawings, active low signals are designated by a line over the time of the signal name.

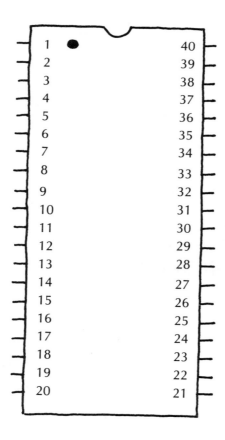

Figure 10–1.   IC Pin-Numbering Scheme.

Z80

The Z80, an 8-bit microprocessor developed by Zilog, can be thought of as a sophisticated 8080 (the CPU that started the microcomputer industry). Among the Z80 computers are the Osborne, earlier Kaypros, and Heath/Zenith 89 series.

Pins 1–5, 30–40. Sixteen address lines (A0-A15). Active high (1).

Pins 7–10, 12–15. Eight bidirectional data lines (D0-D7). Active high (1).

Pin 6. Clock. Clock signal comes from an external clock circuit, usually controlled by a crystal.

Pin 11. +5VDC power input.

Pin 16. INT (Maskable Interrupt Request.) The CPU can be interrupted in current operations by a call to this line from an external source. *Maskable* means that the request can be ''masked'' or overriden by a software instruction. Active low (0).

Pin 17. NMI (Nonmaskable Interrupt Request). Same as INT, but cannot be overriden by software. Active low (0).

Pin 18. HALT. A CPU signal that idles the system while the CPU awaits an interrupt call. Active low (0).

Pin 19. MREQ (Memory Request). A CPU signal that tells the system that a *memory read* or *memory write* operation is underway. Active low (0).

Pin 20. IORQ (Input/Output Request). A CPU signal that tells the system that a *read* (from a port) or *write* (to a port) operation is underway. Active low (0).

Pin 21. RD (Read). A CPU signal notifying the system that it is about to read from memory or from an input port. Active low (0).

Pin 22. WR (Write). A CPU signal notifying the system that it is about to write to memory or to an output port. Active low (0).

Pin 23. BUSAK (Bus Acknowledge). The CPU's signal of compliance to the devices that made a BUSREQ (Bus Request, see Pin 25). Active low (0).

Pin 24. WAIT. A signal on this line tells the CPU to idle while pokey memory or other devices catch up on the current operation. In some computers, wait states for certain key devices (disk drives, etc.) can be set by jumpers.

Pin 25. BUSREQ (Bus Request). Forces the CPU to pay attention to an external device. CPU operations are driven into a temporary wait state until the calling device has its way. Active low (0).

Pin 26. RESET. A signal on this line tells the CPU to "return to GO." Active low (0).

Pin 27. M1 (Machine Cycle 1). A CPU signal that tells the system that a program *fetch* cycle is in progess.

Pin 28. RFSH (Refresh). A CPU signal that governs the *refresh* cycle required by dynamic RAMs. This cycle is necessary to keep DRAMs from "forgetting." Static RAMS are in a permanent state of refresh (so long as the power is left on!) and have no need for this function. Active low (0).

Pin 29. GND (Ground). Power return line.

6502

This 8-bit CPU, developed by MOS Technology as an enhancement of Motorola's 6800, was for a time the dominant "home computer" microprocessor. Versions of it are used today in some Commodore, Atari, and Apple computers.

Pins 9–20, 22–25. Address (AB0-AB15).

Pin 1. V_{ss} (Ground). Power return line.

Pin 2. RDY (Ready). A signal to the CPU to wait for requested or current operation to take place. Used also for DRAM refresh cycling. Active low (0).

Pin 3. Clock input. Signal comes from external clock circuit.

Pin 4. IRQ (Interrupt Request). *See* Z80. Active low (0).

Pin 5. Not used.

Pin 6. NMI (Nonmaskable Interrupt). *See* Z80. Active low (0).

Pin 7. SYNC (Synchronization). A CPU signal that tells the system that a program *fetch* cycle is in progess. Active high (1).

Pin 8. V_{cc} (+5VDC). Power input.

Pin 21. V_{ss} (Ground). Power return.

Pin 34. R/W (Read/Write). A signal from the CPU indicating direction of data movement on the data bus to memory or port, or from memory or port. A high (1) indicates a read; a low (0), a write.

Pins 35–36. Not used.

Pin 37. Phase-One Clock. Timing signal sent by CPU.

Pin 38. SO (Set Overflow). A signal to the CPU to set the *Overflow Flag* of the *Status Register*. The Overflow Flag is one of several flags that the software can use to manage computer operations. (If flag is set, do this; if not, do that, etc.)

Pin 39. Phase-Two Clock. The second of the CPU clock outputs. The two clock-output signals form the master clock.

Pin 40. RESET. *See* Z80. Active low (0).

8086/8088

These popular CPUs are 16-bit descendants of Intel's 8-bit 8080 and 8085. Strictly speaking, the 8088 should be termed an 8/16-bit microprocessor because its internal 16-bit data bus becomes an 8-bit bus in the outside world. The 8086 is 16 bits all the way. All things being equal (and they rarely are), the 8086 will run a given operation faster than an 8088. But there are ways around this 8088 limitation, as many hardware and software developers have discovered. Since the pinouts of both chips are almost identical, a single listing will suffice.

The IBM PC/XT computer and most of the compatibles use the 8088. A few use the 8086. To the software, both microprocessors look alike.

Pin 1. GND (Ground). Power return.

Pins 2–16, 39. 8086 Address/Data lines (AD14-AD0, AD15). These lines are used for both addressing and data by *multiplexing*, a technique whereby the function is alternated.

Pins 35–38. 8086 Address lines (A19-16) and Status lines (S6-S3). Multiplexed for address and the status of the address lines.

Pins 2–8.   8088 Address lines (A14-A8).

Pins 9–16.   8088 Address/data lines (AD7-AD0).

Pins 35–39.   8088 Address lines (A19-A15) and status lines (S6-S3). Multiplexed.

Pin 17.   NMI (Nonmaskable Interrupt). Used by external devices to force the CPU to suspend current operations and give its complete attention to the calling device. Active high (1).

Pin 18.   INTR (Interrupt Request). A maskable interrupt used by external devices to get the CPU's attention. Active high (1).

Pin 19.   CLK (Clock). Input to CPU from clock oscillator circuit.

Pin 20.   GND (Ground). Power return.

Pin 21.   RESET. Used to return the CPU to the start line. Active high (1).

Pin 22.   READY. A signal to the CPU READY line tells the processor to go into an idling (wait-state) mode until the calling device catches up.

Pin 23.   TEST. A signal to the CPU that it evaluates for its next action. A low will tell it to execute the next instruction, a high that it should wait. The CPU will ignore the TEST line until instructed otherwise by the software. Active low (0).

Pin 24.   INTA/QS1 (Interrupt Acknowledge/Queue Status 1). INTA is a signal from the CPU indicating that it has recognized an Interrupt Request (INTR). Active low (0). The QS1 and QS0 signals are used in the *maximum mode* (multiprocessor environments).

Pin 25.   ALE/QS0 (Address Latch Enable/Queue Status 0). ALE is a CPU signal indicating the presence of address information on the address lines. This is one of the signals used by external devices to demultiplex (separate) information. ALE allows for the latching ("grabbing") of address information. Active high (1). *See* above for QS.

Pin 26.   DEN/S0 (Data Enable/Status line 0). DEN is a CPU signal used to enable operation of external data buffers like the 8286 Data Bus Transceiver. This IC acts as a holding tank for data on the bus while certain operations take place. Active low (0). The status signals indicate the nature of bus operations in maximum mode operations.

Pin 27. DT/R,S1 (Data Transmit/Receive, Status line 1). A CPU signal used to control the flow of data to and from a data bus transceiver. Transmit is active high (1); receiver is active low (0). *See* S.

Pin 28. IO/M,S2 (Memory/Input-Output, Status line 2). A CPU signal specifying whether the current operation is to be directed to memory or to a port. A high (1) indicates memory, a low (0) I/O. *See* S.

Pin 29. WR/LOCK (Write/Lock). WR is the CPU's signal indicating that the current operation will be an output to memory or a port. The LOCK signal, used in multiprocessor environments, is issued by the CPU to deny an external processor access to the bus.

Pin 30. HLDA/RQ/GT1 (Hold Acknowledge/Bus Request/Grant line 1). An HLDA signal from the CPU indicates that it has recognized a request by an external device to use the system buses. An active high (1), it goes low when the CPU reassumes control of the buses. RQ/GT signals are use for similar purpose in the maximum (multiprocessor) mode.

Pin 31. HOLD/RQ/GT2 (Hold/Bus Request/Grant line 2). A signal sent to the CPU by an external device demanding use of the buses. Active high (1). *See* RQ/GT.

Pin 32. RD (Read). A CPU signal indicating that a read or input operation impends. Active low (0).

Pin 33. MN/MX (Minimum Mode/Maximum Mode). Signal to CPU selecting minimum (stand-alone) or maximum (multiprocessor) system configuration. This configuration is set by the computer designer. A high selects MN, a low MX.

Pin 34. 8086 only. BHE/S7 (Bus High Enable/Status line 7). BHE is used by the CPU to signal place data on the high byte (most significant byte) end of the data bus. This is so in order that 8-bit devices tied to the high byte can avail themselves of this byte. Active low (1). *See* S.

Pin 34. 8088 only. SSO (Status Line Out). A CPU signal used in combination with IO/M and DT/R to define current operation as memory read, memory write, I/O read, etc.

Pin 40. V_{cc} (+5VDC). Power input.

68000

Motorola's 16-bit CPU, properly 16/32 because of its 32-bit internal operations, can address 64 megabytes of memory and is the most powerful of the microprocessors in common use. It is the heart of the Amiga, the new Atari, and, most visibly, the Macintosh. Its full addressing capability is not used by these computers.

An appreciable part of its computing power derives from the fact that this 64-pin giant has separate address and data lines, hence need not multiplex its operations.

Pins 1–5, 54–64. Data lines (D4-D0, D15-D5).

Pins 29–48, 50–52. Address lines (A1-A20, A21-A23).

Pin 6. AS (Address Strobe). When the addess bus contains a valid address, the CPU pulls this line low. Active low (0).

Pin 7. UDS (Upper Data Strobe). Used with LDS (Lower Data Strobe), pin 8, by the CPU to specify the size and the location on the bus of a data word being transmitted. Valid data is indicated by a low on both lines. Combinations of highs and lows identify which byte on which line is invalid.

Pin 8. LDS (Lower Data Strobe). *See* Pin 7.

Pin 9. R/W (Read/Write). This CPU signal indicates whether an input (read) or an output (write) operation is taking place.

Pin 10. DTACK (Data Transfer Acknowledge). A signal from memory or I/O apprising the CPU that a transfer of data has been completed. Active low (0).

Pin 11. BG (Bus Grant). When the CPU receives a BR (Bus Request), it pulls this line low, a signal to the calling device that the bus is available. Active low (0). *See* BGBACK and BR.

Pin 12. BGBACK (Bus Grant Acknowledge). The calling device issues a low in response to the BG signal. Active low (0). *See* BG and BR.

Pin 13. BR (Bus Request). A signal from a calling device to the CPU requesting control of the bus. Active low (0). *See* BG and BGBACK.

Pin 14. V_{cc} (+5VDC). Power input.

Pin 15.   CLK (Clock). The line from the clock circuitry.

Pin 16.   GND (Ground). Power return.

Pin 17.   HALT. A signal that forces the CPU to wait. Operations are frozen until the line is pulled high. Active low (0).

Pin 18.   RESET. A low on this line causes the CPU to cease current operations and return the system to its startup state. Since this is a bidirectional line, the CPU can use it to issue a reset signal to other components in the system. Active low (0).

Pin 19.   VMA (Valid Memory Address). A signal from the CPU to 6800-family peripheral devices that CPU is synchronized with the peripheral and that the bus contains a valid address. *See* VPA. Active low (0).

Pin 20.   E (Enable). A clock signal from the CPU used to enable 6800-family peripherals. See VPA. One E clock period equals ten 68000 clock periods, namely, six lows and four highs. The difference between this clock and the 68000 clock is based on the difference in operating speed between the 6800-family devices and the 68000.

Pin 21.   VPA (Valid Peripheral Address). A signal to the CPU from 6800-family peripheral devices establishing synchronization with the 68000 E signal. *See* VMA. Active low (0).

Pin 22.   BERR (Bus Error). An input to the CPU indicating trouble, that is, devices that don't answer the call to duty, illegal requests, and so on. Active low (0).

Pin 23.   IPL2 (Interrupt Priority Line 2). The IPL lines (see also pins 24 and 25) are inputs to the CPU requesting attention from as many as seven external devices. The programmer assigns each device a priority level, and when an interrupt is issued by a device, it is queued according to the predetermined level. Active low (0).

Pin 24.   IPL1 (Interrupt Priority Line 1). *See* above.

Pin 25.   IPL0 (Interrupt Priority Line 0). *See* above.

Pin 26.   FC2 (Function Code 2). The FC lines (see also pins 27 and 28) are signals from the CPU indicating the status of various operations (interrupt acknowledge, data memory, program memory, etc.). The mix of highs and lows specifies the particular status.

Pin 27. FC1 (Function Code 1). *See* Pin 26.

Pin 28. FC0 (Function Code 0). *See* Pin 26.

Pin 49. V$_{cc}$ (+5VDC). Power input.

Pin 53. GND (Ground). Power return.

FINAL WORDS

Here, in a brief reprise, are a few comments and suggestions on the art of tinkering (troubleshooting and maintenance). Approach your sick or cranky computer with a logician's eye and a touch of insoucience. It's the only way. Panic just won't do.

Don't let your computer system intimidate you. It's just a collection of human-made gadgets. Should it falter, it can be fixed. Its breakdowns shouldn't be the cause of your breakdowns!

Before disaster strikes, do everything reasonable—within the limits of time, strength, cash, and patience—to avert disaster. "He that lives on hope will die fasting," said Ben Franklin.

Set up a computer journal in which you chronicle everything pertinent to your computer operations: maintenance schedule, breakdowns and cures, new purchases, interfacing problems, and solutions.

Establish a "clean" electrical environment.
Establish a clean, dry working environment.
Establish a pleasantly cool working environment.
Establish neat working habits with respect to computer use and disk handling.
Establish a maintenance schedule and stick to it: daily, weekly, monthly cleaning and lubrication, as appropriate.
Check cabling regularly, and repair or replace as needed.
Backup and replace disks on a regular basis.
After disaster strikes, proceed to a solution in a calm, relaxed manner. Getting yourself into a blue funk won't do anything useful for your psyche or your computer.
Make a note of symptoms and attendant circumstances.
Use the troubleshooting aids in this book.
Hand the defective item over to a professional repairperson before attempting to do a job you don't really understand, or lack the skills, or proper equipment for.

> I should be sorry
> To see my labours . . .
> Got by long watching and large patience,
> Not prosper where my love and zeal hath plac'd 'em:
> Which . . . in all my ends,
> Have look'd no way but unto public good . . . .
>
> —Ben Jonson, *The Alchemist*, II, iii.

GLOSSARY

ABBREVIATIONS

Abbreviations marked with * will be defined in the main glossary.

AC	Alternating current.
ACE	Asynchronous Communications Element.
ACIA	Asynchronous Communications Interface Adapter.
ADC	Analog-to-digital converter.
ALU	Arithmetic-logic unit. *
ANSI	American National Standards Institute.
ASCII	American Standard Code for Information Interchange.
bps	Bits per second.
CMOS	Complementary metal-oxide semiconductor (an IC fabrication technology).
CP/M	Control Program for Microcomputers, a disk operating system.
cps	Cycles per second (*see* Hz).
CPU	Central processing unit. *
CRC	Cyclic redundancy check. *
CRT	Cathode ray tube.
CTS	Clear to send (RS-232-C).
DAC	Digital-to-analog converter.
DC	Direct current.
DCE	Data communication equipment (RS-232-C).
DIP	Dual-in-line package (IC package).
DOS	Disk operating system. *
DP	Data processing.
DRAM	Dynamic random-access memory (*see* RAM).
DSR	Data set ready (RS–232–C).
DTE	Data terminal equipment (RS-232-C).
DTR	Data terminal ready (RS-232-C).
EAROM	Electrically alterable read-only memory.
EBCDIC	Extended Binary Coded Decimal Interchange Code (IBM equivalent of ASCII/USASCII).
EEPROM	Electrically erasable read-only memory.
EIA	Electronic Industries Association.
EMF	Electromotive force, volts.
EOF	End of file.
EPROM	Erasable/Programmable read-only memory.

FDC	Floppy disk controller.
GPIB	General purpose interface bus.
GIGO	Garbage in/garbage out.
GND	Ground (in electrical circuitry).
HDC	Hard disk controller.
Hz	Hertz (frequency in cycles per second).
IC	Integrated circuit.
IEEE	Institute of Electrical and Electronics Engineers.
I/O	Input/output.
Kb	Kilobit (1,024 bits).
KB	Kilobyte (1,024 bytes).
KHz	Kilohertz (1,000Hz).
I	Symbol for electrical current.
LAN	Local area network.
LCD	Liquid crystal display.
LED	Light-emitting diode.
LSB	Least significant bit. *
LSD	Least significant digit. *
LSI	Large-scale integration (IC gate density).
Mb	Megabit (1,000,000 bits).
MB	Megabyte (1,000,000 bytes).
MHz	Megahertz (1,000,000Hz).
MPU	Main processing unit. *
MSB	Most significant bit. *
MSD	Most significant digit. *
MS-DOS	Microsoft disk operating system.
MTBF	Mean time between failures.
ns	Nanosecond (one billionth of a second).
OS	Operating system.
P	Symbol for electrical power (also W).
PAL	Programmable array logic (type of IC). *
PC	Personal computer.
PCB	Printed circuit board. *
PIA	Programmable interface adapter.
PROM	Programmable read-only memory.
R	Symbol for electrical resistance.
RAM	Random-access memory. *
ROM	Read-only memory. *
RTS	Request to send (RS–232–C).
RxD	Received data (RS–232–C).
SRAM	Static random-access memory (*see* RAM).
TPI	Tracks per inch.
TxD	Transmitted data.
UART	Universal asynchronous receiver/transmitter.
USART	Universal synchronous/asynchronous receiver/transmitter.

USASCII	United States of America standard code for information interchange (same as ASCII).
V	Volt.
VAC	Volts AC.
VDC	Volts DC.
VDE	Voice data entry.
VDU	Video display unit.
VSLI	Very large-scale integration (IC gate density).
W	Watt, unit of electrical power, also P.

DEFINITIONS

address   A location in memory.

address bus   The electrical pathway over which addressing information is sent. *See* **bus**.

Arithmetic-logic unit   The central processor of the CPU; that part of the CPU that carries out numerical calculations and logical comparisons.

backplane   *See* motherboard.

base-2   The number system built on a root of 2; the numerical basis of digital computer operations. *See* binary.

baud rate   The transfer rate of data bits measured in bps.

binary   (1) The base-2 number system. (2) A two-choice system represented by the digits 1 and 0, which can stand for "yes" and "no," "on" and "off," "go" or "no go," etc.

bit   Binary digit, 1 or 0; the fundamental unit of digital data.

boot   Short for *bootstrap*, the (1) process whereby the computer is brought to operating status, and (2) the program for accomplishing this end.

bus   An electrical pathway. In a typical computer, there are four: *address bus*, *data bus*, *control bus*, and *power bus*.

byte   Eight bits in a coherent string.

central processing unit (CPU)   The system of circuits that controls the basic operations of a computer, commonly a single IC called a *microprocessor; see also* MPU.

character   Any symbol: alphabetic, numeric, etc.

checksum   Summation check, a method of checking for the accuracy of transmitted data.

chip   An integrated circuit.

clock   **(1)** the timing system that keeps the computer operations organized; **(2)** an add-on device that keeps ''real time,'' just like a wristwatch, hence called *real-time clock*.

code   The representation of meanings with symbols. In computer usage, the term usually means *program* material.

compatibility   The ability of one computer to run the programs written for another computer.

control bus   The electrical pathway over which the clock and other control signals are sent.

cyclic redundancy check   An error-checking method, often used in disk operating systems.

data   Information entered into and retrieved from a computer.

databit   *See* bit.

data bus   The electrical pathway over which databits are sent, generally a *byte* or a *word* at a time.

data transmission   The movement of data from one part of the computer to another, or from one computer system to another. To achieve successful communication, both sides of the communication loop must follow the same communication protocols for data transmission rate and *handshaking*, and certain other parameters. (*See* Chapter 8.)

diode   A semiconductor device that allows electricity to flow in one direction but not in another, a process called *rectification*. *See* rectifier and zener.

disk   Any of several types and sizes of disk-shaped magnetic storage media.

disk drive   An electromechanical device for reading from and writing to disks.

disk operating system A program, stored mainly on disk, for controlling the normal operations of a computer. CP/M, MS-DOS, and UNIX are examples of currently popular disk operating systems.

dot pitch The width of pixel spacing. Smaller is better. A figure in the neigborhood of .3mm is acceptable.

dual-in-line package A method of packaging electronic components, particularly ICs, such that there are two parallel rows of pins for insertion into holes or into sockets mounted on *printed circuit boards*.

dump Displaying some (or all) of the contents of memory on a display device (usually a video monitor or a printer) with debugging or other programmer's *utilities*. The dump is most commonly done in *hexadecimal* numbers.

edgecard connector A connector arrangement whereby the circuit board provides a male mating element as a part of the board itself and etched with several fingers that match with connectors in the female element, a slot on another board or a cable. Also called *card-edge connector*.

expansion slot A connector—usually on the main circuit board of a computer—designed to accept memory boards and other circuit boards that enhance the basic capabilities of the computer.

firmware Program material permanently fixed in the ROM type of memory chips. *See* monitor.

floppy disk A flexible magnetic disk permanently sealed in a thin plastic envelope. The first floppies were eight inches in diameter. Now 5¼-inch and 3½-inch sizes predominate. *See* Chapter 4.

formatting The process of preparing a disk or other magnetic medium for use by writing certain information to the disk. The formatting routine establishes the electrical identity of tracks and sectors. *See* Chapter 4.

garbage Useless, unwanted, meaningless information; generally the result of a computer or software malfunction.

gate An electrical circuit (mainly transistors) used to control the flow of databits in a computer to produce desired arrangements of these bits. Integrated circuits consist mainly of gates.

handshaking   The establishment and maintenance of data transfer between two devices by a set of signals specifying that one device is ready to send and the other is ready to receive data. Handshaking can be accomplished in two ways: via control codes sent on the transmit and receive lines (software handshaking) or via separate lines (hardware handshaking). (See data transmission, and Chapter 8.)

hardcopy   ASCII-coded and graphics data printed on paper with a printer or a plotter.

hard disk   A nonflexible disk-shaped magnetic storage medium, also called **fixed disk** and **Winchester**.

hardware   Equipment: computer, printer, video unit, etc.

head   The electromagnetic read/write (playback/record) element of a disk drive. A magnetic flux is produced across the *head gap*, a narrow region between the electromagnetic poles.

head stepper   The *stepper motor* that moves the head back and forth across the surface of a disk during read/write operations.

heat sink   A heat-dissipating metal device (usually finned) mounted on electronic components that tend to get very hot (e.g., voltage regulators)

hexadecimal   Number base-16, consisting of alphanumeric digits 0,1,2,3,4,5,6,7,8,9,A,B,C,D,E,F. Commonly used in assembly language programming because of its convenience. Very large numbers can be represented by a small number of hex digits, for example, 1111111111111111_2 ($65,535_{10}$) = $FFFF_{16}$. Further, like *octal*, hex is both byte- and powers-of-2-oriented.

integrated circuit   Highly miniaturized electronic circuitry fabricated in specially prepared silicon. Degrees of miniaturization, hence component density, are given terms like *large-scale integration* (LSI) and *very large-scale integration* (VSLI). The silicon chips are sealed in plastic or ceramic packages and typically provided with two parallel rows of pins for insertion into *printed circuit boards*. This type of chip unit is called a DIP, *dual inline package.*

interface   The circuitry needed to establish communication between two different pieces of electronic equipment, such as a computer and a printer.

input/output The process of getting data into and out of a computer. A keyboard is a representative input device; a video display is a representative output device.

jack A socket, such as that on a video monitor, for receiving the video cable plug.

junction The region in a *semiconductor* where the *p-type material* meets the *n-type material*. This is the region where *transistor* action occurs.

kilo- (1) As a prefix in designations of computer memory size, 1,024 (thus, one *kilobyte* = 1,024 bytes). (2) As a prefix in other numerical designations; 1,000, thus, one *kilovolt* = 1,000 volts. *See* **mega-.**

least significant bit The "rightmost" bit of a *byte* or computer *word*, the bit with the least numerical weight.

least significant byte The "rightmost" byte of a computer *word*, the byte with least numerical weight. Sometimes called the *low-order byte*.

least significant digit The rightmost digit, the digit with the least numerical weight.

mass storage General term for *disk, tape*, and other external storage systems.

mega- (1) As a prefix in designations of computer memory size, 1,048,576; thus, one *megabyte* = 1,048,576 bytes. (2) As a prefix in other numeric designations, 1,000,000; thus, one *megawatt* = 1,000,000 watts.

memory The region in a computer into which data is stored and retrieved in order for the computer to carry out its activities. Each location in memory has a unique address. Some addresses are reserved for the computer's own use, but a large block is available for user programming or applications software. *See* memory map. The memory of a computer is located in banks of RAM (*random-access memory*) and in ROM (*read-only memory*). Most of the RAM is open; the ROM is reserved.

memory map   (1) The way in which memory is allocated in a particular computer system; (2) a printed representation of this allocation.

main processing unit   Another name for the CPU or microprocessor.

microprocessor   Commonly called the CPU, a highly complex *integrated circuit* used to control the basic operations of a computer. Some microprocessors act as *slaves* or *coprocessors*, taking over certain processing functions to speed up overall operational efficiency, hence speed. *See* Chapter 10.

monitor   (1) A program permanently set into one or more ROMs designed to control certain operations of the CPU; can be said to act as an intermediary between the computer user and the CPU; (2) a *video display unit*.

most significant bit   The leftmost bit of a *byte* or computer *word*, the bit with the greatest numerical weight.

most significant byte   The leftmost *byte* of a computer **word**, the byte with the greatest numerical weight; sometimes called the *high-order byte*.

most significant digit   The leftmost digit, the digit with the greatest numerical weight.

motherboard   The main system board in a computer, containing the basic circuitry as well as slots for expansion boards. Sometimes erroneously called the *backplane*, which is really just the set of system *bus* connections in certain types of computers.

multiplexing   The process whereby a single resource is *time shared* for several applications more or less simultaneously. Many *networks* use some form of multiplexing. At the chip level, two different signals can be multiplexed on a single bus, effectively allowing the chip to perform two different functions or manage two packets of data at the "same" time. The two signals or packets are split apart by a *demultiplexing* process.

network   A system of linking computers and/or terminals in a way that allows them to share common resources (e.g., large capacity hard disk) and to work at several different tasks concurrently.

n-type material Semiconductor material rich in electrons; *negatively charged* material.

octal Base-8 number system. Numerals are 0,1,2,3,4,5,6,7. *See* hexadecimal.

peripheral Any external equipment used to expand the capabilities of the computer and its convenience to the operator. Printer, plotter, spooler, etc.

pixel Picture element, a single point on a video screen. The number of pixels a video monitor can display is one measure of its resolution. The greater the number of small clumps of pixels (ideally, single pixels) the computer can control, the sharper the picture.

port A gateway in a computer through which data is transmitted. The printer port connector, for example, is the user-accessible hardware manifestation of the computer's parallel or serial port. Each port has its own address in the memory management scheme of the computer.

power Electricity for running the computer. Compare *signal*.

power bus The electrical pathway over which the electrical power for running the computer travels, starting at the computer power supply.

printed circuit board A board in which the wiring for the one or more electronic circuits provided for results from etching a copper coating. Etching leaves behind copper traces representing the basic circuit interconnections. The board is drilled and marked for the insertion of the electronic parts—ICs, resistors, capacitors, etc.—that constitute the circuit(s).

program A set of instructions written in a language for the purpose (*i.e.*, a programming language) and designed to cause a computer to perform some useful function at the will of the user. The form of the instructions is called *code*. Someone who turns a program design into specific lines of code is called a *coder*. The programmer and the coder may be the same person.

programmable array logic This type of IC can be field-programmed for "instant upgrades" or certain on-the-spot engineering changes in system design. Bears a certain resemblance to the ROM in the programming hardware required, but is different in that PALs are not merely memory devices, but customizable *gate* arrays.

p-type material   In a *semiconductor*, the positively charged or *hole-rich* material.

queue   A waiting line; term can apply to instructions awaiting processing by the CPU or to files of text waiting to be printed.

qwerty   The standard typewriter/computer keyboard arrangement for the letters of the alphabet and the numerals.

random access   Getting at data stored in memory or in a mass storage device by no fixed rules of precedence. One type: bypassing the CPU to go directly to memory (direct-memory access).

random-access memory   (1) a type of memory IC that allows for reading and writing (e.g. loading and retrieving data); (2) the read/write memory area of a computer, most of which is accessible to the user.

raster   The pattern of scanning lines on a video display tube.

read-only memory   (1) a type of memory IC that can be read from, but, once it has been (factory) programmed, not written to; (2) the computer *firmware* that uses this type of memory.

rectifier   A device commonly made of diodes for turning *AC* into *DC*. Because of the ability of a diode to allow current to flow in only one direction, the rectifier prevents half of the AC sine wave from flowing in the circuit. A flow of electricity consisting of only one half of the sine wave is called *rippling DC*, which must be filtered to be usable by most electronic equipment. A *bridge rectifier* consists of four diodes connected in such a way as to allow them to use both halves of the sine wave (*full-wave rectification*) and still produce DC. *See* Chapter 7.

register   Registers are temporary storage and data manipulation areas in a microprocessor, called by such names as *accumulator, index register, segment register, instruction register,* and others.

scan rate   The speed at which the electron beam scans from the top to the bottom of the video display. American TV scans at the "official" rate of 525 lines per second. More lines provide better resolution.

screen dump   A literal printout (**hardcopy**) of the material currently visible on the video screen.

semiconductor   A device, usually made of a silicon-based material, that can be made to conduct or to block electricity. *See* transistor, diode, n-type material, and p-type material.

sensor   An external analog device that reads "real world" values like temperature and moisture and transduces them into voltages for processing by an analog-to-digital converter. A *transducer* changes one form of energy into another form. *See* Chapter 7.)

signal   Electricity of very low power used for the data processing and control operations of a computer. All the internal signals take the form of binary digits, 1 and 0, manifested as voltages (at negligible current), 0 to .8VDC for binary 0, 2 to 5VDC for binary 1.

sine wave   The characteristic curve of alternating electrical current (AC). One *cycle*, which consists of a positive and a negative swing, adds up to 360°, that is, a complete circle. But since the wave is moving in time, a sine-wave plot appears as a series of peaks and valleys.

software   Program material, including programs to write programs. Software can be input via data-entry devices (keyboard, optical scanner, etc.), *mass storage* (disk, tape, CD-ROM, etc.), and plug-in cartridges, which are circuit boards containing *firmware*.

speech recognition system   A computerized speech system capable of acting predictably on spoken commands.

speech synthesis system   A system capable of producing undestandable imitations of human speech.

stepper motor   A motor capable of moving in small, precise increments, used, for example, in disk drives to move the *head* and, in printers to move the paper-advance mechanism (platen or tractor).

syntax   As applies to programming, the accepted usages of the programming language. For example, misspelling a command or statement in a programming language will result in a "syntax error" message.

terminal   A computer slaved to another computer, or a video display device with no computing capabilities of its own, though perhaps provided with one or more interfaces for data communication.

trace An electrical interconnect ("wire") on a *printed circuit board*.

transducer A device that converts one form of energy into another. A temperature transducer changes the registered temperature value into a voltage value; a loudspeaker changes voltages into sounds.

transistor A semiconductor device; the fundamental electronic element of most ICs, where transistors act as switches to form *gates*. Transistors are also discrete devices used for switching, and current or voltage amplification. Any simple transistor consists of three electrodes: *collector*, *emitter*, and base. The base acts as the toggle for switching the transistor on, or as the controller for the transistor's output at any given moment.

utilities *Programs* designed to facilitate the use of the computer system. *See* Chapter 4.

video bandwith Bandwidth identifies a range of frequencies used for some particular purpose. In the case of video, the higher the frequency bandwidth, the more detail can be transmitted. A good-quality color monitor should have a bandwidth no lower than 15Mhz.

volatile memory Memory that will not hold data after the power has been shut off; the normal state of affairs in the memory of most computer systems. In some desktop computers, memory is retained by a battery backup system after the main power is turned off. Contrast volatile memory with *mass storage*.

voltage regulator An integrated circuit designed to maintain voltage at a fixed level. Most microcomputers use voltage regulators are rated at +5V and +12V.

word In microcomputers, two *bytes* as a coherent unit constitute a word—not to be confused with words in ordinary language. A word is divided into a *low-order byte* and a *high-order byte*, the former containing the *least significant bit*, the latter the *most significant bit*.

X-Y plotter An ordinary plotter, capable of locating points along the vertical (X) axis and horizontal (Y) axis.

yoke   The electromagnetic coil around the neck of a CRT, used for truing the picture horizontally and adjusting color purity. Not to be fooled with by amateurs!

zener diode   A type of **diode**, also known as a *breakdown diode* because of its ability to *avalanche* when a critical voltage is reached. This characteristic makes it useful as a protective device. When the voltage is below the avalanche threshold, the zener blocks the passage of electricity, but when the voltage exceeds the critical point, the diode conducts and the overvoltage can be directed safely to ground.

NAMES

NOTE: The terms named for these scientists are referenced principally in Chapter 7.

Ampère, Andre Marie (1775–1836), French physicist: *ampere, amp.*

Baudot, Emile (1728–1804), French engineer: *baud.*

Boole, George (1815–1864), Anglo-Irish mathematician and logician: *Boolean algebra, Boolean logic.*

Faraday, Michael (1791–1867), English physicist and chemist: *farad.*

Henry, Joseph (1797–1878), American physicist: *henry.*

Ohm, Georg Simon (1787–1854), German physicist: ohm.

Volta, Alessandro (1745–1827), Italian physicist: volt.

Watt, James (1736–1819), Scottish inventor: *watt.*

Zener, Clarence Melvin (1905–), American physicist: zener effect.

INDEX

About the Author

Although Henry F. Beechhold has been interested in electronics since the late 1930's, his academic career of more than 32 years has been as a college teacher of writing, literature, and linguistics. He holds a doctorate in English and comparative literature from Pennsylvania State University and is professor of English and chairman of the linguistics program at Trenton State College.

Outside the world of computers, Professor Beechhold has written poetry, plays, and opera libretti, as well as books, articles, and reviews on such diverse subjects as education, linguistics, and Irish literature. He was a member of the production group that won an Emmy for Grammar Rock (ABC-TV); has served as executive editor of *Bitterroot*, a poetry journal; and is presently associate editor of *Eire-Ireland*, a quarterly journal of Irish studies. His computer-related writing includes articles and reviews for *Computer Consultant*, *InfoWorld*, *Family Computing*, *A+*, *PC*, *Collegiate Microcomputing*, and *Lotus*, as well as two books on microcomputer care and repair. *The Plain English Repair and Maintenance Guide for Home Computers* (Simon & Schuster) was the first popularly written book of its kind.

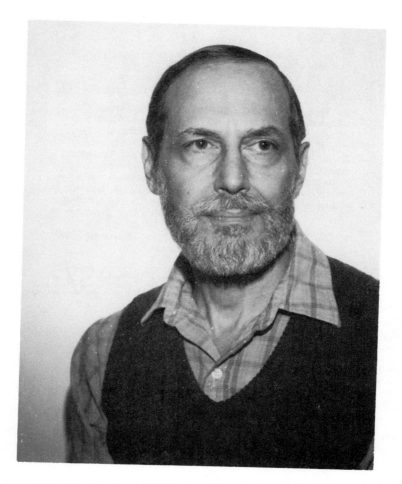